Grade Aid with Practice Tests

for

Kosslyn and Rosenberg

Psychology
The Brain, The Person, The World

Second Edition

prepared by

Marcia J. McKinley
Mount St. Mary's College

PEARSON

Boston   New York   San Francisco
Mexico City   Montreal   Toronto   London   Madrid   Munich   Paris
Hong Kong   Singapore   Tokyo   Cape Town   Sydney

ISBN 0-205-39538-4

Printed in the United States of America

10 9 8 7 6 5   08 07 06 05 04 03

Acknowledgements

This Grade Aid was not a lone venture. Rather, I am grateful to many people for its completion. Specifically, I thank:

- The authors of this text, Stephen M. Kosslyn and Robin S. Rosenberg, for writing a textbook that my students and I find educational and entertaining. I am honored to have had a small part in creating such a wonderful resource.

- The authors of previous editions of the Grade Aid (Marjorie S. Hardy and Wendy Domjan) for providing a firm foundation on which I could build.

- My editor extraordinaire, Erin K. Liedel, who provided patience and support beyond the call of duty and made the publication process much more enjoyable than it otherwise would have been.

- My research assistants and students who pilot-tested these materials, especially Jack Whitney, Tom Fitzgerald, and Jessica Podlaskowich.

- My son, Nathan D. McKinley-Pace, for enduring my long hours during the writing process, although I suspect that I missed him far more than he missed me.

- The support team which ensured Nathan's care while I wrote, especially Jeff Pace, Megan Laird, Judy McKinley, and the Lindquist family.

    After You Read…Practice Tests...188

    When You Are Finished…Puzzle It Out...205

Chapter 6: Learning

    Before You Read…...206

    Chapter Objectives...206

    As You Read…Term Identification…...207

    As You Read…Questions and Exercises...207

    After You Read…Thinking Back...232

    After You Read…Thinking Ahead...233

    After You Read…Practice Tests...234

    When You Are Finished…Puzzle It Out...249

Chapter 7: Memory

    Before You Read…...250

    Chapter Objectives...250

    As You Read…Term Identification…...251

    As You Read…Questions and Exercises...251

    After You Read…Thinking Back...263

    After You Read…Thinking Ahead...264

    After You Read…Practice Tests...265

    When You Are Finished…Puzzle It Out...284

Chapter 8: Language and Thinking

    Before You Read…...285

    Chapter Objectives...285

    As You Read…Term Identification…...286

    As You Read…Questions and Exercises...287

    After You Read…Thinking Back...301

    After You Read…Thinking Ahead...302

    After You Read…Practice Tests...303

    When You Are Finished…Puzzle It Out...318

Chapter 9: Types of Intelligence

    Before You Read…...319

    Chapter Objectives...319

    As You Read…Term Identification…...320

    As You Read…Questions and Exercises...321

    After You Read…Thinking Back...336

    After You Read…Thinking Ahead...337

    After You Read…Practice Tests...338

    When You Are Finished…Puzzle It Out...353

Chapter 10: Emotion and Motivation

    Before You Read…...354

    Chapter Objectives...354

    As You Read…Term Identification…...355

    As You Read…Questions and Exercises...355

    After You Read…Thinking Back...371

    After You Read…Thinking Ahead...372

    After You Read…Practice Tests...373

    When You Are Finished…Puzzle It Out...392

Chapter 11: Personality
Before You Read..393
Chapter Objectives..393
As You Read...Term Identification..394
As You Read...Questions and Exercises..394
After You Read...Thinking Back..408
After You Read...Thinking Ahead..409
After You Read...Practice Tests..410
When You Are Finished...Puzzle It Out..427

Chapter 12: Psychology over the Life Span
Before You Read..428
Chapter Objectives..428
As You Read...Term Identification..429
As You Read...Questions and Exercises..429
After You Read...Thinking Back..451
After You Read...Thinking Ahead..452
After You Read...Practice Tests..453
When You Are Finished...Puzzle It Out..470

Chapter 13: Stress, Health, and Coping
Before You Read..471
Chapter Objectives..471
As You Read...Term Identification..472
As You Read...Questions and Exercises..472
After You Read...Thinking Back..485
After You Read...Thinking Ahead..486
After You Read...Practice Tests..487
When You Are Finished...Puzzle It Out..500

Chapter 14: Psychological Disorders
Before You Read..501
Chapter Objectives..501
As You Read...Term Identification..502
As You Read...Questions and Exercises..502
After You Read...Thinking Back..520
After You Read...Thinking Ahead..521
After You Read...Practice Tests..522
When You Are Finished...Puzzle It Out..541

Chapter 15: Treatment
Before You Read..542
Chapter Objectives..542
As You Read...Term Identification..543
As You Read...Questions and Exercises..543
After You Read...Thinking Back..561
After You Read...Thinking Ahead..562
After You Read...Practice Tests..563
When You Are Finished...Puzzle It Out..581

Chapter 16: Social Psychology

Before You Read...582
Chapter Objectives...582
As You Read...Term Identification...............................583
As You Read...Questions and Exercises.......................584
After You Read...Thinking Back...................................602
After You Read...Practice Tests...................................603
When You Are Finished...Puzzle It Out.......................614

Answer Keys

Chapter 1: Psychology..615
Chapter 2: The Research Process.................................618
Chapter 3: The Biology of Mind and Behavior..............620
Chapter 4: Sensation and Perception............................623
Chapter 5:Consciousness...625
Chapter 6: Learning..627
Chapter 7: Memory...629
Chapter 8: Language and Thinking...............................632
Chapter 9: Types of Intelligence..................................634
Chapter 10: Emotion and Motivation............................636
Chapter 11: Personality...638
Chapter 12: Psychology over the Life Span...................640
Chapter 13: Stress, Health, and Coping........................643
Chapter 14: Psychological Disorders............................645
Chapter 15: Treatment..648
Chapter 16: Social Psychology.....................................650

Chapter 1
The Science of Psychology: Yesterday & Today

Before You Read. . .

In this chapter, you will learn what psychology is and what psychologists do. The chapter also presents a theme that runs throughout the book: "levels of analysis." Basically, this means that we can understand most psychological concepts at the levels of the brain, person, and group.

In addition, you will learn how psychology has evolved. Be sure you learn the various schools of thought in psychology and the famous people in these schools, because you will be seeing these names again and again throughout the book!

Hollywood might lead you to believe that most psychologists practice therapy (often badly), and that many of them behave unethically (e.g., *Mumford* and *Prince of Tides*). In this chapter, you will learn the facts: psychologists do lots of different things and all psychologists are bound by ethical principles, both in research and clinical practice.

Chapter Objectives

After reading this chapter, you should be able to:

♦   Define psychology.

♦   Describe the concept of "levels of analysis," and how it can be used to better understand psychology.

♦   Describe how psychology has evolved over time.

♦   Define the different fields of psychology.

♦   Discuss what the different types of psychologists do.

♦   Discuss proper ethics in research, with humans and animals and in clinical practice.

As You Read. . . Term Identification

Make flashcards using the following terms as you go. Use the definitions in the margins of this chapter for help. If you write the definitions in your own words, though, you will remember them better!

Academic psychologist
Applied psychologist
Behavior
Behaviorism
Clinical psychologist
Cognitive psychology
Cognitive neuroscience
Counseling psychologist
Debriefing
Evolutionary psychology
Functionalism
Gestalt psychology
Humanistic psychology
Informed consent
Introspection
Level of the brain
Level of the person

Level of the group
Mental processes
Psychiatrist
Psychiatric nurse
Psychodynamic theory
Psychology
Psychotherapy
Reinforcement
Science
School psychologist
Self-actualization
Social psychologist
Social worker
Sport psychologist
Structuralism
Unconscious

As You Read. . . Questions and Exercises

The Science of Psychology: Getting to Know You

What is psychology?

Kosslyn and Rosenberg define **psychology** as the _____ of _____ and _____. Look at each part of this definition:

Part #1: Science

Which of your classes this semester are **sciences**?_____
_____

Which of your classes this semester are non-**sciences**? _____
_____

How do your **science** and non-**science** classes differ? _____
_____

Because it is a **science**, psychology requires ideas to be tested by collecting additional facts. Some questions can be answered through science; others can't be. In the table below, decide whether or not you could answer the question with scientific methods. Explain why or why not.

Question	Answer with Science?		Why or why not?
Is there a God?	YES	NO	
Should marijuana be legalized?	YES	NO	
What makes people angry?	YES	NO	
How does stress affect health?	YES	NO	
What happens after we die?	YES	NO	

Part #2: Mental Processes

Name some **mental processes** that you are using as you answer these questions._____
_____

Part #3: Behaviors

Name some **behaviors** that you are doing as you answer these questions._____
_____

Which usually come first: **mental processes** or **behaviors**? Why?_____
_____

Kosslyn and Rosenberg describe the four **goals** of psychologists as:

Goal #1: To DESCRIBE mental processes and behavior.
How could you use research that *describes* mental processes and/or behavior in your own life?
_____
_____

Goal #2: To EXPLAIN mental processes and behavior.
How could you use research that *explains* mental processes and/or behavior in your own life?
_____
_____

Goal #3: To PREDICT mental processes and behavior.
How could you use research that *predicts* mental processes and/or behavior in your own life?
_____
_____

Goal #4: To CONTROL mental processes and behavior.
How could you use research about *how to control* mental processes or behavior in your own life?
_____
_____

Name _____

WHY SHOULD I STUDY PSYCHOLOGY?

Hopefully, you are taking this class because you really want to, not JUST because it fits into your schedule, you like the professor (although, hopefully you do!), or your friends are taking it. But, if not, take a moment to see how much you can really learn from the field of psychology.

Look at both the *skills* you can learn in a psychology course, as well as the *material*. List some of the things you hope to learn here. To get some ideas, you may want to flip through your textbook (to look at all the different topics that you will be covering) or

GO SURFING...

...at one of the many school websites that lists the benefits of studying psychology.

Skills I will learn in psychology:

1. _____

2. _____

3. _____

4. _____

5. _____

Material I hope to learn in psychology:

1. _____

2. _____

3. _____

4. _____

5. _____

Levels of Analysis

We can study phenomena at various **levels: the brain, person,** and **group**. Identify a question that can be asked at each level in the following situations:

Phenomenon	Brain	Person	Group
Fighting with your roommate			
Falling in love			
Drinking too much			
Acing a test			
Wrecking your car			

Looking at Levels

Throughout the Grade Aid, you will be asked to consider the events that occur at the levels of the brain, the person, and the world to influence various psychological phenomena. You should list the factors in the charts provided and indicate how they may interact by drawing arrows between the columns. Below is an example of a completed chart, using the information contained in "Drought Among the Masaii" on pages 8-9. Use this as a model for the other Looking at Levels charts in this Grade Aid.

The Brain	The Person	The Group
Child's temperament	Mom's belief that she should care for only when fussing Mom's feeding behavior Mom's stress level	Nomads=dependent on naturally occurring resources (e.g., water) Extended families

On September 11, 2001, Al Queda terrorists flew planes into the World Trade Centers and the Pentagon. Name some of the factors, at each of the **three levels**, that may have influenced the terrorists' decision to do this. Draw arrows indicating how events at the different levels may interact.

The Brain	The Person	The Group

Name some of the factors, at each of the **three levels**, that influenced your decision to attend college. Draw arrows indicating how events at the different levels may have interacted to influence your decision.

The Brain	The Person	The Group

TRY PRACTICE TEST #1 NOW!
GOOD LUCK!

Then & Now: The Evolution of a Science

Fill in the following. Who are the key people and what are the key ideas of each **school of psychology**? Which level(s) does each theory concentrate on most?

School of Thought	Key People	Key Ideas	Levels of Analysis (Brain, Person, World)
Structuralism			
Functionalism			
Gestalt Psychology			
Psychodynamic Theory			
Behaviorism			
Humanistic Psychology			
Cognitive Psychology			
Cognitive Neuroscience			
Evolutionary Psychology			

In October, 2002, two snipers terrorized the Washington, D.C. area, killing 10 people and injuring 3 more. In the days after the snipers were caught, numerous TV shows hosted specials about the snipers. Suppose that the following psychologists were asked to participate in one of these special broadcasts. How would each of them explain the snipers' actions?

Psychologist	Explanations
Psychodynamic Theorist	
Behaviorist	
Humanistic Psychologist	
Cognitive Psychologist	
Cognitive Neuroscientist	
Evolutionary Psychologist	

GO SURFING...

...to put faces with the names and to find out more about your favorite psychologists. Some places to start are:

♦ **The History of Psychology Website**:
  http://elvers.stjoe.udayton.edu/history/welcome.htm
  This site allows you to search by birthdays (do you have the same birthday as any famous psychologist?), people, and categories. Although some of the trivia questions aren't covered in this chapter, others are. Test yourself!

♦ **The History of Psychology**: http://www.ship.edu/~cgboeree/historyofpsych.html
  This site is an e-book, written by Dr. C. George Boeree at Shippensburg University. It tells more about the early, early days of psychology. Scroll down for more recent happenings.

♦ **Today in the History of Psychology**: http://www.cwu.edu/~warren/today.html
  With over 3100 events included, chances are good that something important happened today in the history of psychology. Find out!

♦ **Centre for Psychology Resources**: http://psych.athabascau.ca/html/aupr/history.shtml
  This site, sponsored by Athabascu University, has tons of links for various schools of psychology and famous psychologists.

WHAT KIND OF PSYCHOLOGIST ARE YOU?

1.   Human beings are driven by:
    a.   irrational passions.
    b   external events.
    c.   brain-based mental processes.
    d.   their desire to be the best they can be.
    e.   instincts.

2.   We can learn more about humankind by studying:
    a.   people's dreams.
    b.   people's behaviors.
    c.   people's brains.
    d.   model humans.
    e.   their predecessors, animals.

3.   How do parents most influence their children?
    a.   By causing pain, which becomes hidden and will be uncovered later.
    b.   By rewarding and punishing their children.
    c.   By providing a model for future relationships.
    d.   By providing a good environment to help them develop to their fullest potential.
    e.   By passing on their genetics.

4.   Humans:
    a.   are basically aggressive people.
    b.   can be bad or good, depending on their environments.
    c.   are basically rational, reasoning beings.
    d.   are basically good, although some may be corrupted by bad experiences in life.
    e.   are basically selfish people, who are driven to reproduce.

5.   Mental illness:
    a.   results from repressed pain.
    b.   results from negative experiences.
    c.   results from negative thoughts.
    d.   results from a person not being valued unconditionally.
    e.   is inborn, a result of bad genetics.

6.   What kind of evidence is needed to prove a psychological fact?
    a.   anecdotal evidence from cases of people seeing psychologists
    b.   behaviors, observed in lab settings
    c.   evidence of brain functioning (e.g., from a brain scan)
    d.   anecdotal evidence from cases of exceptional human beings
    e.   evidence that a certain phenomenon exists in multiple cultures

Compare your answers with those at the end of the book to find out what kind of psychologist you are. (Although you could probably take a good guess as to which theory is represented by each letter!) Do you agree with these results?

Early Days

When did the interest in **mental processes** and **behavior** start? Who started it? _____
_____
_____

Was this the same time that the field of **psychology** started? Why or why not? _____
_____
_____

How did the schools of **structuralism** and **functionalism** differ? _____
_____
_____

Has **functionalism** made any contributions to psychology that endure until today? If so, what are
they? _____
_____
_____

How are **structuralism** and **Gestalt psychology** similar and different? _____
_____
_____

How is **Gestalt psychology** related to current psychological research? _____
_____
_____

Psychodynamic Theory

What are the drawbacks to **psychodynamic theory** (as proposed by **Freud**)?_____
_____
_____

List some of the positive consequences of **psychodynamic theory**:

1. _____

2. _____

3. _____

4. _____

5. _____

Behaviorism

Behaviorists pointed out that the consequences of a people's behavior influence whether the behavior is repeated. If the consequences are good, then a person will be more likely to repeat a behavior. If the consequences are bad, then a person will be less likely to repeat it.

Describe a situation in which you were more or less likely to do something because you had previously experienced the consequences of that behavior. _____
_____
_____

Humanistic Psychology

How do you think **humanistic psychology** has influenced many of the therapies now used? (You can check your answers in Chapter 15.) _____
_____
_____

Cognitive Revolution

The **Cognitive Revolution** led to a tremendous change in American psychology. Before the **Cognitive Revolution**, the predominant theory had been **behaviorism**. Afterwards, it became **cognitive psychology**. How are **cognitive psychology** and **behaviorism** different?
_____
_____

What effects have new technologies, such as **brain-scanning** equipment, had on the field?
_____
_____

Evolutionary Psychology

How is **evolutionary psychology** similar to **functionalism**? _____
_____
_____

How does **evolutionary psychology** differ from **functionalism**? _____
_____
_____

What evidence do **evolutionary psychologists** look for? Why?_____
_____
_____

What is the fundamental limitation of **evolutionary psychology**?_____
_____

Looking at Levels

Researchers have found that men claimed they would be more upset if their mates had sex with someone else, but women claimed they would be more upset if their mates became emotionally involved with someone else. The difference between men and women was larger in the United States than in European countries. Name some of the factors, at each of the **three levels**, that may have influence men and women's feelings. Draw arrows indicating how events at the different levels may interact.

The Brain	The Person	The Group

TRY PRACTICE TEST #2 NOW!
GOOD LUCK!

The Psychological Way:
What Today's Psychologists Do

Do you know any **psychologists**? If so, what do they do? _____
_____

Kosslyn & Rosenberg identify 3 main types of psychologists: **clinical/counseling psychologists**, **academic psychologists**, and **applied psychologists**. For each of these types of psychologists, give their job descriptions and what degrees they have.

Type of Psychologists	Job Description	Degree
Clinical/counseling psychologists		
Academic psychologists		
Applied psychologists		

The following are jobs related to **psychology**. Describe the jobs and the degrees these professionals must have.

Job	Job Description	Degree
Psychiatrist		
Psychiatric nurse		
Social worker		

Clinical/Counseling Psychologists

Students often say that they want to be **clinical or counseling psychologists** so they can "help people." What skills do you think a **clinical or counseling psychologist** must have, beyond this motivation? _____

_____

What difficulties do you think **clinical or counseling psychologists** might face? _____

_____

_____

How might the recent health-care events (such as the increase in managed care) affect **clinical and counseling psychologists**? _____

_____

_____

Academic Psychologists

GO SURFING...

...to find out all the different specialties within psychology. (Your book lists only a few.) All the divisions of the American Psychology Association (APA) will give you an idea of all the different subfields. Here is the official APA website: http://www.apa.org/. Follow the Quick Links to Divisions.

List some of the other subfields not mentioned in your text here:

_____

_____

_____

Do any of them sound especially interesting to you? Which ones?

_____

_____

Visit your school's website and discover what types of **psychologists** are on faculty at your school. Below, list some of the professors and their specialties. Keep this for later reference, especially if you are considering a major in psychology!

Professor	Specialty

What do they do? You may wonder what your professors do all day—after all, they just teach a few classes a week and hold a few office hours, right? You might be surprised! Here are just a few of the things that professors do. Take a guess about how many hours a week they spend on each task. Then, ask your psychology professor for his or her estimate.

Task	Your Estimate	Your Professor's Estimate
Teaching (including preparing for class, in-class time, grading, consulting with students, & holding office hours)		
Research/Scholarly Activity (including planning and conducting studies, writing studies for publication, & other writing projects--like your textbook!)		
Service (work on university committees, on psychology-related committees, presentations in various venues, & service in community organizations		
Advising Students (formally and informally)		

Applied Psychologists

How do the jobs of **academic** and **applied psychologists** differ? How are they similar?

_____

_____

Where might each of these types of **applied psychologists** look for jobs? What kind of companies could they work for? What would they be doing?

Type of Applied Psychologist	Job Possibilities	Companies	Job Description
Cognitive psychologist			
Developmental psychologist			
Human factors psychologist			
Industrial/ organizational psychologist			
Personality psychologist			
Physiological psychologist			
School (educational) psychologist			
Social psychologist			
Sport psychologist			

GO SURFING...

...to find out what the job outlooks are like for various types of psychologists, holding various degrees. Use this to fill out the chart on the next page. Some places to start are:

♦ **Occupational Outlook Handbook, by the U.S. Department of Labor**
http://www.bls.gov/oco/home.htm
Allows you to search by occupation. Be sure to notice all the subspecialties of psychology.

♦ **O*Net OnLine, by the National O*Net Consortium**
http://online.onetcenter.org/
Provides information about the working environments and tasks of various jobs, including psychologists.

♦ **American Psychological Association**
www.apa.org
Use the APA search engine to find out what recent psychology majors and Psychology Ph.D.'s are doing with their degrees.

Type of Psychologists	Working Environment
Clinical/counseling psychologists	
Academic psychologists	
Applied psychologists	

If you were going to be a **psychologist**, what type would you want to be? Why? _____
_____

Would you have a preferred sub-field (e.g., developmental, social, personality, etc.)?_____
_____

What is the outlook like for this type of psychologist? _____
_____

What type of degree would you need to be this type of psychologist? _____

What could you do with a bachelor's degree in psychology?_____
_____

Looking at Levels

Here are some commonly heard statements. Take a guess as to whether these statements are true or false. Then, check your book (page references provided) to see if you were right.

Statement	Your Guess	Fact
If someone talks about suicide, she just wants attention. (p. 584)	TRUE FALSE	TRUE FALSE
People become homosexual because they were mistreated as children. (p. 428)	TRUE FALSE	TRUE FALSE
Opposites attract. (p. 696)	TRUE FALSE	TRUE FALSE
Out of sight – out of mind. (p. 696)	TRUE FALSE	TRUE FALSE
This generation is dumber than the last. (p. 359)	TRUE FALSE	TRUE FALSE

TRY PRACTICE TEST #3 NOW!
GOOD LUCK!

Ethics: Doing It Right

Ethics in Research

GO SURFING...

...to find out more about the controversy about whether Nazi research should be used. Here is a starting point: *The ethics of using medical data from Nazi experiments*, by Baruch Cohen, at http://www.jlaw.com/Articles/NaziMedEx.html.

The Nazis conducted horrific studies on Holocaust victims. List some of those studies here:

_____
_____

Some people argue that the results of these studies should be used, if appropriate. Again, surf the web. Then, summarize this position. What do *you* think? Should data collected in an unethical way ever be used? Under what conditions? Why or why not?

_____

_____

Briefly summarize, *in your own words*, the five general **ethical principles** of psychologists:

PRINCIPLE A:

_____

_____

_____

PRINCIPLE B:

_____

_____

_____

PRINCIPLE C:

_____

_____

_____

PRINCIPLE D:

_____

_____

_____

PRINCIPLE E:

_____

_____

_____

Now, suppose that you were a member of your school's **Institutional Review Board** (IRB). Consider the following scenarios. What are the ethical considerations in each of them?

SITUATION #1: You plan to study the effects of competition on ability to solve math problems. Half of the subjects will be told that you want to see what approach they take in solving math problems. The other half will be told that you want to see which person chooses the best approach.

Ethical considerations: _____

_____

_____

SITUATION #2: You plan to compare the intellectual skills of retired people to those of sophomores. To recruit sophomores, you plan to arrange for volunteers to receive an A in their psychology course and for nonvolunteers to have their grades lowered. To recruit retired people, you plan to go to a retirement community each evening next week, knock at people's doors, and ask them to work some puzzles without explaining all of the details of the study because most would not understand.

Ethical considerations: _____
_____
_____

SITUATION #3: To study self-esteem in children, you plan to have 8-year-olds draw pictures of themselves and their friends and to answer some questions. You plan to ask a teacher friend of yours to let you test some of her students.

Ethical considerations: _____
_____
_____

Ethics in Clinical Practice

Name three specific things that it would be unethical for a clinical psychologist to do. Explain which of the general **ethical principles** is involved in this situation.

Unethical Action	Related General Ethical Principle

Looking at Levels

How can psychologists justify trying new treatments and thus delaying the use of established treatments? Consider the factors at the **three levels** that might influence psychologists' decisions. Draw arrows between the factors to indicate how they may interact.

The Brain	The Person	The Group

TRY PRACTICE TEST #4 NOW!
GOOD LUCK!

After You Read. . . Thinking Ahead

The theories that you learned in this chapter will come up again and again, throughout the textbook.
Can you imagine what some of these theorists would say about these topics? Take a shot!
Check your answers as they come up.

Theory	Emotion	Personality	Psychological Disorders	Therapy
Psychodynamic Theorist				
Behaviorist				
Humanistic Psychologist				
Cognitive Psychologist				
Cognitive Neuroscientist				
Evolutionary Psychologist				

After You Read. . . Practice Tests

PRACTICE TEST #1:
THE SCIENCE OF PSYCHOLOGY

True/False Questions

Circle TRUE or FALSE for each of the following statements.

1.   TRUE   FALSE   Psychologists want to predict and control behavior. (p. 5)

2.   TRUE   FALSE   Psychology avoids speculation. (p. 10)

3.   TRUE   FALSE   Psychology does not study observable behaviors. (p. 15)

4.   TRUE   FALSE   The level of the brain never influences the level of the group. (p. 7)

5.   TRUE   FALSE   Relationships would be events at the level of the group. (p. 7)

Multiple-Choice Questions

For each question, circle the best answer from the choices given.

1.   Psychology is defined by the authors as the science of: (p. 4)
    a.   Mental processes and behavior.
    b.   Behavior and emotions.
    c.   Human and animal behavior.
    d.   Normal and deviant behavior.

2.   Which of the following is NOT a mental process? (p. 4)
    a.   Thinking.
    b.   Memorizing.
    c.   Feeling happy.
    d.   Jumping for joy.

3.   Talking involves: (p. 5)
    a.   A behavior.
    b.   A mental process.
    c.   The level of the brain.
    d.   All of the above.

4. Which of the following questions would be <u>least</u> likely to be answered by a psychologist? (p. 7)
    a. How do people store memories?
    b. Are there basic human rights?
    c. Are personalities more influenced by genetics or the environment?
    d. How would damage to the frontal lobes affect a person's thinking?

5. How does psychology differ from philosophy? (p. 10)
    a. Psychologists are interested in the study of behavior, whereas philosophers are interested in the study of mental processes.
    b. Psychologists are interested in the study of mental processes, whereas philosophers are interested in the study of behaviors.
    c. Psychologists use logic and data to answer questions, whereas philosophers use only logic to answer questions.
    d. Psychologists use data to answer questions, whereas philosophers use logic.

6. The four goals of psychology are to: (p. 5)
    a. Predict, describe, explain, control.
    b. Predict, contribute, describe, answer.
    c. Theorize, control, describe, explain.
    d. Describe, explain, hypothesize, answer.

7. At the level of the _____, psychologists focus on beliefs, desires, and feelings. (p. 7)
    a. Brain
    b. Person
    c. Group
    d. Culture

8. Which of the following is not likely to happen? (p. 8)
    a. Events at the level of the person affect events at the level of the brain.
    b. Events at the level of the group affect events at the level of the brain.
    c. Events at the level of the person affect events at the level of the group.
    d. All are likely to happen.

9. The brain damage that a person suffered during a car accident would be an event at: (p. 8)
    a. The level of the brain.
    b. The level of the person.
    c. The level of the group.
    d. All levels.

10. Among the Maasai, the infants who were most likely to survive the drought were the ones who were: (p. 8)
    a. Calm and cooperative.
    b. Testy and demanding.
    c. Small in size.
    d. Cared for by a single person.

PRACTICE TEST #2:
PSYCHOLOGY THEN AND NOW

Fill-in-the-Blank Questions
Fill in each blank with a word from the word bank.

WORD BANK	
behavior	information processing
behaviorism	introspection
brain	mental processes
brain scans	philosophy
cognitive	physiology
cognitive neuroscience	psychodynamic
computer	psychology
evolutionary	science
functionalism	structuralism
Gestalt	unconscious drives

In 1879, Wilhelm Wundt established the first _____ laboratory in Leipzig, Germany. This new field shared its interests with _____; however, because it is a _____, its methods are more similar to _____. Over time, the field has evolved and many theories have emerged. Wundt's school of psychology was called _____. These psychologists used _____ as the primary method of data collection. Other schools of psychology with European roots include _____ psychology, which takes its name from the German word for "whole," and Freud's _____ school, which focused on people's _____.

William James brought psychology to America. His school of psychology, _____, was strongly influenced by Charles Darwin, as was the more recent school of _____ psychology. However, the predominant school of psychology in America in the early 20th century was _____. As its name suggests, this school focused primarily on people's _____. In fact, _____ were not much studied by American psychologists until after the _____ revolution in the 1950s. Many psychologists taking this perspective used a _____ metaphor to study human _____. Recent technologies, such as _____, have been important in the development of _____, which blends cognitive psychology with neuroscience (the study of the _____). (p. 10-18)

Matching Questions

Match the following names with the school of thought. Write the matching letter in the blank on the left.

_____1.   Wilhelm Wundt (p. 10)   A.   Psychodynamic

_____2.   Max Wertheimer (p. 13)   B.   Cognitive

_____3.   William James (p. 12)   C.   Gestalt

_____4.   Sigmund Freud (p. 14)   D.   Behaviorism

_____5.   James B. Watson (p. 15)   E.   Structuralism

_____6.   Carl Rogers (p. 16)   F.   Evolutionary

_____7.   Herbert Simon (p. 17)   G.   Functionalism

_____8.   David Buss (p. 18)   H.   Humanism

Multiple-Choice Questions

For each question, circle the best answer from the choices given.

1. Gestalt psychologists focused primarily on the level of the: (p. 13)
   a. Brain.
   b. Person.
   c. Group.
   d. All of the above

2. The key idea of psychodynamic theory is that: (p. 14)
   a. The whole is greater than the sum of its parts.
   b. Some individuals possess characteristics that enable them to survive and reproduce more fruitfully than others.
   c. Only directly observable behavior should be the subject matter of psychology.
   d. Behavior is driven by mental processes often hidden from conscious awareness.

3. According to behaviorists, people behave in certain ways because: (p. 16)
   a. They are reinforced for their behaviors.
   b. They want to.
   c. It is part of the basic human desire to self-actualize.
   d. They unconsciously wish to be successful.

4. Self-actualization is a goal of _____ psychology. (p. 16)
   a. Behavioral.
   b. Humanistic.
   c. Gestalt.
   d. Cognitive.

5. Cultural universality is the best source of evidence for _____ psychology. (p. 19)
   a. Behavioral
   b. Evolutionary
   c. Humanistic
   d. Cognitive

6. Gestalt psychology has influenced the modern study of: (p. 13)
   a. Perception.
   b. The brain.
   c. Memory.
   d. Psychotherapy.

7. Which of the following is NOT one of the long-term influences of Freud's psychodynamic theory? (pp. 14-15)
   a. The idea that some mental processes are hidden from awareness.
   b. The creation of new approaches to treating psychological problems.
   c. Attention to different kinds of observations, like tip-of-the-tongue phenomena
   d. An emphasis on cultural relativism.

8. How are behaviorism and cognitive psychology different? (p. 17)
   a. Behaviorism relies on the scientific method, whereas cognitive psychology does not.
   b. Mental processes play no part in behaviorism, whereas they are central to cognitive psychology.
   c. Behaviorists do not believe that there is such a thing as mental illness, whereas cognitive psychologists do.
   d. Cognitive psychologists attach no importance to social experiences, whereas behaviorists do.

9. Which of the following has NOT been influenced by behaviorism? (p. 16)
   a. Recognition of need for rigor in psychological studies
   b. Education
   c. Psychotherapy
   d. Neuro-imaging technologies

10. Which of the following was the first American school of psychology? (p. 12)
    a. Structuralism
    b. Functionalism
    c. Gestalt psychology
    d. Behaviorism

PRACTICE TEST #3:
THE PSYCHOLOGICAL WAY

Matching Questions

Match the following psychologists and other task-related individuals with the activities they would typically engage in. Put the matching letter in the space at the left.

_____1.	Clinical psychologist (p. 21)	A.	Prescribes medication
_____2.	Clinical neuropsychologist (p. 22)	B.	Studies individual differences in preferences
_____3.	Counseling psychologist (p. 22)	C.	Studies thinking, memory, and related topics
_____4.	Psychiatrist (p. 22)	D.	Diagnoses the effects of brain damage
_____5.	Social worker (p. 23)	E.	Studies biological structures and functions related to psychological phenomena
_____6.	Psychiatric nurse (p. 23)	F.	Does teaching and scholarship
_____7.	Academic psychologist (p. 24)	G.	Helps people with serious problems
_____8.	Developmental psychologist (p. 24)	H.	Helps athletes improve performance
_____9.	Cognitive psychologist (p. 23)	I.	Studies how groups function
_____10.	Social psychologist (p. 25)	J.	Works with educators to help children in schools
_____11.	Personality psychologist (p. 25)	K.	Helps people with normal stressors
_____12.	Physiological psychologist (p. 25)	L.	Focuses on using psychology in the workplace
_____13.	Industrial/organizational psychologist (p. 25)	M.	Has master's degree in nursing with specialization and works closely with medical doctors
_____14.	Sport psychologist (p. 25)	N.	Studies how people during life
_____15.	School psychologist (p. 25)	O.	Has an MSW and frequently works with families

Multiple-Choice Questions

For each question, circle the best answer from the choices given.

1.   Psychiatrists are able to _____ and most psychologists are not. (p. 22)
        a.   Prescribe drugs
        b.   Sleep with their patients
        c.   Use psychotherapy
        d.   Work in a hospital setting

2.   A _____ psychologist is likely to study obedience, conformity, and prejudice. (p. 22)
        a.   Clinical
        b.   Humanistic
        c.   Social
        d.   Personality

3.   Which of the following professionals would be least likely to perform psychotherapy? (p. 22)
        a.   Psychiatrist
        b.   Counseling psychologist
        c.   Social psychologist
        d.   Social worker

4.   How are academic and applied psychology different? (pp. 23-24)
        a.   There are many sub-specialties of academic psychology (e.g., developmental, social, etc.), whereas there are not with applied psychology.
        b.   Applied psychologists do research whereas academic psychologists do not.
        c.   Academic psychologists do research whereas applied psychologists do not.
        d.   By definition, applied psychologists help to solve specific practical problems, whereas academic psychologists may study practical or theoretical problems.

5.   Which of the following are there more of? (pp. 24-25)
        a.   Clinical psychologists
        b.   Counseling psychologists
        c.   School psychologists
        d.   Human factors psychologists

6.   The mere-exposure effect would say that you are more likely to prefer: (p. 26)
        a.   Professor Sleepy, who teaches your English class on Monday nights
        b.   Professor Sneezy, who teaches your Chemistry class on Mondays, Wednesdays, and Fridays (and the Thursday labs)
        c.   Professor Happy, who teaches your Tuesday/Thursday Psychology class
        d.   Professor Grumpy, who teaches your Monday/Wednesday/Friday History class

7. In which location would you be LEAST likely to find an applied psychologist? (pp. 24-25)
    a. A company
    b. A school
    c. A government office
    d. A college

8. How are clinical and counseling psychology different? (pp. 21-22)
    a. Clinical psychologists tend to use behavioral therapies, whereas counseling psychologists are more likely to use psychotherapy.
    b. Clinical psychologists will prescribe medications, whereas counseling psychologists don't.
    c. Clinical psychologists have Ph.D.s, whereas counseling psychologists have only master's degrees.
    d. Clinical psychologists would be more likely to deal with people with mental disorders, whereas counseling psychologists deal with issues that we all face.

9. Which of the following is NOT typically a function of an academic psychologist? (p. 23)
    a. Teaching
    b. Counseling students about personal problems
    c. Advising students about their classes
    d. Research

10. Social psychology and industrial-organizational psychology are alike in that they both: (p. 23 & p. 25)
    a. Focus on the level of the person.
    b. Focus on the level of the brain.
    c. Study people in a group context.
    d. Work in applied settings.

PRACTICE TEST #4:
ETHICS

Matching Questions

Match the given situation to the general ethical principle it violates. Write the matching letter in the space at the left.

_____1.   Beneficence &   A.   Falsifying some data
            Nonmaleficence (p. 29)

_____2.   Fidelity & Responsibility   B.   Overburdening a student assistant
            (p. 29)   with work, to the point that the
                                              assistant becomes ill

_____3.   Integrity (p. 29)   C.   Failing to publish some data, because it
                                        doesn't support the psychologist's
                                        political agenda

_____4.   Justice (p. 29)   D.   Providing therapy to both spouses
                                        during a messy divorce, without telling
                                        either spouse

_____5.   Respect for People's   E.   Deciding not to hire a young female
            Rights & Dignity (p. 29)   applicant to be a new professor
                                           because she may need maternity
                                           leave soon

Multiple-Choice Questions

For each question, circle the best answer from the choices given.

1. Before a study commences, participants must sign a(n) _____; after the study, they
    must be _____. (p. 27)
    a.. Debriefing; informed.
    b.   Informed consent; debriefed.
    c.   Affidavit; paid.
    d.   Contract; reimbursed.

2. An informed consent must include: (p. 27)
    a.   A description of what the participants will be asked to do.
    b.   A description of any risks and benefits of the procedure.
    c.   A statement that they can withdraw from the study at any time without penalty.
    d.   All of the above.

3.   In California (and most other states), if a client threatens the life of another individual, his/her therapist must: (p. 28)
      a.   Inform the individual of the threat.
      b.   Do nothing – it would be a breech of confidentiality.
      c.   Place the client under house arrest.
      d.   Discontinue treatment with the client.

4.   Research has found that people with schizophrenia benefit greatly if: (p. 29)
      a.   They receive psychotherapy.
      b.   They are placed in a group home.
      c.   They are medicated immediately.
      d.   They are allowed to leave their jobs.

5.   Which of the following would be *unethical* for a clinical psychologist to do? (p. 28)
      a.   Use a new technique in therapy after being trained appropriately.
      b.   Break confidentiality to tell a person that his/her life has been threatened by the clinician's patient.
      c.   Engage in sexual relations with a patient.
      d.   Advertise his/her services.

6.   Which of the following would NOT be included in an informed consent? (p. 27)
      a.   Information about the risks of the study
      b.   Information about the benefits of the study
      c.   Information about what journal will publish the results of the study
      d.   A notice that the participants can withdraw from the study at any time

7.   In what situations are psychologists allowed to deceive research participants? (p. 27)
      a.   When they obtain approval from the participants' parents
      b.   When they debrief participants
      c.   When they obtain informed consent
      d.   When participants will not be harmed and the knowledge to be gained outweighs the use of dishonesty

8.   In animal studies, what is the role of the IRB? (p. 28)
      a.   None
      b.   To ensure that they are not mistreated
      c.   To ensure that they are adopted, after the study is finished
      d.   To prohibit any studies that involve inflicting pain

9.   What spurred the development of codes of professional ethics? (p. 26)
      a.   The 1996 study of suicidal teens in New York
      b.   Nuremberg trials following World War II
      c.   Animal rights movement
      d.   Cognitive Revolution

10. Who is on an IRB? (p. 27)
    a. Psychologists
    b. Representatives from the local community
    c. Clergy
    d. All of the above

COMPREHENSIVE PRACTICE TEST

True/False Questions

Circle TRUE or FALSE for each of the following statements.

1. TRUE   FALSE   The founder of psychology was Sigmund Freud. (p. 10)

2. TRUE   FALSE   Early behaviorists focused on mental processes. (p. 15)

3. TRUE   FALSE   Humanistic psychology emphasizes free will and personal growth. (p. 16)

4. TRUE   FALSE   Evolutionary theories are easy to test. (p. 19)

5. TRUE   FALSE   Clinical psychologists must hold a Ph.D. to practice psychology. (p. 22)

6. TRUE   FALSE   William James established the first psychological laboratory in America. (p. 12)

7. TRUE   FALSE   Psychologists want to know how to control people's behavior. (p. 5)

8. TRUE   FALSE   In some states, clinical psychologists can prescribe medications. (p. 22)

9. TRUE   FALSE   Developmental psychologists do psychotherapy with children. (pp. 23-24)

10. TRUE   FALSE   Psychologists are never allowed to deceive research participants. (p. 27)

Matching Questions

Match the motto (or, in some cases, quotes) that would best describe each theory. Write the matching number in the space to the left.

_____1   Structuralism   (p. 11)   A.   "The whole is more than just the sum of its parts."

_____2.   Functionalism (p. 12)   B.   "Be all you can be."

_____3.   Gestalt psychology (p. 13)   C.   "Tell me about your mother."

_____4.   Psychodynamic theory (p. 14)   D.   "The mind is what the brain does."

_____5.   Behaviorism (p. 16)   E.   "The real question is not whether machines think but whether men do."

_____6.   Cognitive psychology (p. 17)   F.   "The brain can be explained by natural selection." (p. 17)

_____7.   Cognitive neuroscience (p. 18)   G.   "The human mind is like a computer."

_____8.   Humanistic psychology (p. 16)   I.   "What is that for?"

_____9.   Evolutionary psychology (p. 18) J.   "Look within."

Multiple-Choice Questions

For each question, circle the best answer from the choices given.

1.   Psychologists who focus on culture study events at the level of the: (p. 7)
    a.   Brain.
    b.   Person.
    c.   Group.
    d.   Neuron.

2.   Among the Maasai, the difficult babies were more likely to survive the drought than were the easy babies because they: (p. 8)
    a.   Were healthier.
    b.   Were older.
    c.   Had better immune systems.
    d.   Were more demanding.

3.   The first formal movement in psychology was: (p. 10)
    a.   Behaviorism.
    b.   Structuralism.
    c.   Psychoanalysis.
    d.   Functionalism.

4.	The problem with the research method of introspection was: (p. 11)
	a.	That it couldn't be verified.
	b.	That it relied on expensive equipment that most psychologists couldn't afford.
	c.	That it ignored the level of the group.
	d.	That it didn't focus on mental processes.

5.	It was the _____ who led us to realize that the observation of animals could provide clues to human behavior. (p. 12)
	a.	Structuralists
	b.	Functionalists
	c.	Behaviorists
	d.	Psychoanalysts

6.	Which of the following would behaviorists be LEAST interested in studying? (p. 15)
	a.	Environmental antecedents
	b.	Unconscious processes
	c.	Stimulus—response associations
	d.	Reinforcements

7.	The cognitive neuroscience approach considers events at the three levels of analysis, but with a primary focus on the: (p. 18)
	a.	Brain.
	b.	Group.
	c.	Person.
	d.	Interactions of the three levels.

8.	Which professional would need the LEAST amount of education to get a job? (p. 22)
	a.	A psychiatrist
	b.	A social worker
	c.	An academic psychologist
	d.	A clinical psychologist

9.	A _____ psychologist studies individual differences in preferences and inclinations. (p. 23)
	a.	Social
	b.	Personality
	c.	Neuropsychologist
	d.	Developmental

10.	A therapist may engage in sexual relations with his/her client: (p. 28)
	a.	If he/she knew the client before therapy.
	b.	If he/she terminates therapy.
	c.	If the client is being seen for a non-emotional, behavioral problem.
	d.	Never.

11. In comparing and contrasting the various schools of psychology, which of the following is FALSE? (pp. 16, 18)
    a. Functionalism is similar to evolutionary psychology in that they both were influenced by Darwin.
    b. Cognitive psychology is similar to psychodynamic theory in that they both focus on mental processes.
    c. Psychodynamic theory is similar to evolutionary psychology in that both are hard to test.
    d. Humanistic psychology is similar to evolutionary psychology in that both view humans as generally good.

12. Which of the following would be an event at the level of the person? (p. 7)
    a. Brain injury following a fall from a cliff
    b. The decision to use drugs
    c. Exposure to the media
    d. World War II

13. How do the levels of analysis interact? (p. 8)
    a. Each level interacts with the next "bigger" level (e.g., the brain impacts the person and the person impacts the world).
    b. Each level interacts with the next "smaller" level (e.g., the person impacts the brain and the world impacts the person).
    c. All levels interact one time.
    d. All levels interact continuously.

14. Which of the following disciplines has LEAST influenced psychology? (p. 10)
    a. English
    b. Computer science
    c. Biology
    d. Philosophy

15. Modern psychology is grounded in all previous schools of psychology. Which of the following is a FALSE statement about the roots of modern psychology? (p. 17)
    a. The scientific standards set by behaviorists are still used today.
    b. Gestalt psychology has influenced the modern study of perception.
    c. The humanistic view of people has influenced modern therapy.
    d. The behaviorists' view that behavior is driven by mental processes is still applicable today.

16. Structuralism and modern psychology differ MOST in: (p. 11)
    a. Their methods.
    b. Their ethical standards.
    c. The emphasis they place on mental processes.
    d. Their interest in therapeutic application.

17. Put the following schools of psychology in order of their development (from earliest to latest). (pp. 14, 17, 18)
    a. Psychodynamic, cognitive, evolutionary, behaviorist
    b. Functionalism, behaviorism, cognitive neuroscience, evolutionary
    c. Structuralism, Gestalt, cognitive neuroscience, humanistic
    d. Humanistic, Gestalt, psychodynamic, evolutionary

18. Which of the following schools of psychology did NOT originate in Europe? (p. 15)
    a. Gestalt
    b. Structuralism
    c. Behaviorism
    d. Psychodynamic

19. Evolutionary psychology is difficult to study because: (p. 18)
    a. We don't know much about what our ancestors were like.
    b. Most people are resistant to the idea that we had primate ancestors.
    c. People will not admit to their baser instincts.
    d. It is not an important school of psychology.

20. Which of the following people is most likely to be working as an applied psychologist? (p. 24)
    a. Humpty, who studies how people adjust to prostheses
    b. Jack and Jill, who counsel people who have been through serious traumas
    c. Little Miss Muffet, who studies why people are more afraid of spiders than cars
    d. Old King Cole, who teaches Introduction to Psychology at Harvard

Essay Questions

Answer each question in the space provided.

1. How might a researcher come to understand depression at the levels of the brain, the person, and the group?_____
   _____
   _____
   _____
   _____
   _____
   _____
   _____
   _____
   _____

2.   How might an evolutionary psychologist, a psychodynamic theorist, and a behaviorist interpret a child's fearfulness at separating from his/her mother?_____

_____

_____

_____

_____

_____

_____

_____

_____

_____

3.   Why would it be a bad idea for an academic psychologist who has clinical training to also work in the counseling center at the school at which he or she teaches?_____

_____

_____

_____

_____

_____

_____

4.   How might a psychiatrist, psychologist, and social worker each approach a client suffering from an eating disorder?_____

_____

_____

_____

_____

_____

_____

_____

_____

_____

_____

When You Are Finished. . . Puzzle It Out

Across

3. Psychologist teaching at college
7. Number of levels
9. Established first psychological lab
10. "Whole"
12. Psychologist who studies groups
13. Major figure in behaviorism
15. Degree held by psychiatrist
16. Founder of psychodynamic theory
18. School's ethical committee
19. Influence on functionalism
20. Given after research participation

Down

1. Cognitive neuroscientists' tool
2. Brought psychology to America
4. Newest school of psychology
5. Led to #11 down
6. Human nature per humanists
8. Psychologists solving real problems
11. Revolution during 1950s-1970s
14. Structuralists' method
17. Only allowed if benefit > risk

Puzzle created with Puzzlemaker at DiscoverySchool.com.

Chapter 2
The Research Process: How We Find Things Out

Before You Read . . .

Different academic disciplines gain knowledge in different ways. For example, English professors and students gain knowledge by reading and considering what others have written. Philosophers gain knowledge by thinking logically about different issues. Psychologists are like other scientists (including sociologists, chemists, biologists, and many others) in that they gain knowledge through the scientific method. Can you think of advantages to using the scientific method versus other ways of gaining knowledge?

In this chapter, you will learn about the six steps of the scientific method. You will also learn about how the scientific method is applied to psychology and the advantages of using the scientific method. Because statistics are one part of the scientific method, you will learn about different types of statistics and how psychologists use them. In addition, you will learn about how statistics can be misused by advertisers and others who seek to mislead consumers on certain points. Finally, you will learn tips about how to read research reports and write up your own research.

Chapter Objectives

After studying this chapter, you should be able to:

♦   Describe the benefits of using the scientific method to gain knowledge.

♦   Discuss each of the six steps of the scientific method, including how to perform the step and its significance.

♦   Describe the differences between experimental, correlational, and descriptive research and when you would want to use each kind.

♦   Calculate the various measures of central tendency and variability and understand when to use each measure.

♦   Understand how advertisers and the media can "lie" with statistics.

♦   Understand how to use the QALMRI method to read and write research reports.

As You Read . . . Term Identification

Make flashcards using the following terms as you go. Use the definitions in the margins of this chapter for help. If you write the definitions in your own words, though, you will remember them better!

Bias
Case study
Central tendency
Confound
Control condition
Control group
Correlation
Data
Dependent variable
Descriptive statistics
Double-blind design
Effect
Experimenter expectancy effects
Hypothesis
Independent variable
Inferential statistics
Mean
Median
Meta-analysis
Mode
Normal distribution
Operational definition

Percentile rank
Placebo
Population
Predictions
Pseudopsychology
Random assignment
Range
Raw data
Reliability
Replicated
Response bias
Sample
Sampling bias
Sampling error
Scientific method
Standard deviation
Statistical significance
Statistics
Survey
Theory
Validity
Variable

As You Read . . . Questions and Exercises

The Scientific Method: Designed to Be Valid

Step 1: Specifying a Problem

What does a "problem" mean, in this context?_____
_____
_____

Where do you think scientists get their "problems"? _____
_____
_____
_____
_____

Name some problems or questions that you have that would be suitable for psychological research:

Problem #1 _____

Problem #2 _____

Problem #3 _____

Problem #4 _____

Step 2: Observing Events

What does it mean for a scientist to **replicate** a study?_____
_____
_____
_____

Why do psychologists prefer to use numerical measurements?_____
_____
_____
_____

What are the two kinds of events in which psychologists are interested?

♦   _____
♦   _____

Look at the questions you listed above, under Step 1. What kind of events could you observe for each of these problems?

Problem #1 _____

Problem #2 _____

Problem #3 _____

Problem #4 _____

Step 3: Forming a Hypothesis

What would the opposite of a **variable** be?_____

Can you think of an example? _____

What is a hypothesis?_____

_____

_____

_____

_____

Look at the questions you listed above, under Step 1. Do you have hypotheses about each of these problems?

Problem #1 _____

_____

Problem #2 _____

_____

Problem #3 _____

_____

Problem #4 _____

_____

Step 4: Testing the Hypothesis

What is an **operational definition**?_____

_____

_____

_____

_____

_____

How is an **operational definition** different from any other type of definition? _____

_____

_____

_____

Offer an **operational definition** for one of the variables in your problems above:

Problem #1 _____

_____

Problem #2 _____

_____

Problem #3 _____

_____

Problem #4 _____

_____

Step 5: Formulating a Theory

Compare and contrast hypotheses and theories in the table below.

	Hypotheses	Theories
Similarities		
Differences		

Step 6: Testing a Theory

How can a **theory** be supported? _____
_____
_____
_____

What happens when a **theory** is supported? _____
_____

What leads to a **theory** being rejected? _____
_____
_____
_____

What does it mean for a theory to be **falsifiable**? _____
_____
_____
_____

Looking at Levels

How do factors at the different **levels** affect whether or not sleep apnea impacts cognitive functioning? Draw arrows to indicate how events at the different levels may interact.

The Group	The Brain	The Person

TRY PRACTICE TEST #1 NOW!
GOOD LUCK!

The Psychologist's Toolbox: Techniques of Scientific Research

Name one advantage and one disadvantage for each of the following types of **research**.

Technique	Advantage	Disadvantage
Experimentation		
Quasi-experimentation		
Correlational research		
Naturalistic observation		
Case studies		
Surveys		

Experimental Research

For each of the following hypotheses, indicate the **independent variable** (IV) and **dependent variable** (DV) and think of one possible confound. If you have trouble remembering which variable is the IV and which is the DV, try using the following sentence to help:

The __(dependent variable)__ is dependent on the __(independent variable)__.

♦ Children who are abused during childhood will have lower self-esteem in adulthood than will children who were not abused.
  IV = _____
  DV = _____
  Possible confound = _____

♦ Seniors have better study skills than do freshmen.
  IV = _____
  DV = _____
  Possible confound = _____

♦ The more children watch TV, the less intelligent they are.
  IV = _____
  DV = _____
  Possible confound = _____

♦ Lawyers are more devious than psychologists.
  IV = _____
  DV = _____
  Possible confound = _____

♦ Lawyers make more money than psychologists.
  IV = _____
  DV = _____
  Possible confound = _____

♦ The happier people are with their jobs, the more hours they will work.
  IV = _____
  DV = _____
  Possible confound = _____

♦ Catholic people are more likely to vote Republican than are non-Catholics.
  IV = _____
  DV = _____
  Possible confound = _____

♦ The more religious people are, the less they will be afraid of death.
IV = _____
DV = _____
Possible confound = _____

♦ People who are underweight live longer than people who are overweight.
IV = _____
DV = _____
Possible confound = _____

♦ People who have more than 12 years of education are less likely to get Alzheimer's disease than others.
IV = _____
DV = _____
Possible confound = _____

Describe two ways that researchers can avoid **confounds** in experimental research.

♦ _____
_____
_____
_____

♦ _____
_____
_____
_____
_____
_____

How is a **quasi-experimental design** like an **experiment**? _____
_____
_____

How is a **quasi-experimental design** different from an **experiment**? _____
_____
_____

Correlational Research

A correlation will be a number between _____ and _____. The sign of the correlation indicates _____, while the number indicates
_____.

In the space below, draw scatterplots showing the following correlations:

- ♦   -.70
- ♦   -1.0
- ♦   +.30
- ♦   +.90

-.70

-1.0

+.30

+.90

Find 10 adult friends (or family members) and ask them for their birthweights and current weights. Record the data in the chart below.

Participant	Birthweight	Current Weight
Friend #1		
Friend #2		
Friend #3		
Friend #4		
Friend #5		
Friend #6		
Friend #7		
Friend #8		
Friend #9		
Friend #10		

Now, draw a scatterplot. Record your data on this scatterplot.

Current Weight

Birthweight

Based on this, does it appear that there is a correlation between birthweight and current weight? _____ What size and direction would you estimate the correlation to be? _____

...at one of the following sites and calculate the correlation coefficient for these data, following the directions at the sites.

♦ http://faculty.vassar.edu/lowry/VassarStats.html
    (Choose the "direct-entry method" of basic linear correlation and regression, then enter 10 for the pop-up screen. The correlation coefficient will be abbreviated as *r* in the results.)
♦ http://calculators.stat.ucla.edu/correlation.php
♦ http://math.uc.edu/statistics/statbook/java/StatCalc.html

What **correlation** coefficient did you obtain at one of these sites? _____

How accurate was your prediction? _____

What factors influenced the size of the **correlation**? _____
_____

Descriptive Research

Why might a researcher want to conduct **descriptive research**, given that it does not say anything about a relationship between two variables?_____
_____
_____

Can you think of another person, or type of person, about whom a **case study** might be meaningful or informative (besides those described in the book)? _____
_____
_____

Under what circumstances might a **case study** be particularly useful?_____
_____
_____

What are some of the difficulties with using **surveys** to collect data?

♦ _____
♦ _____
♦ _____
♦ _____
♦ _____
♦ _____

Be a Critical Consumer of Psychology

Provide an example of a measure that is **reliable** and one that is **unreliable**.

♦   **Reliable:** _____

_____

♦   **Unreliable:** _____

_____

Name and describe, in your own words, two sources of **bias** in a study:

♦   _____

_____

_____

_____

♦   _____

_____

_____

_____

_____

How can a researcher unintentionally affect the results of a study?_____

_____

_____

_____

_____

What can a researcher do to ensure that he or she *doesn't* affect the results of a study?_____

_____

_____

_____

_____

Go to the health or science section of a newspaper and find a brief (1-2 paragraph) article about a research study. Obviously, the study was summarized for inclusion in the paper. What questions about the study does the article leave you with? What is the significance of each of these unanswered questions?

♦   **Question:** _____

Importance:_____

♦   **Question:** _____

Importance:_____

♦ **Question:** _____

_____

Importance: _____

_____

What is **pseudopsychology**? _____

_____

_____

_____

_____

Why is ESP not necessarily **pseudopsychology**? _____

_____

_____

_____

_____

Looking at Levels

Suppose that you were working for a private company as a Human Resources executive. If you were charged with hiring a new manager, what types of characteristics would you look for in a candidate? At what levels are each of these factors? _____

_____

_____

_____

How might the particular group for which you were hiring the manager affect your decision? Why?

_____

_____

_____

TRY PRACTICE TEST #2 NOW!
GOOD LUCK!

Statistics: Measuring Reality

Descriptive Statistics

What are **descriptive statistics**? _____

_____

_____

_____

How do **descriptive** and **inferential statistics** differ?_____

_____

_____

_____

Some studies indicate that **placebos** are equally effective treatment as some medicines. Why might
this be? How might placebos have this effect?_____

_____

_____

_____

Find 10 friends and ask them about their exercise and their sleep schedules. Specifically, ask them
how many hours per day they exercise and then ask them how many hours per night they sleep. List
the **raw data** here.

Participant	Hours of Exercise	Hours of Sleep
Friend #1		
Friend #2		
Friend #3		
Friend #4		
Friend #5		
Friend #6		
Friend #7		
Friend #8		
Friend #9		
Friend #10		

Now, calculate all three **measures of central tendency** for each of these variables.

Hours of Exercise
♦   **Mean =** _____
♦   **Median =**_____
♦   **Mode=**_____

Hours of Sleep
♦   **Mean =** _____
♦   **Median =**_____
♦   **Mode=**_____

Draw a **frequency distribution** of the hours of exercise your friends get. Remember that frequency (or, the number of friends who exercise for a particular amount of time) is on the Y axis; the hours of exercise they get, on the X axis.

**Number of Friends
With this Response
(Frequency)**

Hours of Exercise

Draw a **frequency distribution** showing the number of hours of exercise your friends get. Remember that frequency (or, the number of friends who exercise for a particular amount of time) is on the Y axis; the hours of sleep they get, on the X axis.

**Number of Friends
With this Response
(Frequency)**

Hours of Sleep

Do your frequency distributions appear to be **normal** or **skewed**?

♦   **Hours of Exercise** distribution: _____
♦   **Hours of Sleep** distribution:_____

Given this, which **measure of central tendency** would be the most appropriate to use? _____
_____

Can you think of a situation in which the *only* possible **measure of central tendency** you could use would be the mode? Describe such a situation._____
_____
_____

Calculate the **range** for both the hours of exercise and for the hours of sleep.

- ♦   **Hours of Exercise** range: _____
- ♦   **Hours of Sleep** range:_____

If someone were to say that your work was "**standard**," what would that mean to you?_____
_____
_____

If someone were to call you a "**deviant**," what would that mean to you? _____
_____
_____

So, if you put these words together to get **standard deviation**, what would this mean?_____
_____
_____

Calculate the **standard deviation** for the hours of sleep data obtained above.

First, rewrite your data in the first column. In the second column, calculate **deviation scores** by subtracting the mean from each answer.

Hours of Sleep	Deviation Score (Mean – Answer)

Now, add up all the **deviation scores**. What did you get? _____ You should have gotten 0. (If not, you made an error someplace.) Because you got 0, you cannot calculate an average.

Next take the **deviation scores** and square them.

Deviation Score	Deviation Score Squared

Now, add up the **squared deviation scores**. What did you get? _____

There are two problems with using this number as a **measure of variability**:
♦   This is a *total* number, not an *average* (as called for by the definition of **standard deviation**).
♦   This number represents *squared* hours, not regular hours.

So, you need to take care of both of these problems. First, take the **average (mean) of the squared deviation scores**. What did you get?_____

Next, undo the squaring that you did early by taking the square root of the average you just calculated. What did you get? _____ This is the **standard deviation** of the data set.

The **standard deviation** will tell you how different values fall in the frequency distribution.
♦   Subtract the standard deviation from the mean. What did you get? _____
♦   Add the standard deviation to the mean. What did you get?_____

Approximately 68% of your data points (e.g., your friends' answers about the number of hours of sleep they get) should fall between these two numbers.

Now,
♦   Subtract two standard deviations from the mean. What did you get? _____
♦   Add two standard deviations to the mean. What did you get?_____

Approximately 95% of your data points (e.g., your friends' answers about the number of hours of sleep they get) should fall between these two numbers. Go back to your original **raw data**. Is this true? Do almost all of your data points fall between these numbers?_____

Suppose that your professor came into class and announced that the **mean** on the test was a 92 (out of 100 possible points). Would you be hoping for a large or a small **standard deviation**? Why?

_____

_____

_____

_____

If your professor announced that the **mean** on the test was a 75 with a **standard deviation** of 15 points, what scores would *most* of the students have earned? How do you know that?_____

_____

_____

_____

_____

Suppose that your professor was looking in her grade book and saw the following two sets of scores for two different classes.

Class A: 30, 60, 60, 60, 70, 70, 70, 100

Class B: 60, 60, 60, 60, 70, 70, 70, 75

Which class would have the larger **standard deviation**? _____

Which class would have the larger **range**? _____

Which class would have the higher **mean**?_____

For which class would the **median** be a better measure of central tendency than the **mean**? Why?

_____

_____

_____

GO SURFING...

...at http://www.ruf.rice.edu/~lane/stat_analysis/descriptive.html and enter your data by putting a space between each data point (e.g., friend's answer). For example, your data may look like this:

6 7 8 9 10 5 7 9 8 8

Then, click on "compute."

What are the following **percentile ranks**?

- ♦ 25th percentile: _____
- ♦ 50th percentile: _____
- ♦ 75th percentile: _____

If you were taking a standardized test, such as the GRE's or LSAT's, would you rather have a high or low **percentile rank?** Why? _____
_____
_____

What would it mean if your **percentile rank** was 95?_____
_____
_____

Inferential Statistics

Earlier, you calculated the correlation between birthweight and current weight. If this correlation was **statistically significant**, what would that mean?_____
_____
_____
_____
_____

What do the following expressions mean?

- ♦ $p < .05$ _____
- ♦ $p < .01$ _____
- ♦ $p < .001$_____

Which standard is usually used by psychologists?_____

If you wanted to be really, really sure of your results, what standard would you use?_____
Why do psychologists usually study **samples** instead of **populations**?_____
_____
_____

Suppose that you were testing an AIDS vaccine. You would hope to find a difference between individuals who took the vaccine and those who didn't (e.g., you would hope that those who took the vaccine had fewer symptoms). What could you do to ensure that this difference was "real" and not due to **sampling error**?

- ♦ _____
- ♦ _____

What does a **meta-analysis** do?_____

_____

_____

Why do **meta-analyses** sometimes reveal results that other studies don't?

- ◆ _____
- ◆ _____

Lying with Statistics

Go through magazines and newspapers and see how many of the following statistical "lies" you can spot. Cut them out and attach to these pages as examples!
- ◆ **Selective reporting**
- ◆ **Using an inappropriately large range of values to minimize a difference**
- ◆ **Using 3-dimensional graphics to exaggerate size**
- ◆ **Transforming data before plotting it**
- ◆ **Changing width and height**

Looking at Levels

Consider how the levels of analysis might help advertisers to do their jobs better, so as to design more appealing advertisements. Explain the factors involved at each of the **levels**. Draw arrows indicating how these factors may interact.

The Brain	The Person	The Group

TRY PRACTICE TEST #3 NOW!
GOOD LUCK!

How to Think About Research Studies

Reading Research Reports: The QALMRI Method

For each of the following components of the **QALMRI Method**, identify and briefly discuss the information for which a reader should be looking.

♦   **Q = Question** _____

_____

♦   **A = Alternatives** _____

_____

♦   **L = Logic** _____

_____

♦   **M = Method** _____

_____

♦   **R = Results** _____

_____

♦   **I = Inferences** _____

_____

_____

Writing Your Own Research Papers

Kosslyn and Rosenberg have published numerous research papers and books (including this one). Here, they provide some helpful advice for writing your own reports. For each of the following sections of a research paper, list some of the information that you should include and in what form.

Introduction

♦   _____
♦   _____
♦   _____
♦   _____

Method

♦   _____
♦   _____
♦   _____
♦   _____

Results

◆ _____
◆ _____
◆ _____
◆ _____

Discussion

◆ _____
◆ _____
◆ _____
◆ _____

Looking at Levels

Suppose that you wanted to learn to play golf. Because you can't afford a golf instructor, you decide to go to the courses and imitate the good players you see there. What factors (at each of the three **levels**) influence how well you will learn to play golf? Describe below. Draw arrows to indicate how factors at the different levels may interact.

The Brain	The Person	The Group

TRY PRACTICE TEST #4 NOW!
GOOD LUCK!

After You Read . . . Thinking Back

1. Early philosophers shared some of psychologists' interests. What makes philosophy and psychology different?_____

    _____
    _____
    _____
    _____
    _____
    _____

2. What type of data did the structuralists collect? What were some of the problems with that type of data?_____

    _____
    _____
    _____
    _____
    _____
    _____

3. What type of data do you think Freud collected? What are the problems with that method of data collection? How has this affected the status of Freud's theory?_____

    _____
    _____
    _____
    _____
    _____
    _____

4. Why is humanism considered a "nonscientific approach"? Discuss._____

    _____
    _____
    _____
    _____
    _____

5. Given that many clinical and counseling psychologists do not engage in research, why is it important for them to know about research? Give an example. Why are they still called "psychologists" if they do not conduct research?_____

    _____
    _____
    _____
    _____
    _____
    _____

After You Read . . . Thinking Ahead

1. Flip through the Table of Contents of your textbook. Which of the topics that you will be considering do you think are more likely to use survey methods? Why? _____
   _____
   _____
   _____
   _____
   _____

2. Which topics might lend themselves more easily to experimental methods? Why?_____
   _____
   _____
   _____
   _____
   _____

3. Are there some topics for which it might be impossible to use an experimental technique? Why?_____
   _____
   _____
   _____
   _____
   _____

4. How might a researcher's stereotypes affect the results of his or her studies? What would this be called?_____
   _____
   _____
   _____
   _____

5. Can you think of situations in which it would be difficult to collect numerical data? Describe._____
   _____
   _____
   _____
   _____

6. What topics might lend themselves well to case study research? Why? _____
   _____
   _____
   _____
   _____

After You Read . . . Practice Tests

PRACTICE TEST #1:
THE SCIENTIFIC METHOD

Matching Questions
Match each description with the appropriate stage of the research process.

_____1.   Step 1 (p. 34)   A.   Specify operational definitions

_____2.   Step 2 (p. 35)   B.   Find a research question

_____3.   Step 3 (p. 35)   C.   Compare outcomes to theory

_____4.   Step 4 (p. 36)   D.   Develop an idea about what might happen

_____5.   Step 5 (p. 36)   E.   Develop a set of ideas to explain observations

_____6.   Step 6 (p. 36)   F.   Collect data

Multiple-Choice Questions
For each question, circle the best answer from the choices given.

1.   Amy has just read about a study that she finds very interesting. Unfortunately, the researchers do not provide many details about how they collected their data. As a result, Amy is unable to _____ the study. (p. 35)
   a.   Validate
   b.   Copy
   c.   Replicate
   d.   Repeat

2.   Which of the following is not a variable? (p. 35)
   a.   Individuals' height
   b.   The value of pi
   c.   Batting averages
   d.   The number of phone calls people make per day

3.   Leslie is trying to decide how to collect data on college students' motivation. She is considering asking open-ended questions in individual interview settings. Which of the following is likely to be a particular problem if Leslie uses this method? (p. 35)
   a.   Ensuring the study can be replicated
   b.   Developing operational definitions
   c.   The falsifiability of the theory
   d.   Sorting out the data and her interpretations

4. Which of the following is probably not a hypothesis that would be used in psychological research? (p. 35)
    a. The more students study, the higher their GPAs will be.
    b. Roommates with dissimilar personalities will fight more often than roommates with similar personalities.
    c. The more students drink, the more likely they are to be involved in a sexual assault.
    d. Professors want their students to succeed.

5. Jesika is interested in studying whether first-year college students' reading habits predict their writing abilities. She has decided to measure writing ability by asking students to self-report their grades in Freshman Composition. Jesika has provided _____ of her_____. (pp. 36 & 38)
    a. An operational definition; independent variable
    b. Confound; study
    c. An operational definition; dependent variable
    d. A variable; study

6. Hypotheses and theories are similar in that they both: (p. 36)
    a. Produce predictions.
    b. Are rooted in a web of facts and concepts.
    c. Apply only to specific studies.
    d. Are tentative ideas.

7. How are hypotheses and theories related to each other? (p. 36)
    a. They are the same thing.
    b. Hypotheses are tested in studies; the results of these studies are then woven together into theories.
    c. Hypotheses produce predictions whereas theories report conclusions.
    c. Hypotheses may be either correct or incorrect; theories are always correct.

8. Although it is impossible to directly observe emotions, researchers can learn about them by: (p. 35)
    a. Testing hypotheses.
    b. Observing things that directly correlate to emotions, such as facial expressions.
    c. Replicating others' studies.
    d. Asking subjects.

9. By "problem," psychologists mean: (p. 35)
    a. A conflict.
    b. A question you want to answer.
    c. An occurrence of a particular phenomenon.
    d. An unsolved dilemma.

10. A good theory is falsifiable, meaning that: (p. 37)
    a. It is possible to reject the theory if the predictions are not confirmed.
    b. Is never wrong.
    c. Has not yet been rejected.
    d. Makes correct predictions.

PRACTICE TEST #2:
THE PSYCHOLOGISTS' TOOLBOX

True/False Questions
Circle TRUE or FALSE for each of the following statements.

1.   TRUE   FALSE   Correlational research involves the researcher controlling the situation. (p. 40)

2.   TRUE   FALSE   A quasi-experimental design is similar to an experimental design in that it involves comparing groups. (p. 40)

3.   TRUE   FALSE   The sign of a correlation will tell you if two variables vary in the same or opposite directions. (p. 41)

4.   TRUE   FALSE   Case studies may sometimes involve experimentation, only with a single subject. (p. 43)

5.   TRUE   FALSE   Random assignment involves selecting subjects for your study randomly. (p. 40)

6.   TRUE   FALSE   Correlations can help you establish that one variable causes another. (p. 41)

7.   TRUE   FALSE   Not all psychological research involves examining relationships between two variables. (p. 42)

8.   TRUE   FALSE   Confounds will help to clarify the results of a study. (p. 39)

9.   TRUE   FALSE   In a double-blind study, the participants are not aware of the predictions of the study. (p. 48)

10.   TRUE   FALSE   A study can be reliable but not valid. (p. 45)

Multiple-Choice Questions
For each question, circle the best answer from the choices given.

1.   Pete was interested in whether training students in memory techniques really improved their memory. He randomly assigned students in his class to one of two groups. One group received memory training and the other, did not. A week later, Pete tested the students' memory. This is an example of: (p. 38)
      a.   An experiment.
      b.   A quasi-experiment.
      c.   A correlation.
      d.   A case study.

2. In #1 above, the independent variable is: (p. 38)
   a. Memory.
   b. Memory training.
   c. Pete.
   d. Subjects' intelligence.

3. A possible confounding variable in the study described in #1 is: (p. 39)
   a. Amount of sleep the subjects have had recently.
   b. Their memory.
   c. Their memory training.
   d. Pete.

4. The group that did not receive training in #1 would be called: (p. 39)
   a. The control group.
   b. The control condition.
   c. The experimental group.
   d. Confounding subjects.

5. A quasi-experiment is different from an experiment in that: (p. 40)
   a. It does not involve comparing groups.
   b. It does not involve random assignment.
   c. It does not involve collecting data.
   d. It has fewer confounds.

6. Which of the following is the *weakest* correlation? (p. 40)
   a. -.29
   b. -.78
   c. 1.6
   d. .16

7. Gail is involved in a study comparing a placebo with a prescription medicine for allergies. As she administers the allergy medicine, Gail says to the study participant, "I'm sure you will be feeling well soon." She says nothing to the participants who receive the placebo. This is an example of: (p. 48)
   a. Response bias.
   b. Sampling bias.
   c. Being a dishonest researcher.
   d. Experimenter expectancy.

8. To avoid a situation like that in #7, Gail or the study director could: (p. 48)
   a. Plan a double-blind study.
   b. Use a quasi-experimental design of those already using the medicine.
   c. Use random assignment.
   d. Use a survey.

9. Which of the following is *not* a potential difficulty associated with the use of surveys? (pp. 43-44)
    a. People may lie, especially about sensitive material.
    b. What people say and what they do may be different.
    c. Not everyone who is asked to fill out a survey does.
    d. They are expensive.

10. Greg takes his temperature once and gets 96.7°. Five minutes later, he takes it again and gets 98.1°. Five minutes after that, he gets a reading of 99.2°. Greg's thermometer apparently lacks: (p. 45)
    a. Validity.
    b. Reliability.
    c. Validity but not reliability.
    d. Neither validity and reliability.

PRACTICE TEST #3:
STATISTICS

Fill-in-the-Blank Questions

Fill in the blanks in the paragraph below, using the following words:

WORD BANK	
Central tendency	Normal distribution
Frequency distribution	Range
Mean	Skewed
Median	Standard deviation
Mode	Variability

If you look at a _____ and it appears bell-shaped, it is called a

_____. In this type of distribution, all three measures of

_____ are the same. In other situations, it may be more appropriate to use

one measure rather than another. The most frequently used measure of central tendency is the

_____. However, this measure is strongly affected by an extreme value or score.

When there is an extreme value or score, the distribution is said to be _____. In this

case, it is better to use the _____ or the _____, which usually do not

change much as a result of extreme scores. The more skewed the distribution is, the greater the

spread or _____ of the distribution will be, in general. The simplest measure of

spread to calculate is called the _____ and is calculated by subtracting the low score of

the distribution from the high score. However, this is not the most frequently used measure of

spread. Rather, the most frequently used measure of spread is the

_____, which is a kind of "average variability" of the data. (p.

52-54)

Multiple-Choice Questions

For each question, circle the best answer from the choices given.

For questions #1-5 and #7, use the following scenario: Suppose that you gave a quiz. Your students received the following scores (out of a total of 10 possible points):

4, 4, 4, 3, 2, 1, 10

1.   What is the mean of this set of data? (p. 53)
        a.   1
        b.   2
        c.   4
        d.   10

2.   What is the mode of this set of data? (p. 53)
        a.   1
        b.   2
        c.   3
        d.   4

3.   What is the median of this set of data? (p. 53)
        a.   1
        b.   2
        c.   3
        d.   4

4.   If plotted in a frequency distribution, this data set would probably be: (p. 53)
        a.   Normal.
        b.   Bell-shaped.
        c.   Skewed.
        d.   Bimodal.

5.   The most appropriate measure of central tendency to use for this distribution would probably be: (p. 53)
        a.   The mean.
        b.   The median.
        c.   The mode.
        d.   Any of the above.

6.   Which measure of variability is most commonly used? (p. 54)
        a.   Deviation scores
        b.   The range
        c.   The standard deviation
        d.   None of the above

7.   In the data set in above data set, the range would be: (p. 54)
     a.   from 1 to 10
     b.   6
     c.   10
     d.   9

8.   Suppose that you obtained a correlation that was statistically significant. This would mean: (p. 56)
     a.   It is important.
     b.   It is unlikely to be due to chance.
     c.   You made a mathematical error.
     d.   Nothing.

9.   Which of the following factors will make it more likely that your correlation is statistically significant? (p. 56)
     a.   You have few pairs of data.
     b.   The correlation value is large.
     c.   The probability value is small (e.g., .001 versus .05).
     d.   All of the above.

10. When researchers combine results from different studies into one larger study, this is called: (p. 57)
     a.   A big study.
     b.   A meta-analysis.
     c.   An experiment.
     d.   A quasi-experiment.

PRACTICE TEST #4:
HOW TO THINK ABOUT RESEARCH STUDIES

True/False Questions
Circle TRUE or FALSE for each of the following statements.

1.   TRUE   FALSE   Information about the participants in a study belongs in the Introduction. (p. 65)

2.   TRUE   FALSE   The author of a research paper should not acknowledge that there are multiple possible answers to the research question. (p. 63)

3.   TRUE   FALSE   When writing a research paper, an author should try to take the perspective of an intelligent reader. (p. 65)

4.   TRUE   FALSE   The researcher should point out possible confounds in the Methods section. (p. 64)

5.   TRUE   FALSE   In the Introduction, the researcher should explain the significance of the research question. (p. 63)

6.   TRUE   FALSE   Questionnaires used in a study should have demonstrated validity. (p. 63)

7.   TRUE   FALSE   Statistical information is found in the Results section. (p. 64)

8.   TRUE   FALSE   Measures of central tendency and variability are often best presented in a graph format. (p. 65)

9.   TRUE   FALSE   The Introduction should include all previous relevant studies on your topic. (p. 65)

10.   TRUE   FALSE   The logic of the study should be expressed in an *If....then* format. (p. 63)

Multiple-Choice Questions
For each question, circle the best answer from the choices given.

1.   The apparatus used in the study should be included in which of the following sections of a research paper? (p. 64)
    a.   Introduction
    b.   Methods
    c.   Results
    d.   Discussion

2. Which measure of variability is typically included in a research paper? (p. 64)
   a.   Mode
   b.   Mean
   c.   Range
   d   Standard deviation

3. If a study is well-designed: (p. 64)
   a.   There shouldn't be any confounds in the study.
   b.   You should be able to rule out at least one alternative answer.
   c.   It should be consistent with previous studies on the same topic.
   d.   The results can be generalized to related topics and populations.

4. If a "p value" is .05 or less: (p. 64)
   a.   The results are probably due to chance.
   b.   The results are important.
   c.   The results probably indicate real differences in the population.
   d.   There was a mathematical error made in calculating this statistic.

5. Which of the following is *not* included in the Methods section of a research paper? (p. 62)
   a.   Descriptions of the questionnaires used
   b.   Descriptions of the procedures followed
   c.   Description of the guiding theory
   d.   Description of the participants

6. In the Discussion section of a research paper, which of the following should the researcher consider? (p. 64)
   a.   The effects of any possible confounds
   b.   The generalizability of the results
   c.   Why the study is important
   d.   All of the above

7. The methods of the study should be described so clearly that: (p. 65)
   a.   A reader could have a visual image of the study.
   b.   The reader can walk through the study from the participant's perspective.
   c.   The study could be replicated.
   d.   The reader wants to conduct follow-up research on the study.

8. Another way to think about the hypothesis is that it is: (p. 65)
   a.   Your prediction of what will not happen in the study.
   b.   Your favorite alterative of the possible outcomes of the study.
   c.   The result of the study.
   d.   An explanation of the logic of your study.

9.	Mary is writing a research report in which she compares the emotional skills of American and Japanese children. She should ensure that the two groups of children are: (p. 65)
	a.	Comparable on important factors, such as age and education.
	b.	From the same population, as indicated by the p-value.
	c.	From different populations, as indicated by the p-value.
	d.	Recruited in the same way.

10.	Participants should be: (p. 63)
	a.	Similar to the population they represent.
	b.	Similar to each other.
	c.	Similar to the population in general.
	d.	Very different from each other.

COMPREHENSIVE PRACTICE TEST

Identification Questions
Identify the following as positive or negative correlations. (p. 41)

1. POSITIVE   NEGATIVE   As clouds gather, temperature drops.

2. POSITIVE   NEGATIVE   As inflation increases, interest rates drop.

3. POSITIVE   NEGATIVE   As children age, they grow taller.

4. POSITIVE   NEGATIVE   As hours spent studying decrease, grades decrease.

5. POSITIVE   NEGATIVE   As alcohol consumption increases, motor control decreases.

Matching Questions
Match the research technique with the best description.

_____ 1.	Experiment (p. 38)	A.	Involves looking in real-world habitats
_____ 2.	Quasi-experiment (p. 40)	B.	Do not examine the relationship between variables
_____ 3.	Correlational (p. 40)	C.	Uses random assignment
_____ 4.	Case study (p. 43)	D.	Limited by participants' honesty
_____ 5.	Naturalistic observation (p. 42)	E.	An example would be a comparison of males and females on some variable
_____ 6.	Surveys (p. 43)	F.	Does not prove causation
_____ 7.	Descriptive (p. 42)	G.	Difficult to generalize from

Identification Questions
Identify the dependent variable (DV) and independent variable (IV) in each of the following hypotheses. (p. 38-39)

1. The more water you drink, the less likely you are to have kidney stones.
   DV = _____
   IV = _____

2. Rats are bigger than mice.
   DV = _____
   IV = _____

3.	Female gymnasts are more likely to be anorexic than other females of the same age.
	DV = _____
	IV = _____

4.	Students who complete their study guide activities will have better grades than those who don't.
	DV = _____
	IV = _____

5.	Parents who have books in their homes are more likely to have children who like to read.
	DV = _____
	IV = _____

Multiple-Choice Questions

For each question, circle the best answer from the choices given.

1.	A tentative idea that might explain a set of observations is a(n): (p. 35)
	a.	Theory.
	b.	Variable.
	c.	Hypothesis.
	d.	Prediction.

2.	Dr. Speramental is interested in the effects of caffeine on memory in lab rats. In setting up an experiment, the independent variable is _____ and the dependent variable is _____. (p. 38)
	a.	The rats; caffeine
	b.	Caffeine; memory
	c.	Memory; the rats
	d.	Memory; caffeine

3.	To test his hypothesis, Dr. Speramental decides to inject one group of rats with caffeine every day for a week, but to leave the other group alone. At the end of the week, he will measure the rats' memory for a maze they had previously learned. To avoid a confound, Dr. Speramental should probably: (p. 39)
	a.	Inject all the rats, some with caffeine and some with water.
	b.	Use a correlational study.
	c.	Allow only one group of rats to learn the maze before the injections.
	d.	Groom the rats every day.

4. Dr. Figerout is interested in whether a new teaching technique she learned at a conference is an effective means of making her classroom presentations more interesting to students. To test her hypothesis that the new technique is more effective, she uses her old technique with her 8:00 a.m. class and her new technique with her 11:00 class. What is a confound in this study? (p. 39)
    a. The students
    b. The old technique
    c. The time of day
    d. The new technique

5. If interested in studying the differences between existing groups (e.g., those with depression and those without), a researcher would have to use a(n): (p. 39)
    a. Correlational study.
    b. Meta-analysis.
    c. Experiment.
    d. Quasi-experiment.

6. Which of the following correlations affords the greatest predictive value? (p. 41)
    a. 2.3
    b. -.76
    c. 0
    d. .54

7. Which of the following techniques would offer the greatest control? (p. 40)
    a. An experiment
    b. A case study
    c. A quasi-experiment
    d. Naturalistic observation

8. A technique that combines the results from different studies is a(n): (p. 57)
    a. Case study.
    b. Experiment.
    c. Meta-analysis.
    d. Naturalistic observation.

9. If a study can be replicated, it is said to be: (p. 45)
    a. Confounded.
    b. Reliable.
    c. Explicated.
    d. Valid.

10. Children typically give the same response over and over again, without regard for the questions asked. This type of bias is called: (p. 47)
    a.   Sampling bias.
    b.   Kid bias.
    c.   Population bias.
    d.   Response bias.

11. The first step in the scientific method is: (p. 34)
    a.   Forming a hypothesis.
    b.   Replication.
    c.   Systematically observing events.
    d.   Specifying a problem.

12. The variable a researcher manipulates is called the _____ variable. (p. 38)
    a.   Independent
    b.   Hypothetical
    c.   Dependent
    d.   Confounding

13. Which of the following correlation coefficients would probably best describe the relationship between how sociable people are and how much time they spend at a party? (p. 41)
    a.   0.2
    b.   1.7
    c.   0.8
    d.   −0.2

14. In a _____ experiment, neither the participant nor the investigator knows the predictions of the experiment or the condition to which the participant has been assigned. (p. 48)
    a.   Single-blind
    b.   Completely confounded
    c.   Double-blind
    d.   Quasi-experimental

15. If you wanted to replicate another researcher's study, you should look at his or her: (p. 65)
    a.   Resume.
    b.   Introduction section.
    c.   Methods section.
    d.   Website.

Essay Questions

Answer each question in the space provided.

1.   Design a study to investigate the influence of morality on willingness to cheat in an academic setting. Identify the independent and dependent variables, and discuss the ethical considerations of such a study._____

_____

_____

_____

_____

_____

_____

_____

_____

_____

_____

_____

_____

_____

_____

_____

_____

_____

_____

_____

_____

_____

2.   Discuss each of the following sources of error in a study, including what stage of the research process it arises and its possible effects:
   ♦   Sampling bias
   ♦   Response bias
   ♦   Experimenter expectancy effects

_____

_____

_____

_____

_____

_____

_____

_____

_____

3. Provide examples of studies for which you would be likely to use correlational, quasi-experimental, and experimental research designs. Why would each of these designs be most appropriate in these situations?

_____
_____
_____
_____
_____
_____
_____
_____
_____
_____
_____
_____
_____
_____
_____
_____
_____
_____

4. What kinds of problems must you be careful to avoid when using surveys? Explain._____

_____
_____
_____
_____
_____
_____
_____
_____
_____
_____

5. If you had your choice, what type of research design would you want to use? Why?_____

_____
_____
_____
_____
_____
_____
_____
_____
_____
_____

6. Think of a situation in which you might want to use statistics to "lie" about your data. Describe._____

_____

_____

_____

_____

_____

_____

_____

_____

_____

_____

7. Describe a situation in which you would want to use each of the three measures of central tendency: mean, median, and mode._____

_____

_____

_____

_____

_____

_____

_____

_____

_____

_____

When You Are Finished. . . Puzzle It Out

Across
5. Largest score minus smallest score
7. Variable that depends on another
11. Careful observations or numerical measurement
12. Subset of the population
13. Getting results over and over
15. Questionnaire
16. Tentative idea to explain data
18. How spread out scores are
19. Distribution that is bell-shaped
20. Entire set of relevant people

Down
1. Example is your GPA
2. Most frequently occurring score
3. Can range from -1 to +1
4. Combining results from different studies
6. Occurs when no random sampling
8. Numbers that summarize measurement
9. Redoing study and getting similar data
10. Scientific study of one person
14. Type of definition indicating how data measured
17. Number of steps in scientific method

Puzzle created with Puzzlemaker at DiscoverySchool.com.

Chapter 3
The Biology of Mind and Behavior

Before You Read. . .

Have you ever known any who has suffered brain damage…perhaps someone who has had a stroke or Alzheimer's Disease? How did this damage affect their functioning?

In this chapter, you will learn the basics of how the brain works, beginning with the basic cell of the nervous system: the neuron. Communication within the brain and across the nervous system is an electrochemical process that results in neurotransmitters being released into the synapses between neurons. You will also learn how the brain and the nervous system are organized.

The chapter also discusses two other systems of the body that interact with our brains to keep our bodies healthy: the neuroendocrine system and immune system. You will discover how researchers have learned about the brain, using neuroimaging, lesions, and strokes. Finally, the chapter ends with a discussion of genetic influences on behavior, and the dynamic interaction of genes and the environment.

Chapter Objectives

After reading this chapter, you should be able to:

♦ Describe how neurons work and what could cause neurons to die.

♦ Explain how chemicals allow neurons to communicate and what happens if healthy neurons can no longer communicate.

♦ Name and describe the major parts of the brain and the nervous system and their functions.

♦ Understand how the functions of the two sides of the brain differ.

♦ Name and explain the techniques used to study the brain.

♦ Describe the role of genes in behavior and how genes and the environment interact as the brain develops and functions.

♦ Explain what *heritability* means and how evolution shaped the functions of the brain.

As You Read…Term Identification

Make flashcards using the following terms as you go. Use the definitions in the margins of this chapter for help. If you write the definitions in your own words, though, you will remember them better!

Action potential
Active interaction
Adaptation
Adoption study
Agonist
All-or-none law
Amygdala
Antagonist
Autonomic nervous system (ANS)
Axon
Basal ganglia
Behavioral genetics
Brain circuit
Brainstem
Cell body
Cell membrane
Central nervous system (CNS)
Cerebellum
Cerebral cortex
Cerebral hemisphere
Complex inheritance
Computer-assisted tomography (CT)
Corpus callosum
Cortisol
Dendrite
Deoxyribonucleic acid (DNA)
Dizygotic
Electroencephalogram
Electroencephalograph (EEG)
Endogenous cannabinoids
Estrogen
Evocative (or reactive) interaction
Evolution
Forebrain
Frontal lobe
Functional magnetic resonance imaging (fMRI)
Gene
Genotype
Glial cell
Gyrus

Heritability
Hindbrain
Hippocampus
Hormone
Hypothalamus
Interneuron
Ion
Knockin mice
Knockout mice
Lesion
Limbic system
Lobes
Magnetic resonance imaging (MRI)
Medulla
Mendelian inheritance
Meninges
Microelectrode
Midbrain
Monozygotic
Motor neuron
Motor strip
Mutation
Myelin
Natural selection
Neuroendocrine system
Neuroimaging
Neuromodulator
Neuron
Neurotransmitter
Occipital lobe
Parasympathetic nervous system
Parietal lobe
Passive interaction
Peripheral nervous system (PNS)
Phenotype
Pituitary gland
Plasticity
Pons
Positron emission tomography (PET)
Pruning
Receptor

Reflex
Resting potential
Reticular formation
Reuptake
Selective serotonin-reuptake inhibiter (SSRI)
Sensory neuron
Skeletal system
Somatosensory strip
Spinal cord
Split-brain patient
Stroke
Subcortical structure

Sulcus
Sympathetic nervous system
Synapse
Synaptic cleft
Temporal lobe
Terminal button
Testosterone
Thalamus
Transcranial magnetic stimulation (TMS)
Twin study
Ventricle

As You Read. . . Questions and Exercises

Brain Circuits: Making Connections

The Neuron: A Powerful Computer

For each of the following types of neurons, offer a definition and an example.

Type of Neuron	Definition	Example
Sensory Neuron		
Motor Neuron		
Interneurons		

In addition to approximately 100 billion neurons, the brain also contains 10 times as many
_____ cells, which fill the gaps between neurons and have the following functions:

♦ _____

♦ _____

♦ _____

♦ _____

What are brain circuits and how do they work? _____
_____
_____
_____

Think of an analogy for brain circuits that will help you to remember them and their functions.
Describe. _____
_____
_____
_____
_____

In the space below, draw a picture of two connecting neurons.

Then, label each part on the previous page to correspond with its number below. Also, complete the following chart to provide the function of each part of the **neuron**.

	Neural Structure	Function
1	Cell membrane	
2	Cell body	
3	Dendrites	
4	Axon	
5	Myelin sheath	
6	Terminals (terminal branches)	
7	Terminal buttons	
8	Synapse	
9	Synaptic cleft	
10	Receptor sites	
11	Neurotransmitters	

What is the **all-or-none law**? Describe._____
_____
_____
_____
_____

Neurotransmitters and Neuromodulators: Bridging the Gap

GO SURFING...

...at http://faculty.washington.edu/chudler/synapse.html to read more (and see pictures) of how an action potential travels. Send your professor a postcard to let him or her know you were there!

Describe the difference in the functions of **neurotransmitters** and **neuromodulators**.

Neurotransmitters	Neuromodulators

When neurotransmitters or neuromodulators **bind** to receptors, they can have one of two effects. Explain each:

♦   **Excitatory:** _____
_____
_____

♦   **Inhibitory:** _____
_____
_____

Do **neurotransmitters** and **neuromodulators** always have the same effect? Why or why not?
_____
_____
_____
_____
_____

What happens to any extra **neurotransmitter** that is released by the terminal buttons, but not taken up by receptors?_____
_____
_____
_____
_____
_____

Name and describe 3 ways that drugs may affect **neurotransmitters**:

♦   _____
_____
_____

♦   _____
_____
_____

♦   _____
_____
_____

Looking at Levels

Michael J. Fox quit working on his successful hit series "Spin City," citing his fight against Parkinson's Disease and his need to spend more time with his family as the primary reasons. Describe how Michael's disease has affected him at the various levels of functioning. Use arrows to indicate how factors at the different levels may interact with each other.

The Brain	The Person	The Group

TRY PRACTICE TEST #1 NOW!
GOOD LUCK!

The Nervous System:
An Orchestra with Many Members

Overview

Together, the brain and the **spinal cord** make up the **central nervous system (CNS)**. What are the functions of the spinal cord?

♦ _____
♦ _____
♦ _____

Explain how **reflexes** work. _____
_____
_____
_____
_____

The **CNS** hooks into the **peripheral nervous system (PNS)**, which has two parts: the **autonomic nervous system** and the **skeletal** (or **somatic**) **nervous system**. In the table below, for each system note which muscles are controlled, the appearance of these muscles and other characteristics of these muscles.

	Autonomic Nervous System	Skeletal (or Somatic) System
Muscles Controlled		
Appearance of Muscles Controlled		
Other Characteristics of Muscles Controlled		

The **autonomic nervous system** also has two parts: the **sympathetic nervous system** and the **parasympathetic nervous system**. Provide the following characteristics of each.

	Sympathetic Nervous System	Parasympathetic Nervous System
What is the purpose of the system?		
What activates the system?		
What are the effects of activation of the system?		

If you could see under someone's skull, what would you see (in order)? Name and describe each feature.

- ♦ _____
- ♦ _____
- ♦ _____

Under all this, you would see two **cerebral hemispheres**.

♦　　Why are these parts named hemispheres?_____
　　　_____

♦　　What does each hemisphere do?_____
　　　_____
　　　_____

GO SURFING…

…at http://www.pbs.org/wnet/brain/3d/ to see more pictures of the brain.

Each hemisphere is divided into **four lobes**. List the location of each of the lobes. (An example is given for **temporal lobes**.)

	Occipital	Temporal	Parietal	Frontal
Location		At the temples		

Why is the **cerebral cortex** so "crumpled-up"? _____
_____
_____
_____
_____

What would you find if you looked underneath the cortex? List and describe each feature.

♦　　_____

♦　　_____

♦　　_____

Cerebral Cortex: The Seat of the Mind

	Function	Result of Damage to This Part
Occipital Lobes		
Temporal Lobes		
Parietal Lobes		
Frontal Lobes		

The Dual Brain: Thinking with Both Barrels

Who are **split-brain patients**? What information can studies of split-brain patients provide?

_____

_____

_____

_____

_____

Mark an "X" in the column headed "left" or "right" to indicate in which **hemisphere** the following functions typically take place.

Function	Left	Right
Captures the details of shapes		
Carries out most aspects of language		
Makes the pitch of a voice rise at the end of a question		
Extracts the metaphors and allusions of language		

Function	Left	Right
Captures the overall shape of objects		
Registers the literal meaning of a message		

Why must generalizations about the specializations of each **hemisphere** be made cautiously?

_____

_____

_____

_____

_____

If you had to suffer damage to one **hemisphere**, which one would it be? Why?_____

_____

_____

_____

_____

_____

GO SURFING...

...at http://faculty.washington.edu/chudler/rightl.html to determine how strong your hand preference is.

Take one of the Handedness Questionnaires. How strong is your hand preference?_____

_____

What is the relationship between handedness and hemispheric specialization? See http://faculty.washington.edu/chudler/split.html and then briefly explain here._____

_____

_____

_____

_____

_____

Beneath the Cortex: The Inner Brain

For each of the following **brain parts**, explain its function and then provide a personal example of when you use this brain part in your life.

Brain Part	Function	Personal Example
Thalamus		
Hypothalamus		
Hippocampus		
Amygdala		
Basal Ganglia		
Brainstem		
Cerebellum		

The Neuroendocrine System: It's Hormonal

How is the **CNS** related to the **neuroendocrine system**?_____

_____

_____

_____

What are **hormones**? Define in your own words._____

_____

_____

What role does the **pituitary gland** play in the neuroendocrine system? Explain._____

_____

_____

_____

_____

What are the effects of the following **hormones**?

Hormone	Effects
Testosterone	
Estrogen	
Cortisol	

In addition to physical effects, sexual hormones (e.g., testosterone and estrogen) may have psychological effects. Can you think of any psychological or behavioral changes you experienced in adolescence that may have resulted from hormonal changes?_____

_____

_____

_____

_____

_____

Looking at Levels

There is some research to suggest that riding roller coasters may sometimes cause brain damage. Explain the factors at each of the **three levels** that may be involved in creating brain damage. Draw arrows to indicate how these factors may interact to cause brain damage.

The Brain	The Person	The Group

TRY PRACTICE TEST #2 NOW!
GOOD LUCK!

Probing the Brain

The Damaged Brain: What's Missing?

What are **strokes** and **lesions**, and how do they help us to understand the brain's functions?

_____
_____
_____
_____
_____
_____
_____
_____

What are the limitations of using natural experiments to inform us about brain functioning?

♦   _____
       _____
       _____
♦   _____
       _____
       _____

Recording Techniques: The Music of the Cells

The following two techniques record the activity of neurons. For each technique, explain how it works, its advantages and its limitations.

	Description of technique	Advantages	Disadvantages
Electroencephalograph (EEG)			
Single-cell Recording			

Neuroimaging: Picturing the Living Brain

How has **neuroimaging** transformed psychology? _____
_____
_____
_____
_____

In the following chart, explain how each technique works, as well as its advantages and its limitations.

	Description of Technique	Advantages	Disadvantages
Techniques Allowing Visualization of Brain Structure			
Computer-assisted tomography (CT or CAT)			
Magnetic resonance Imaging (MRI)			
Techniques Allowing Visualization of Brain Function			
Positron emission tomography (PET)			
Functional magnetic resonance imaging (fMRI)			

Stimulation: Tickling the Neurons

In your own words, describe the three types of **neural stimulation techniques** and the disadvantages of each.

Technique & Description	Disadvantages

GO SURFING...

...at http://www.pbs.org/wgbh/aso/tryit/brain/ to electronically recreate one of Wilder Penfield's studies.

What does this activity tell you about how much of the **motor cortex** is devoted to different brain parts? Discuss._____

_____

_____

_____

_____

Looking at Levels

Consider some ability or talent that you have (e.g., musical talent). List actors at the **three levels** (brain, person, group) that have influenced your ability. Draw arrows to indicate how these factors may interact to affect your ability.

The Brain	The Person	The Group

TRY PRACTICE TEST #3 NOW!
GOOD LUCK!

Genes, Brain, and Environment: The Brain in the World

Genes as Blueprints: Born to be Wild?

What are the two key ideas of **Mendelian inheritance**?

- ♦ _____
  _____
  _____
- ♦ _____
  _____
  _____

Name and describe a characteristic for which you apparently received **recessive alleles** from both of your parents: _____
_____
_____

Name and describe a characteristic for which your **phenotype** demonstrates the **dominant allele** of one parent. _____
_____
_____

What are **knockout mice**? What do they tell us about the role of genes in the brain and behavior?
_____
_____
_____
_____

What are **knockin mice**? What do they tell us about the role of genes in the brain and behavior?
_____
_____
_____
_____

Given the discussions in the book about **knockout** and **knockin mice**, how do you feel about animal research in neuroscience? Why? _____
_____
_____
_____

Why do some neural connections get **pruned**? _____
_____
_____
_____
_____

Do you think there could be any good results of **pruning**? If so, what would those be? _____
_____
_____
_____

Pruning is one aspect of the brain's **plasticity**, which is its ability to change with experience. Name and briefly describe the other ways that the brain changes with experience:

♦ _____
_____
_____

♦ _____
_____
_____
_____

♦ _____
_____
_____
_____

♦ _____
_____
_____
_____

When is **plasticity** most evident?

♦ _____
_____
♦ _____
_____
♦ _____
_____
♦ _____
_____

Give original examples from your own life of **passive interaction**, **evocative interaction**, and **active interaction**.

Type of Interaction	Example
Passive	
Evocative	
Active	

Behavioral Genetics

What types of questions might someone in **behavioral genetics** ask?

♦ _____
_____
♦ _____
_____
♦ _____
_____
♦ _____
_____

In your own words, define **heritability**. _____
_____
_____
_____
_____
_____

Describe the following types of studies, which allow researchers to study the relative contributions of genes and environment to a particular trait.

♦   **Twin studies:** _____
_____
_____
_____
_____

♦   **Adoption studies:**_____
_____
_____
_____
_____
_____

Evolution and the Brain: The Best of All Possible Brains?

Consider the giraffe, the elephant, and the human. What characteristics of each species may have evolved over time (been reproduced over and over again) because they ensured survival and helped the animals adapt to the environment?

Animal	Characteristic	Reason for adaptation
Giraffe		
Elephant		
Human		

Looking at Levels

Some Mormons and Muslims *do* drink, and some become alcoholics. Considering the **levels of analysis**, what might lead an individual whose religious convictions do not allow drinking to become alcoholic anyway? Draw arrows to indicate how events at the different levels may interact to allow this.

The Brain	The Person	The Group

TRY PRACTICE TEST #4 NOW!
GOOD LUCK!

After You Read . . . Thinking Back

1. What must researchers do to ensure that their use of animals in research settings is ethical? Discuss._____
    _____
    _____
    _____
    _____
    _____
    _____
    _____

2. Of the different theories of psychology discussed in Chapter 1, which ones do you think rely the most on the brain research described in this chapter? Why? _____
    _____
    _____
    _____
    _____
    _____

3. Which theories do you think rely the least on this research? Why? _____
    _____
    _____
    _____
    _____
    _____

4. Explain how a neuropsychologist might use experimental, quasi-experimental, and correlational research designs
    ◆   **Experimental:** _____
        _____
        _____

    ◆   **Quasi-experimental:** _____
        _____
        _____
        _____

    ◆   **Correlational:**_____
        _____
        _____
        _____

5. What are some of the difficulties with using case studies to make conclusions about brain functioning?_____
    _____
    _____
    _____

After You Read . . . Thinking Ahead

1. Based on what you have learned about the function of different brain parts, what brain parts might be involved in the following:
    ♦   Depression_____
    ♦   Anxiety disorders_____
    ♦   Sleep disorders_____

2. What parts of the brain would you think would be undergoing the most development at the following ages? Why?
    ♦   0 – 6 months_____
        _____
    ♦   18-24 months_____
        _____
    ♦   Early school-age years _____
        _____
    ♦   Teenage years_____
        _____

3. What outcome would you predict for a child who suffered brain damage, as opposed to an older person who suffered the same type of damage?_____
    _____
    _____
    _____
    _____

4. How could the research on plasticity explain the fact that it is easier to learn second languages as a child rather than as an adult? Discuss._____
    _____
    _____
    _____
    _____

5. What do you think the role of the brain is in intelligence? What brain parts do you think are especially relevant? Why?_____
    _____
    _____
    _____
    _____
    _____

6. Can you think of ways to use the idea of brain connections, as described in this chapter, to develop better memory techniques? Discuss._____
    _____
    _____
    _____
    _____

After You Read . . . Practice Tests

PRACTICE TEST #1:
BRAIN CIRCUITS

Fill-in-the-Blank Questions
Fill in the blanks in the paragraph below with the following words.

WORD BANK	
Excitatory	Neurotransmitters
Glial	Reuptake
Inhibitory	Synapse
Neuromodulators	

Communication between neurons takes place at the _____, the place where the axon of the sending neuron comes closest to the receiving neuron. Two types of chemicals are released from the terminal buttons into the cleft:_____, which are the chemical messengers, and _____, which are chemicals that alter the effects of the neurotransmitters. _____ cells may also influence chemical activity between neurons by producing a substance that either increases or decreases a neuron's sensitivity to input from other neurons. When chemicals bind to the receptors of the receiving neuron, they can be _____, causing the receiving neuron to fire; or they can be _____, making the receiving neuron less likely to fire. After being released into the space between neurons, the chemicals are reabsorbed in a chemical reaction called _____. (pp. 73-78)

Matching Questions

Match the following parts of the neuron with their functions.

_____	1. Cell body (p. 74)	A. The sending end of the neuron
_____	2. Cell membrane (p. 74)	B. The receiving end of the neuron
_____	3. Channel (p. 75)	C. Contains the nucleus
_____	4. Axon (p. 74)	D. Contains neurotransmitters or neuromodulators
_____	5. Terminal button (p. 74)	E. The skin of the neuron
_____	6. Dendrite (p. 74)	F. A small hole in the skin of a neuron

Multiple-Choice Questions

For each question, circle the best answer from the choices given.

1. Most of the neurons in the brain are: (p. 73)
   a. Sensory neurons.
   b. Motor neurons.
   c. Channel neurons.
   d. Interneurons.

2. There are ten times as many _____ as there are neurons in the human brain. (p. 73)
   a. Glial cells
   b. Hormones
   c. Blood cells
   d. Leukocytes

3. The sending end of the neuron is the: (p. 74)
   a. Axon.
   b. Dendrites.
   c. Cell body.
   d. Nucleus.

4. The _____ of a neuron receive messages from the axons of other neurons. (p. 74)
   a. Cell bodies
   b. Dendrites
   c. Axons
   d. Glial cells

5. During an action potential, _____ ions move into the neuron and _____ ions move out. (p. 75)
    a.   Sodium; potassium
    b.   Sodium; chloride
    c.   Potassium; sodium
    d.   Hydrogen; potassium

6. Neurons obey the _____ law, meaning that if enough stimulation reaches the neuron, it fires. (p. 75)
    a.   Excitatory potential
    b.   All-or-none
    c.   Sodium-potassium exchange
    d.   Dendritic expression

7. Most axons are covered with _____, a fatty substance that helps impulses travel more quickly. (p. 75)
    a.   Glial cells
    b.   Sodium
    c.   Myelin
    d.   Potassium

8. The gap between sending and receiving neurons is called the: (p. 77)
    a.   Glial gap.
    b.   Myelin mile.
    c.   Synaptic cleft.
    d.   Brain bridge.

9. Neurotransmitters that make the receiving neuron more likely to fire an action potential are said to be _____ neurotransmitters. (p. 79)
    a.   Excitatory
    b.   Ignitatory
    c.   Inhibitory
    d.   Modulatory

10. Drugs that mimic the effects of a neurotransmitter by activating a particular type of receptor are called: (p. 80)
    a.   Antagonists.
    b.   Hormones.
    c.   Agonists.
    d.   Neuromodulators.

PRACTICE TEST #2:
THE NERVOUS SYSTEM

Matching Questions

Match each of the terms with the appropriate description.

_____	1.	Cranial nerves (p. 82)	A.	Reflexes occur at this level
_____	2.	Spinal cord (p. 82)	B.	Controls the smooth muscles and some glandular functions
_____	3.	Central nervous system (p. 82)	C.	Readies an animal to cope with emergencies
_____	4.	Peripheral nervous system (p. 83)	D.	Protective membranes that cover the brain
_____	5.	Autonomic nervous system (p. 83)	E.	Affects the organs one at a time to slow them down after an emergency passes
_____	6.	Skeletal system (p. 84)	F.	The 12 nerves that send and receive information to and from the brain
_____	7.	Sympathetic system (p. 84)	G.	Where most of the brain's mental processes take place
_____	8.	Parasympathetic system (p. 85)	H.	The system of nerves attached to voluntary muscles
_____	9.	Meninges (p. 86)	I.	The brain and spinal cord
_____	10.	Corpus callosum (p. 86)	J.	Hooks the central nervous system to the organs
_____	11.	Cerebral cortex (p. 86)	K.	Connects the two hemispheres of the brain

Matching Questions

Match the following brain structures with their functions.

_____ 1. Thalamus (p. 94)   A. Controls many bodily functions, including eating and drinking, maintaining temperature and blood pressure, and sexual behavior.

_____ 2. Hypothalamus (p. 95)   B. Important in the automatic control of breathing, swallowing, and blood circulation

_____ 3. Hippocampus (p. 96)   C. Involved in planning and producing movement, and in forming habits

_____ 4. Amygdala (p. 96)   D. Involved in coordinated motor movements

_____ 5. Basal ganglia (p. 96)   E. Relay station in the brain; also involved in attention and sleep control

_____ 6. Medulla (p. 97)   F. A bridge connecting the brainstem and cerebellum

_____ 7. Reticular formation (p. 97)   G. Plays a role in expressing and reading emotions such as fear and anger

_____ 8. Pons (p. 97)   H. Plays a key role in the storage of new memories

_____ 9. Cerebellum (p. 97)   I. Plays a key role in arousal and alertness

Matching Questions

Match the following terms with their descriptions.

_____ 1. Testosterone (p. 98)   A. Causes breasts to develop in women

_____ 2. Estrogen (p. 98)   B. The "master gland" of the endocrine system

_____ 3. Cortisol (p. 98)   C. Causes males to develop facial hair and build up muscle

_____ 4. Pituitary gland (p. 98)   D. Helps the body cope when under stress by breaking down protein and fat to sugar

Multiple-Choice Questions

For each question, circle the best answer from the choices given.

1.   There are _____ cranial nerves. (p. 82)
     a.   10
     b.   14
     c.   12
     d.   16

2.   The central nervous system is composed of the: (p. 82)
     a.   Brain and spinal cord.
     b.   Sympathetic and parasympathetic systems.
     c.   Limbic and hippolimbic systems.
     d.   Sensory and motor neurons.

3.   Reflexes happen with the: (p. 83)
     a.   Cerebral cortex.
     b.   Spinal cord.
     c.   Occipital lobe.
     d.   Hypothalamus.

4.   When you clench your fist, you are using your _____ system. (p. 84)
     a.   Skeletal
     b.   Hypothalamic
     c.   Autonomic
     d.   Peripheral nervous

5.   The two major divisions of the autonomic nervous system are the: (pp. 84-85)
     a.   Brain and spinal cord.
     b.   Skeletal and muscular.
     c.   Sympathetic and parasympathetic.
     d.   Forebrain and midbrain.

6.   The creases in the cerebral cortex are called: (p. 86)
     a.   Sulci.
     b.   Collosi.
     c.   Gyri.
     d.   Ventricles.

7.   Chemicals that are produced by glands and that can act as neuromodulators are called: (p. 98)
     a.   Neurotransmitters.
     b.   Hormones.
     c.   Leukocytes.
     d.   Cerebral fluids.

8. The male puberty hormone is _____, and the female puberty hormone is _____. (p. 98)
    a. Testosterone; estrogen
    b. Cortisol; estrogen
    c. Estrogen; testosterone
    d. Testosterone; cortisol

9. The "master gland" of the endocrine system is the _____ gland. (p. 99)
    a. Pineal
    b. Thalamus
    c. Thyroid
    d. Pituitary

10. The "white matter" of the brain is _____ and the "gray matter" is _____. (p. 86)
    a. The sulci, the gyri
    b. The ventricles, the cortex
    c. Subcortical structures, the ventricles
    d. Myelin, subcortical structures

PRACTICE TEST #3:
PROBING THE BRAIN

Fill-in-the-Blank Questions
Fill in the blanks with words from the following word bank.

WORD BANK	
Computer-assisted tomography (CT)	Magnetic resonance imaging (MRI)
Functional magnetic resonance	Neuroimaging techniques
Imaging (fMRI)	Positron emission tomography (PET)

Because they produce an actual picture of neuronal structure and function, scanning techniques are referred to as _____. _____ is the oldest technique and involves taking a series of X-rays and building up a three-dimensional image, slice by slice. _____ _____ makes use of the magnetic properties of different atoms, producing an even sharper image. Small amounts of radiation are introduced into the blood, which is then taken up into different brain areas to show how hard neurons are working, when a _____ _____ is used. The most popular type of neuroimaging today is _____ _____, which reveals function by detecting oxygen usage in the brain. (pp. 100-105)

Multiple-Choice Questions
For each question, circle the best answer from the choices given.

1.   The most frequent source of damage to the brain is a(n): (p. 100)
       a.   Aneurysm.
       b.   Stroke.
       c.   Lesion.
       d.   EEG.

2.   EEG stands for: (p. 100)
       a.   Electroencephalograph.
       b.   Excitatory encephalogram.
       c.   Electric event graphing.
       d.   Entrance and exit graphing.

3. Which of the following provides a visual picture of brain structure? (p. 102)
    a. MRI
    b. MEG
    c. EEG
    d. TMS

4. The most popular type of neuroimaging, the fMRI, has the problem of: (p. 104)
    a. Comparing brain processing to a task done during rest, when researchers don't yet know what the brain does during rest.
    b. It introduces radioactive material into the brain.
    c. It is impossible to detect precise locations of the processing.
    d. It does not show brain function, only brain structure.

5. Cathy suffers a stroke that causes her to lose basically all of her short-term memory. The doctors are eager to ascertain exactly where the damage occurred. Cathy is most likely to have: (p. 103)
    a. Single-cell recordings.
    b. X-rays.
    c. MRI scan.
    d. fMRI.

6. Penfield and colleagues delivered mild electricity to different parts of the brains of people about to undergo brain operations. From this, he concluded that people experience different images, memories and feelings depending on the area in the brain that is stimulated. One problem with this technique is that: (p. 104)
    a. It is dangerous to the patient.
    b. Researchers can't be sure whether the memories are real or fabricated.
    c. Different people have different kinds of memories.
    d. This is a very expensive technique.

7. The problem with conclusions about brain function based on stroke victims is: (p. 100)
    a. Victims are usually older and therefore not representative of the population.
    b. Victims usually have not led healthy lives and are therefore not representative.
    c. Stroke damage can extend over multiple areas of the brain.
    d. All of the above.

8. One problem with using electroencephalograms (EEGs) is that: (p. 101)
    a. EEGs cannot determine where exactly electrical currents occur.
    b. EEGs do not indicate how groups of neurons work together.
    c. EEGs require invasive surgery.
    d. EEGs requires introduction of radioactive materials to the brain.

9. _____ show that certain neurons respond to some words but not others. (p. 101)
    a. EEGs
    b. PET scans
    c. Single-cell recordings
    d. fMRIs

10.   MRIs provide information about _____, whereas fMRIs provide
       information about: (pp. 102-103)
       a.   The function of brain parts, the structure of the brain.
       b.   Brain activity, the damage that has occurred to certain parts of the brain.
       c.   What specific neurons do, the function of brain parts.
       d.   Brain structure, the brain at work.

PRACTICE TEST #4:
GENES, BRAIN, AND ENVIRONMENT

True/False Questions

Circle TRUE or FALSE for each of the following statements.

1. TRUE   FALSE   A gene is a stretch of DNA that produces a specific protein. (p. 107)

2. TRUE   FALSE   Scientists can alter genes to produce alterations in behavior. (p. 108)

3. TRUE   FALSE   There were fewer connections in your brain at birth than you have now. (p. 109)

4. TRUE   FALSE   Neural connections are lost but not made as we experience the world. (p. 100)

5. TRUE   FALSE   Genes and the environment are two interlocking systems working together. (p. 111)

6. TRUE   FALSE   Genes can be "turned on" to produce proteins and other substances. (p. 110)

Multiple-Choice Questions

For each question, circle the best answer from the choices given.

1. Genes produce _____, which in turn form(s) the building blocks of our bodies. (p. 107)
   a. DNA
   b. Fats
   c. Proteins
   d. Sugars

2. The process by which certain neural connections are eliminated is called: (p. 109)
   a. Cutting.
   b. Pruning.
   c. Lesioning.
   d. Ablating.

3. A protein that is produced at the "instruction" of genes is said to be: (p. 110)
   a. Pruned.
   b. Expressed.
   c. Turned on.
   d. Stimulated.

4. A famous pianist has a child and introduces her to the piano at the age of two, in an example of _____ interaction. (p. 111)
   a. Passive
   b. Active
   c. Evocative
   d. Reactive

5. Difficult babies tend to elicit punitive reactions from their caregivers. This is an example of a(n) _____ interaction. (p. 111)
   a. Passive
   b. Active
   c. Evocative
   d. Reactive

6. Saying that intelligence is 50% heritable means: (p. 113)
   a. You get 50% of your intelligence from you mom, and 50% from your dad.
   b. You get 50% of your intelligence from your parents, and 50% from the environment.
   c. In a specific environment, 50% of the variability in intelligence among people is due to genetics.
   d. In a specific environment, 50% of people are intelligent and 50% are not.

7. Whose genes would be the most similar? (p. 113)
   a. Parent and child
   b. Monozygotic twins
   c. Siblings born at different times
   d. Dizygotic twins

8. Plasticity refers to: (p. 109)
   a. The soft spots on an infant's head.
   b. The fact that people are born with few neural connections.
   c. The ability of the brain to change with experience.
   d. The fluid-filled parts at the center of the brain.

9. Studies with knockout mice can tell researchers: (p. 108)
   a. What happens when a certain part of the genetic code is snipped away.
   b. What happens if a mouse receives brain damage via a blow to the brain.
   c. What happens if a mouse experiences a stroke.
   d. What happens if the researcher removes part of the mouse's brain.

10. Pruning is: (p. 109)
    a. The growth of additional neural pathways.
    b. The death of certain neural connections.
    c. The cultivation of certain parts of the genetic code.
    d. An attempt to grow neurons in a laboratory setting.

COMPREHENSIVE PRACTICE TEST

True/False Questions

Circle TRUE or FALSE for each of the following statements.

1.   TRUE   FALSE   A neuron can fire at different strengths. (p. 75)

2.   TRUE   FALSE   When a neurotransmitter is released, the adjacent neuron always fires. (p. 75)

3.   TRUE   FALSE   Antagonist drugs block particular receptors. (p. 80)

4.   TRUE   FALSE   The sympathetic and parasympathetic systems always work against one another. (p. 85)

5.   TRUE   FALSE   The size and development of the basal ganglia make us uniquely human. (p. 90)

6.   TRUE   FALSE   The hypothalamus controls many automatic bodily functions. (p. 95)

7.   TRUE   FALSE   An EEG allows us to observe brain structure. (pp. 100-101)

8.   TRUE   FALSE   Adult brains can easily create new neurons.   (p. 109)

Multiple-Choice Questions

For each question, circle the best answer from the choices given.

1.   Which of the following is NOT a type of neuron? (pp. 102-103)
    a.   Sensory neuron
    b.   Interneuron
    c.   Motor neuron
    d.   Glial neuron

2.   If enough stimulation reaches a neuron, it: (p. 75)
    a.   Fires.
    b.   Becomes chemically neutral.
    c.   Stops firing.
    d.   Dies.

3.   During an action potential, _____ is actively pushed outside of the neuron. (p. 75)
    a.   Potassium
    b.   Chloride
    c.   Sodium
    d.   Bromine

4.   Multiple sclerosis causes _____ to deteriorate, resulting in impaired sensation, loss of vision, and paralysis. (p. 76)
   a.   Interneurons
   b.   Myelin
   c.   Sensory neurons
   d.   Glial cells

5.   The process by which a surplus of neurotransmitter is reabsorbed back into the sending neuron is called: (p. 80)
   a.   Reuptake.
   b.   Reusage.
   c.   Reabsorption.
   d.   Removal.

6.   The peripheral nervous system is composed of the: (p. 83)
   a.   Brain and spinal cord.
   b.   Sympathetic and parasympathetic systems.
   c.   Skeletal and autonomic divisions.
   d.   Midbrain and the hindbrain.

7.   When under stress, our _____ prepares us for "fight or flight." (p. 86)
   a.   Spinal cord
   b.   Skeletal system
   c.   Reticular formation
   d.   Sympathetic system

8.   The two halves of the brain are connected by the: (p. 86)
   a.   Glial connection.
   b.   Corpus callosum.
   c.   Brain bridge.
   d.   Midbrain.

9.   Damage to the _____ lobes causes partial or complete blindness. (p. 88)
   a.   Occipital
   b.   Parietal
   c.   Temporal
   d.   Frontal

10.   The somatosensory strip is found in the _____ lobes. (p. 89)
   a.   Occipital
   b.   Parietal
   c.   Temporal
   d.   Frontal

11. The subcortical region of the brain that coordinates inputs from sensory and motor systems and plays a crucial role in attention is the: (p. 94)
   a. Cerebral cortex.
   b. Thalamus.
   c. Cerebellum.
   d. Hypothalamus.

12. Damage to the _____ would most likely result in trembling and impaired movement. (p. 96)
   a. Cerebral cortex
   b. Thalamus
   c. Basal ganglia
   d. Hippocampus

13. Farah signed up for a sleep study and the neurologist hooked wires up to her head. Most likely, the neurologist plans to keep a running _____ of the electrical activity in Farah's brain as she descends through the sleep stages. (p. 101)
   a. Transcranial recording
   b. Magnetic resonance imaging
   c. Electroencephalogram
   d. Neuroimage

14. A gene is a stretch of DNA that produces a specific: (p. 107)
   a. Fatty acid.
   b. Neuromodulator.
   c. Neurotransmitter.
   d. Protein.

15. The theory of _____ asserts that more genes arise in a population if those genes allow an organism to have more offspring. (p. 114)
   a. Genetic selection
   b. Darwinism
   c. Natural selection
   d. Adaptation

Essay Questions
Answer each of the questions in the space provided.

1. Explain the passage of the electrical signal along the axon._____
   _____
   _____
   _____
   _____
   _____
   _____
   _____

2.   Explain how the sympathetic and parasympathetic systems of the brain are effective in an immediate emergency, but less effective in situations of chronic stress. _____

_____

_____

_____

_____

_____

_____

3.   If a picture of a fork were flashed to the left visual field of a person whose corpus callosum has been split, what would he see? What would be the best way for him to "tell" you what he is seeing? Explain your answer._____

_____

_____

_____

_____

_____

_____

_____

4.   Why are lesions and strokes an inexact method of studying brain function?_____

_____

_____

_____

_____

_____

_____

5.   Why is it misleading to attribute any differences in intelligence among groups of people to genetics?_____

_____

_____

_____

_____

_____

_____

6.   If glial cells produce myelin, and the deterioration of myelin is responsible for the disease multiple sclerosis (MS), then why can't we just introduce glial cells into the brains of people suffering from MS to cure the disease?_____

_____

_____

_____

_____

7. Suppose you had to give up one part of your brain. Which part would you give up, and why? Which part(s) could you definitely not live without?_____

_____

_____

_____

_____

_____

_____

_____

8. Given the recent research showing that positive mental and emotional states can have a tremendous impact on the immune system and resistance to illness, what should a doctor say to someone who wants to "cure" himself of cancer with *just* positive thought (instead of with traditional medicine)?_____

_____

_____

_____

_____

_____

_____

_____

9. Animal models provide us with the opportunity to study the effects of brain lesions on behavior. Discuss the ethical dilemmas involved in such research. Do the pros outweigh the cons? _____

_____

_____

_____

_____

_____

_____

_____

10. Researchers have worked to map out the entire genetic code for humans. We could one day know whether we carry the gene for a particular illness, whether we will eventually develop an illness that could kill us, and whether we could possibly pass a gene onto a child who would then be at risk for the illness. Do we want to know this much information? Why and why not? How might the information be abused and by whom?

_____

_____

_____

_____

_____

_____

_____

When You Are Finished. . . Puzzle It Out

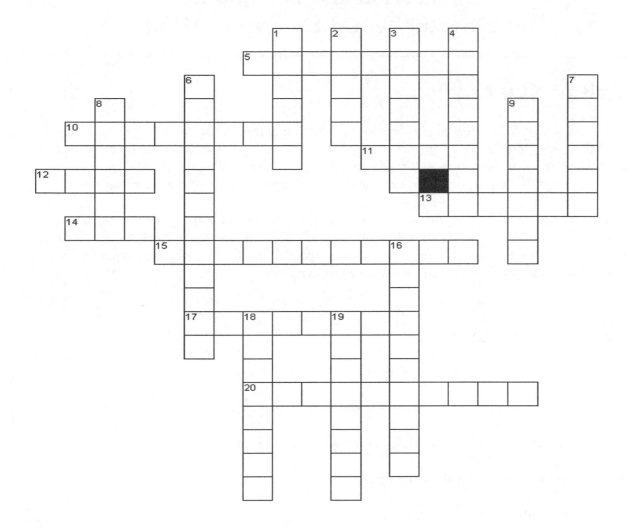

Across
5. Individual's genetic code
10. From the Greek word for tree
11. Blocks reuptake of serotonin
12. Bulges in the cortex
13. Region of impaired tissue
14. Includes the spinal cord and brain
15. Critical to making new memories
17. Often thought of as switching center
20. They fill gaps between neurons

Down
1. Automatic response to an event
2. Four parts of each hemisphere
3. Place where two neurons meet
4. Charge of the resting potential
6. Amount of variability due to genetics
7. Helps impulses travel faster down axon
8. The basic unit of the nervous system
9. Elimination of neural connections
16. Molding of brain by experience
18. Involved in emotions like anger
19. Physical change of a gene

Puzzle created with Puzzlemaker at DiscoverySchool.com.

Chapter 4
Sensation and Perception:
How the World Enters the Mind

Before You Read . . .

Why is your significant other always able to spot the deer at the side of the road when you don't? Why does food taste funny when you have a cold? In this chapter, you will learn how you come to understand the world around you through your senses. Understanding the world depends upon not only sensation, but also upon perception, or our brain's interpretation of the incoming stimuli.

The chapter starts with in-depth coverage of two senses: vision and hearing. Less detailed information is presented about the other senses: smell, taste, and the somasthetic senses (those that have to do with sensing your body and position in space). Finally, the chapter concludes with discussions of magnetic sense and extrasensory perception.

Chapter Objectives

After reading this chapter, you should be able to:

♦ Define sensation and explain how it differs from perception.

♦ Explain how you see, including the sensation of color, shape, and motion.

♦ Describe how you make sense of what you see.

♦ Define attention.

♦ Explain how ears normally register sound.

♦ Describe how the sense of smell works.

♦ Describe how the sense of taste works.

♦ Explain how we sense our bodies.

♦ Understand the evidence for the existence of magnetic sense and extrasensory perception (ESP).

As You Read . . . Term Identification

Make flashcards using the following terms as you go. Use the definitions in the margins of this chapter for help. If you write the definitions in your own words, though, you will remember them better!

Absolute pitch
Absolute threshold
Accommodation
Afterimage
Amplitude
Attention
Attentional blink
Bias
Binocular cues
Bottom up
Categorical perception
Chemical senses
Cocktail party phenomenon
Color blindness
Color constancy
Conduction deafness
Cones
Cornea
Dark adaptation
Dichotic listening
Divided attention
Double pain
Endorphins
Extrasensory perception (ESP)
Figure
Fovea
Frequency
Frequency theory
Gate control
Gestalt laws of organization
Ground
Hair cells
Iris
Just-noticeable difference (JND)
Kinesthetic sense
Loudness
Monocular static cues
Motion cues

Nerve deafness
Opponent cells
Opponent process theory
Optic nerve
Paradoxical cold
Perception
Perceptual constancy
Perceptual set
Pheromones
Pitch
Place theory
Pop-out
Psychophysics
Pupil
Repetition blindness
Retina
Retinal disparity
Rods
Selective attention
Sensation
Sensitivity
Shape constancy
Signal detection theory
Size constancy
Somasthetic senses
Speech segmentation problem
Stereopsis
Taste buds
Texture gradients
Threshold
Tinnitus
Tonotopic organization
Top-down processing
Transduction
Trichromatic theory of color vision
Vestibular sense
Wavelength
Weber's law

As You Read . . . Questions and Exercises

Vision

Visual Sensation: More Than Meets the Eye

Name and describe the two phases of **visual perception**.

♦ _____
_____
_____
_____

♦ _____
_____
_____
_____
_____

First Steps of Visual Perception: Organizing the World

Define each of the following terms and give a personal example of why it could be important in your life.

Term	Definition	Personal Example
Threshold		
Absolute Threshold		
Just-noticeable difference (JND)		

What is the purpose of **signal detection theory**? _____
_____
_____
_____

There are two key concepts that explain why **signals** are detected or missed. Define each of these concepts. Then, explain how these concepts could be used in ensuring that airport security personnel detect any dangerous materials during screening procedures.

Concept	Definition	Impact in Airport Security Screening
Sensitivity		
Bias		

What is **light**?_____

_____

Define the following terms:

♦   **amplitude:** _____

_____

♦   **frequency:**_____

_____

♦   **wavelength:** _____

_____

_____

Name the color with the **lowest frequency** and **longest wavelength**: _____

Name the color with the **highest frequency** and **shortest wavelength**:_____

GO SURFING...

...at http://kidshealth.org/misc_pages/bodyworks/eye.html to see how the eye works. Then, explain the steps involved in **transduction**, or the conversion of electromagnetic energy into nerve impulses:

♦   The **iris** _____.
♦   The **pupil**_____.
♦   The **cornea** _____.
♦   The **lens**_____.
♦   The **retina** _____.
♦   The **fovea**_____.

Why does everything look gray at night? Explain. _____
_____
_____
_____
_____
_____
_____

GO SURFING...

...at http://faculty.washington.edu/chudler/chvision.html and do the experiments on finding your **blind spot**. Why do you have a **blind spot**? Explain. _____
_____
_____
_____
_____
_____
_____

Name two reasons for **dark adaptation**:

♦ _____
_____
_____

♦ _____
_____
_____

What are the **three types of cells** that assist in transforming light into neural impulses? Explain what each type of cell does.

♦ _____
_____

♦ _____
_____
_____

♦ _____
_____
_____

Name and briefly describe the three ways that **colors** can vary.

♦ _____
_____

♦ _____
_____
_____

♦ _____
_____
_____

Recent research has supported the **trichromatic theory of color vision** with some modifications.

This theory says that we can see different hues because we have three different types of cones. Each type is MOST sensitive to a different light in the wavelength. So, one type is most sensitive to light seen as _____ and another to light seen as _____ and yet another to light seen as _____.

For each color, there are at least two different types of cones that are sensitive to it, although one type of cone will be MORE sensitive. The brain registers the **mixture** of the different responses of the three types of cones. However, some materials, such as paint, absorb some light. As a result, not all light is reflected. Only the wavelengths that are

_____, not absorbed, reach your eyes. But, there is more to seeing color than what is explained by this theory. The **opponent process theory of color vision** provides another factor. This theory says that the presence of one color of a pair inhibits the perception of the other color. The opponent pairs are: red/_____, yellow/_____, and black/_____.

Why might one person call a **color** "green," and another person call the color "blue-green"? _____
_____
_____
_____
_____

GO SURFING...

...at http://faculty.washington.edu/chudler/chvision.html. Scroll down the page to the section on visual illusions and do the activities on **afterimages**.

Why can't we see the **mixture** of blue and yellow at the same time? _____
_____
_____
_____
_____

GO SURFING...

...at http://colorlab.wickline.org/colorblind/colorlab/ and see what colors would look like if you were to have different forms of color blindness.

Do you know anyone who has **color blindness**? If so, what form does it take?_____
_____
_____

Who is most likely to have **color blindness**?_____

What causes **color blindness**?

♦ _____

♦ _____

What implications would it have in your life if you were **color-blind**? (For example, the author of this manual once had a karate instructor who was color-blind and could not identify the different colored belts of his students!)_____

_____

_____

_____

_____

_____

GO SURFING...

...at http://www.nei.nih.gov/photo/sims/sims.htm and see photos illustrating **eye disease**. Here, you can see what the world would look like if you had glaucoma or **cataracts**. In fact, fewer than 1/3 of the world's population has perfect **vision**. Others suffer from some of the following problems. State the cause of each problem and any corrective actions that can be taken for it.

Visual Problem	Definition	Cause	Corrective Action(s)
Myopia			
Hypermetropia			
Astigmatism			
Cataract			

In Operation Iraqi Freedom, how did the United States armed forces take advantage of research on separating **figures** from **ground**?_____

_____

_____

_____

_____

Why do you see your desk as a desk, even though it is likely covered by papers and other objects?

_____

_____

_____

_____

_____

_____

_____

How does learning affect your **perception**?_____

_____

_____

_____

_____

_____

Perceptual constancy is the perception of the characteristics of objects as the same even though the sensory information striking the eyes changes. Give a personal example of each of the following types of constancy.

Type of Constancy	Example
Size constancy	
Shape constancy	
Color constancy	

To perceive the world as three-dimensional, the brain uses different types of cues. Briefly describe, and provide an example of each of the following types of **cues**.

Type of Cue	Description	Example
Binocular cues	Cues that come from both eyes working together.	
Retinal disparity		
Convergence		
Monocular cues	Cues that come from only one eye.	
Texture gradient		
Linear perspective (foreshortening)		
Occlusion cue		
Motion cues		
Motion parallax		

GO SURFING...

...at http://psych.hanover.edu/Krantz/SizeConstancy/index.html to see more about size constancy. Be sure to play with the interactive figure. What are the 3 cues that you use to determine if the sizes of objects are constant? Name and briefly describe.

♦ _____
♦ _____
♦ _____

What are two of the **cues** that help you to perceive whether an object is coming closer to you?

♦ _____
♦ _____

GO SURFING...

...at http://faculty.washington.edu/chudler/chvision.html. Scroll down and take a look at the visual illusions there. Some other good sites for viewing illusions are:

♦   www.sandlotscience.com
♦   http://www.optillusions.com/

Which **illusions** are your favorites? Describe here. Explain how they work.

Illusion (Name and Draw)	Explanation

Visual Perception: Recognition and Identification

There are two major neural pathways in the brain:

♦ **The *what* pathway**, which _____
_____

♦ **The *where* pathway**, which _____
_____
_____

What is involved in the final stages of **perceptual processing**? _____
_____
_____
_____
_____
_____
_____

Give the definition and an example of each of the following:

Type of Processing	Description	Example
Bottom-up processing		
Top-down processing		

How do **bottom-up** and **top-down processing** interact? _____
_____
_____
_____
_____
_____
_____

What are **perceptual expectancies** and where do they come from? _____
_____
_____
_____
_____
_____
_____

Kosslyn (one of your textbook authors) proposes that the brain uses two different ways to **code space**. Describe each of these two ways and the hemisphere primarily responsible for these tasks.

Method of Coding Space	Purpose of this Coding Method	Hemisphere
Categorical spatial relations		
Coordinate spatial relations		

There are two reasons why people **pay attention** to something.

Type of Attention	Brain Part Involved	How It Works	Function
Pop-out			
Voluntary (vigilance)			

Name a factor at each of the **levels of analysis** that would help to explain **attention**:

♦   **Level of the brain:** _____

_____

♦   **Level of the person:**_____

_____

♦   **Level of the group:**_____

_____

Name and explain each of the three **limits of attention** and give a personal example of each.

Name & Explanation	Personal Example

How is it possible for **blind people to see**?_____

_____

_____

_____

_____

Define the following phenomena and give an example of how they may affect an editor's job.

Phenomena	Explanation	Effect
Repetition Blindness		
Attentional Blink		

Looking at Levels

What body parts do you find most attractive in others? Analyze your **preferences** at each of the **three levels**. Draw arrows to indicate how factors at the different levels may interact.

The Brain	The Person	The Group

TRY PRACTICE TEST #1 NOW!
GOOD LUCK!

Hearing

Auditory Sensation: If a Tree Falls, but Nobody Hears It, Is There a Sound?

Why do some people **make sounds** from their **ears**, sometimes so loud that others can hear it!
_____
_____
_____
_____

Why can't we **hear** anything in outer space? _____
_____
_____
_____

Name and describe the two phases of **auditory processing**.

◆   _____
_____
_____
_____

◆   _____
_____
_____
_____

If a tree falls in the forest but nobody hears it, is there a sound? Explain your answer. _____
_____
_____
_____
_____

GO SURFING...

...at http://kidshealth.org/misc_pages/bodyworks/ear.html to see how the ear works. Now, explain the steps involved in **auditory processing**:

♦   **Waves** _____.
♦   The **eardrum**_____.
♦   The **three bones in the middle ear (hammer, anvil and stirrup)**_____
_____.
♦   The **basilar membrane**_____.
♦   **Hair cells sticking up from the basilar membrane** _____
_____.

There are two main theories about the way the **basilar membrane** converts pressure waves to sound: **frequency theory** and **place theory**. Which of these theories appears to be correct? Explain the theory. _____
_____
_____
_____
_____

Explain some of the ways that **vision** and **hearing** are similar.

Idea	...As Applied to Vision	...As Applied to Hearing
Brain parts involved in identifying stimuli		
Registering spatial relations		

More than 28 million Americans have some sort of **hearing** difficulty. Describe each of the following problems.

Auditory Problem	Explanation
Genetics	
Nerve deafness	
Tinnitus	
Aspirin usage	
Conduction deafness	

How does **deafness** with an onset in childhood demonstrate the **brain's plasticity**? _____
_____
_____
_____
_____

First Steps of Auditory Perception: Organizing the Auditory World

The first column of this chart lists some of the ways that **vision** and **hearing** are similar. In the last two columns, explain how this idea relates specifically to vision and hearing.

Idea	...As Applied to Vision	...As Applied to Hearing
Gestalt Laws		
Categorical Perception		
Use of Two Sensory Organs (e.g., Two Eyes or Two Ears)		

Idea	...As Applied to Vision	...As Applied to Hearing
Use of Many Different Cues		
Filling-in Effect		

How important is **awareness** to the **processing of sound**? _____
_____
_____
_____
_____
_____

Auditory Perception: Recognition and Identification

Explain the evidence that there is a **genetic component** to **music perception**? _____
_____
_____
_____
_____
_____

Looking at Levels

Explain how, at the **levels of the brain, person, and group**, Beethoven was able to become one of the greatest composers, despite the fact that he was deaf. Draw arrows to indicate how events at the different levels may have interacted.

The Brain	The Person	The Group

TRY PRACTICE TEST #2 NOW!
GOOD LUCK!

Sensing and Perceiving in Other Ways

Smell: A Nose for News?

What are the two **chemical senses**? _____

Why are they called that? _____
_____
_____

What are some of the characteristics of people who are particularly good at **identifying smells**?

♦   _____
♦   _____
♦   _____

Explain the steps involved in **olfaction**:

♦   **Molecules** _____.
♦   **Receptors** _____.

There are two major neural tracks by which odors can travel into the brain:

♦   _____
♦   _____

Female **pheromones** can attract men. Women who wore perfume with the pheromone reported:

♦   _____
♦   _____
♦   _____
♦   _____

Would you ever wear a **pheromone**? Why or why not? _____
_____
_____
_____
_____

Taste: The Mouth Has It

Where can **taste buds** be found?_____
_____

What is the relationship between **smell** and **taste**?_____
_____
_____

Somasthetic Senses: Not Just Skin Deep

Briefly describe each of the following **somasthetic senses** in the chart below.

Sense	Description/Definition	Source
Kinesthetic Sense		
Vestibular Sense		
Touch		
Temperature		

What are the two different kinds of **pain**?

♦ _____
♦ _____

Explain the role of **bottom-up** and **top-down processing** in creating **pain** below.

Bottom-Up Processing	Top-Down Processing

Research indicates that people differ widely in the amount of pain that they can withstand. Do you think that you have a **low** or **high pain threshold**?_____
_____
_____
_____

Other Senses

What impact would it have on the medical field if it were found that humans respond to **magnetic fields** as strongly as do birds?_____

_____

_____

_____

_____

_____

Briefly describe each of the following forms of **extrasensory perception (ESP)**.

Form	Description
Telepathy	
Clairvoyance	
Precognition	
Psychokinesis (PK)	

What are the three reasons why most psychologists are **skeptical** about **ESP**?

- ◆ _____
- ◆ _____
- ◆ _____

Looking at Levels

Given that some cultures hold less rigid standards for body odor, would you expect the effects of **pheromones** to be stronger in those cultures than in ours? Explain why or why not, at the **levels of the brain, person, and group**. Draw arrows to indicate how events at the different levels may interact.

The Brain	The Person	The Group

TRY PRACTICE TEST #3 NOW!
GOOD LUCK!

After You Read . . . Thinking Back

1. What is the relationship between the **sense organs** and **neural impulses in the brain**?

   _____
   _____
   _____
   _____
   _____
   _____

2. In Chapter 1, you learned about **evolutionary psychology**. Name some examples of how evolutionary psychologists have explained facts about sensation and perception. (For example, what would an evolutionary psychologist say is the purpose of pain?) Describe.

   ◆ _____
   _____
   ◆ _____
   _____
   ◆ _____
   _____
   ◆ _____
   _____

3. In Chapter 2, you learned about the importance of **replication**. Why is the ability to replicate studies on ESP so important? Why does the failure to be able to replicate studies make psychologists so skeptical about ESP?_____

   _____
   _____
   _____
   _____
   _____

4. Despite the differences between the **sense organs**, there are many similarities in how sensory information is processed in the **brain**. Give some examples.

   ◆ _____
   _____
   ◆ _____
   _____
   ◆ _____
   _____

After You Read . . . Thinking Ahead

1. At what time in life do you think the different **senses** develop? Do some develop before others? Which ones? When? _____

    _____

    _____

    _____

    _____

    _____

    _____

    _____

    _____

    _____

2. How does your **memory** (both its contents and its processes) affect what you **sense and perceive**? _____

    _____

    _____

    _____

    _____

    _____

    _____

3. How does what you **sense and perceive** affect your **memory** (both the contents and processes)?_____

    _____

    _____

    _____

    _____

4. How might a person's **stereotypes and/or prejudices** influence his or her **sensation and/or perception**? _____

    _____

    _____

    _____

    _____

    _____

5. How might your **sensations and perceptions** influence your **social interactions**? _____

    _____

    _____

    _____

    _____

    _____

After You Read . . . Practice Tests

PRACTICE TEST #1:
VISION

Matching Questions

For the following figures, indicate which Gestalt law of organization is at work: (p. 135)

1. _____

XX XX XX XX

2. _____

XXXXxxxx

3. _____

4. _____

       – – – – – – – – –

      a.   Proximity
      b.   Continuation
      c.   Similarity
      d.   Closure

Multiple-Choice Questions

For each question, circle the best answer from the choices given.

1.   The willingness to report noticing a stimulus is called: (p. 125)
     a.   Sensitivity.
     b.   Reactivity.
     c.   Bias.
     d.   Vigilance.

2.   Weber's law states that: (p. 125)
     a.   A neuron must only be stimulated slightly to fire.
     b.   To notice a stimulus, one must attend to the event.
     c.   Individual differences determine which signals are perceived and which are not.
     d.   A constant percentage of a magnitude change is necessary to detect a difference.

3. The color red has a _____ frequency and a _____ wavelength. (p. 126)
   a. High;short
   b. Low;short
   c. High;long
   d. Low;long

4. The conversion of electromagnetic energy (light) into nerve impulses is called: (p. 126)
   a. Accommodation.
   b. Transduction.
   c. Opponent processing.
   d. Trichromation.

5. There are three types of cones in the eye which correspond to three wavelengths. Which of the following is a wavelength for which there is not a unique type of sensor? (p. 130)
   a. Yellow
   b. Green
   c. Violet
   d. Blue

6. An object that is camouflaged has similar _____and: (p. 134)
   a. Hue; saturation.
   b. Saturation; intensity.
   c. Brightness; hue.
   d. Figure; ground.

7. Stereopsis is: (p. 137)
   a. Hearing more than one soundwave at a time.
   b. Seeing more than one wavelength of light at the same time.
   c. Figuring out depth from binocular disparity.
   d. Figuring out hue from the shape of objects.

8. A stroke that affects the bottom parts of the temporal lobes impairs a person's ability to: (p. 140)
   a. Perceive depth.
   b. See colors.
   c. Recognize objects by sight.
   d. Register locations.

9. The words in bold in the text of your book stand out because of: (p. 145)
   a. Bias.
   b. Selectivity.
   c. Vigilance.
   d. Pop-out.

10. Carol was paying close attention to the light on the corner, waiting for it to turn green. This form of attention is called: (p. 146)
    a. Vigilance.
    b. Pop-out.
    c. Hypersensitivity.
    d. Reactivity.

PRACTICE TEST #2:
HEARING

Multiple-Choice Questions

For each question, circle the best answer from the choices given.

1. We are most sensitive to the frequencies of: (p. 152)
    a. Music.
    b. A baby's cry.
    c. Speech.
    d. A dog's bark.

2. If you emit a humming sound from your ears, it probably: (p. 152)
    a. Acts like sonar to help you locate the objects around you.
    b. Impairs your hearing.
    c. Is feedback from the brain to the ear.
    d. Is your ear sending signals to your brain.

3. According to place theory: (p. 153)
    a. The higher the frequency, the greater the neural firings.
    b. Different frequencies activate different places on the basilar membrane.
    c. Different sounds will activate different parts of the eardrum.
    d. The direction of the sound will indicate how well it is heard.

4. Rods and cones in vision are analogous to _____ in auditory processing. (p. 153)
    a. The eardrum
    b. The hammer, anvil and stirrup
    c. The auditory canal
    d. Hair cells on the basilar membrane

5. Which of the following is the pathway that a sound wave takes in the ear? (p. 153)
    a. Cochlea → basilar membrane → eardrum → bones in the middle ear
    b. Eardrum → bones in the middle ear → basilar membrane → auditory nerve
    c. Eardrum → basilar membrane → bones in the middle ear → auditory nerve
    d. Bones in the middle ear → eardrum → cochlea → auditory nerve

6. The theory that best explains how we hear sounds at a high frequency is the _____ theory. (p. 153)
    a. Place
    b. Opponent-processing
    c. Frequency
    d. Tonotopic

7. The spatial pattern of activation on the basilar membrane: (p. 154)
   a. Is mimicked on the eye.
   b. Is mimicked in the visual cortex.
   c. Is mimicked in the primary auditory cortex.
   d. Mimics the outside world.

8. Nerve deafness occurs when the _____ is/are damaged. (p. 154)
   a. Bones in the middle ear
   b. Eardrum
   c. Hair cells
   d. Auditory nerve

9. The process by which we distinguish the sounds we want to hear (figure) from background noise (ground) is called: (p. 155)
   a. Tonotopic processing.
   b. Opponent-processing analysis.
   c. Frequency processing.
   d. Auditory scene analysis.

10. Like visual perception, auditory perception: (pp. 155-156)
    a. Adheres to the principles of thresholds.
    b. Relies on many different cues to assess where an object is in space.
    c. Involves categorizing perceptions.
    d. All of the above.

11. After riding New York subways for years, Neal found that he had constant ringing in his ears. This is called: (p. 155)
    a. Nerve deafness.
    b. Tinnitis.
    c. Conduction deafness.
    d. Normal aging processes.

12. In auditory perception, Gestalt laws: (p. 155)
    a. Help you determine where the beginnings and endings of words are.
    b. Help you know what to pay attention to.
    c. Help sounds "pop-out" at you.
    d. Help people locate sounds.

13. Which part of the brain is likely to be more developed in a person who is deaf? (p. 155)
    a. The visual cortex
    b. The frontal lobes
    c. The auditory cortex
    d. The parietal lobes

14. To distinguish figure from ground in auditory processing, you: (p. 155)
    a.   Conduct an auditory scene analysis.
    b.   Pay close attention.
    c.   Use cues from both of your ears.
    d.   Rely on tonotopic organization of auditory information.

15. Having two ears: (p. 156)
    a.   Allows us to categorize perception better.
    b.   Helps us to assess the distance of a sound source.
    c.   Helps us to identify a sound more easily.
    d.   Balances our heads.

16. Because we have two ears, there are important differences in the stimuli that reach both ears including: (p. 156)
    a.   The difference in the phase of the sound wave in which they reach the ear.
    b.   The difference in loudness at the two ears.
    c.   The difference in the timing of when they reach each ear.
    d.   All of the above.

17. Suppose that you are at a party, talking to a friend, when all of a sudden you hear someone several feet away say your name. This is an example of: (p. 157)
    a.   Gestalt laws of processing.
    b.   Absolute pitch.
    c.   Plasticity.
    d.   The cocktail party phenomenon.

18. Dichotic listening studies indicate that: (p. 157)
    a.   Attention is required for hearing.
    b.   People hear out a single ear at a time.
    c.   People "fill-in" sounds that they didn't hear.
    d.   Even when not paying attention, people register some information from an unattended ear.

19. If you are in the middle of a conversation and your partner's speech is disrupted by the dog barking, you will: (p. 157)
    a.   Probably still understand what your partner said, due to the phonemic restoration effect.
    b.   Have to ask your partner to repeat the disrupted words.
    c.   Probably still understand what your partner said, because you have two ears.
    d.   Not understand your partner at all because attention is required for hearing.

20. If you have absolute pitch, you: (p. 158)
    a.   Are an excellent musician.
    b.   Can identify a note in relation to others.
    c.   Can identify a note by itself.
    d.   Sing out of tune.

PRACTICE TEST #3:
SENSING AND PERCEIVING IN OTHER WAYS

True/False Questions
Circle TRUE or FALSE for each of the following statements.

1.   TRUE   FALSE   Once burned and lost, taste buds never regenerate. (p. 161)

2.   TRUE   FALSE   Sensitivity to taste diminishes as we age. (p. 161)

3.   TRUE   FALSE   Taste buds are found on the tongue, in the throat, and inside the cheeks. (p. 161)

4.   TRUE   FALSE   There are five types of taste buds: sweet, sour, salty, bitter, and spicy. (p. 162)

5.   TRUE   FALSE   Bitter tastes are best detected in the front of your mouth. (p. 162)

6.   TRUE   FALSE   Taste buds are found on every part of the mouth. (p. 162)

7.   TRUE   FALSE   One type of cell that senses balance information can be found in the inner ear. (p. 163)

8.   TRUE   FALSE   The more cortex devoted to a particular area of the skin, the more sensitive we are to it. (p. 163)

9.   TRUE   FALSE   The mix-and-match principle means that we can feel more types of sensations than we have receptors for. (p. 163)

10. TRUE   FALSE   In mice, magnetic fields can disrupt spatial learning. (p. 165)

Matching Questions
Match the following types of extrasensory perception with their definitions: (p. 165)

_____1.   Telepathy   A.   The ability to move objects without touching them

_____2.   Clairvoyance   B.   The ability to foretell future events

_____3.   Precognition   C.   The ability to send and transmit thoughts mind-to-mind

_____4.   Psychokinesis   D.   The ability to know about events directly, without using the ordinary sense or reading someone's mind

Multiple-Choice Questions

For each question, circle the best answer from the choices given.

1. Who is likely to be best at distinguishing among different smells? (p. 159)
    a. An elderly person
    b. A woman
    c. A 10-year-old boy
    d. A 5-year-old girl

2. Pheromones are similar to hormones in that they: (p. 160)
    a. Modulate the functions of various organs.
    b. Are released inside the body.
    c. Are released by the pituary gland.
    d. Are accessed by the nose.

3. In one study, participants who wore pheromones reported: (p. 161)
    a. Having more sex.
    b. Feeling sexier.
    c. More informal dates.
    d. More masturbation.

4. The reason that smells can evoke strong emotions is because: (p. 160)
    a. One neural track sends signals about odors to the thalamus.
    b. One neural track sends signals about odors to the limbic system.
    c. Both a & b
    d. Neither a nor b

5. Free nerve endings in the mouth are irritated by: (p. 162)
    a. Salty food.
    b. Bitter food.
    c. Spicy food.
    d. Sweet food.

6. Being able to clap your hands together is made possible by the _____ sense. (p. 163)
    a. Somasthetic
    b. Kinesthetic
    c. Vestibular
    d. Limbic

7. Damage to the _____ can cause disruption in a person's vestibular sense. (p. 163)
    a. Inner ear
    b. Occipital lobe
    c. Somasthetic nerve
    d. Thalamus

8.   The role of top-down processing of pain is shown in: (p. 164)
      a.   Acupuncture.
      b.   The placebo effect.
      c.   Double pain.
      d.   Paradoxical cold.

9.   The gate control mechanism may explain: (p. 164)
      a.   Why some people are more sensitive to pain than others.
      b.   How hypnosis can control pain.
      c.   Why the menstrual cycle can influence pain perception.
      d.   How the vestibular sense works.

10.   Which of the following is one of the reasons most psychologists are skeptical about ESP? (pp. 165-166)
      a.   Studies that have been found to support ESP are difficult to replicate.
      b.   The brain mechanisms underlying ESP are unknown.
      c.   It is unknown what form ESP signals might take.
      d.   All of the above.

COMPREHENSIVE PRACTICE TEST

True/False Questions

Circle TRUE or FALSE for each of the following statements.

1. TRUE FALSE Top-down processing is guided by knowledge, expectations, or beliefs. (p. 143)

2. TRUE FALSE It is only in late visual processing that what we see becomes meaningful. (p. 140)

3. TRUE FALSE Rods are extraordinarily sensitive to light and color. (p. 128)

4. TRUE FALSE Most color blindness is present from birth. (p. 132)

5. TRUE FALSE At distances greater than 10 feet, motion cues are more important for depth perception than is stereopsis. (p. 137)

6. TRUE FALSE Repetition blindness results when the visual system is "locked up" for a brief period of time. (p. 150)

7. TRUE FALSE If a tree falls in the forest and nobody hears it, no sound is produced. (p. 152)

8. TRUE FALSE Distinct spots on the skin register hot, cold, or warm stimuli. (pp. 163-164)

9. TRUE FALSE Most people are very good at identifying odors. (p. 159)

10. TRUE FALSE There is a substantial genetic component to pain thresholds. (p. 164)

Identification

Identify the following events as bottom-up or top-down: (p. 143)

Experience	Bottom-up or Top-down?
Unexpectedly seeing a friend walking down the street.	
"Hearing" strange noises in the night when you're alone in the house but nothing is there.	
Tasting something new for the first time.	
Thinking you recognize a friend you are expecting in a passing group of strangers.	

Multiple-Choice Questions

For each question, circle the best answer from the choices given.

1. While watching television, sometimes Jeffrey hears his mother calling his name and sometimes he doesn't. _____ seeks to explain why. (p. 125)
    a. Signal detection theory
    b. JND theory
    c. Weber's law
    d. Absolute threshold theory

2. Perception occurs _____ stage of processing. (p. 134)
    a. Early in the
    b. Late in the
    c. In the middle
    d. In the first

3. The study of the relation between physical events and the corresponding experience of those events is called: (p. 124)
    a. Psychophysics.
    b. Psychosensation.
    c. Astrophysics.
    d. Psychoperception.

4. Jamal is lifting a 10-lb weight; Joel is lifting a 5-lb weight. If it takes an additional two pounds to make Jamal's weight feel heavier, then it will only take an additional one pound to make Joel's weight feel heavier. The theory that best explains this is: (p. 125)
    a. Gestalt's law of grouping.
    b. The opponent process theory.
    c. Sensory adaptation.
    d. Weber's law.

5. Suppose that you were taking a hearing test and were asked to raise your hand every time you heard a noise. If, at one point, you failed to raise you hand when a noise had been sounded, this would be called: (p. 125)
    a. A hit.
    b. A miss.
    c. A false alarm.
    d. A correct rejection.

6. An advertiser creates a billboard, with a neon-colored product shown against the black-and-white background. The advertiser is using _____ to draw the audience's attention. (p. 145)
   a. Selectivity
   b. Bias
   c. Pop-out
   d. Weber's law

7. The automatic adjustment of the eye for seeing at different distances is called: (p. 126)
   a. Accommodation.
   b. Transduction.
   c. Induction.
   d. Adaption.

8. Which of the following pairs of color is NOT an opponent pair? (p. 131)
   a. Red/green
   b. Black/white
   c. Yellow/blue
   d. Orange/brown

9. Most color-blind people are unable to distinguish: (p. 132)
   a. Red from green.
   b. Red from yellow.
   c. Yellow from blue.
   d. Any colors.

10. One of the neural tracks that leaves the olfactory bulb passes through the _____, which is particularly involved in memory. (p. 160)
    a. Hypothalamus
    b. Hindbrain
    c. Thalamus
    d. Forebrain

11. The ability to foretell future events is called: (p. 165)
    a. Telepathy.
    b. Precognition.
    c. Clairvoyance.
    d. Psychokinesis.

12. The immediate experience of basic properties of an object or event that occurs when a receptor is stimulated is called: (p. 123)
    a. Sensation.
    b. Processing.
    c. Perception.
    d. Accommodation.

13. Perception is the process by which: (p. 123)
    a. Stimuli are detected.
    b. Stimuli are transformed into neural activity.
    c. Stimuli are organized and interpreted.
    d. Nerve cells fire in an organized fashion.

14. During a hearing test, Matthew couldn't hear many of the tones presented because they were below his: (p. 124)
    a. Absolute threshold.
    b. Difference threshold.
    c. Subliminal threshold.
    d. Amplitude threshold.

15. An airline pilot needs to have great _____ in order to say when she detects an odd noise over the sound of the jet engines. (p. 125)
    a. Bias
    b. Sensitivity
    c. Accommodation
    d. Opponent-processing

Essay Questions

Answer each of the following questions in the space provided.

1. What are the three stages of processing sensory input from the outside world? _____

   _____
   _____
   _____
   _____
   _____
   _____
   _____
   _____

2. Explain how *bottom-up* and *top-down* processing would help us to understand a language we have never heard before. _____

   _____
   _____
   _____
   _____
   _____
   _____
   _____
   _____

3.   Explain why you cannot confuse green and red or blue and yellow._____
_____
_____
_____
_____
_____
_____
_____

4.   Explain how *repetition blindness* and *attentional blink* can affect the proofreading of your own papers. How can you overcome them? _____
_____
_____
_____
_____
_____
_____
_____
_____

5.   If you could choose one sense to enhance, which would it be? If you had to sacrifice one sense, which would you choose? Which sense do you think will be the most important to you in your future career? Why? _____
_____
_____
_____
_____
_____
_____
_____

6.   Given that perception is subjective, and possibly dependent upon a person's unique genetic make-up, how can we have an objective definition of unique colors (e.g., blue). Consider, too, that we cannot sense just one wave of the electromagnetic spectrum, that every color we perceive is a combination of wavelengths. _____
_____
_____
_____
_____
_____
_____
_____

7. Books and movies that have been written about blind individuals gaining sight do not always paint a happy picture. What would be the downsides to gaining sight, if you were previously blind? Would it be worth it?_____

_____
_____
_____
_____
_____
_____
_____
_____

8. If a deaf person is in a forest when a tree falls, does it make a sound? _____

_____
_____
_____
_____
_____
_____
_____
_____

9. The authors describe how we can detect if someone is "interested" in us by the size of their pupils. Could we also tell if someone were angry at us? What features of the person's face do you think you would selectively attend to if you thought the person were angry? How might changes in your brain, in this situation, affect you (the person), and others (the group)?_____

_____
_____
_____
_____
_____
_____
_____
_____

10. How can we tell if an infant has depth perception? Explain.

_____
_____
_____
_____
_____
_____
_____
_____

When You Are Finished. . . Puzzle It Out

Across

3. Person's willingness to report stimuli
9. Opening in eye that light goes through
10. Leftover from previous visual perception
12. Processing guided by knowledge
15. Like hormones, but outside the body
16. When different stimuli are obvious
17. Opponent color of red
18. Strength of a sound
19. Defect in curvature of cornea
20. Retinal cells that register only gray

Down

1. Set of characteristics corresponding to object
2. Sense registering limp position
4. Focusing on particular information
5. Where optic nerve exits retina
6. Just discovered receptor in eye
7. Constant ringing in the ears
8. How high or low a sound seems
11. Sensitive to different tastes
13. Central region of retina
14. Painkilling chemicals produced by brain

Puzzle created with Puzzlemaker at DiscoverySchool.com.

Chapter 5
Consciousness

Before You Read . . .

This chapter opens with a discussion of something you probably don't get enough of—**sleep**! You will learn why you need sleep so much and what happens when you don't get it. In addition, you will learn about the different stages of sleep and the physical changes that occur during sleep. The chapter discusses four different sleep disorders; do you have one of these?

Next, you will learn about **hypnosis**. You may have seen a stage show featuring a hypnotist; however, this is not representative of the use of hypnosis. Rather, hypnosis involves ongoing self-awareness but a decreased awareness of the environment. You will learn that some people are more hypnotizable than others—are you? If you have never been hypnotized, you will learn more about its benefits; perhaps sometime you will want to use this tool. **Meditation** also has many benefits. You will learn more about these benefits, and the different forms of meditation, in this chapter.

Finally, you will learn the criteria for **substance use** and **dependence** so that you know how to identify whether someone has a problem. Next, you will learn more about the properties and effects of several different classes of substances, including **depressants**, **stimulants**, **narcotic analgesics**, and **hallucinogens**.

Chapter Objectives

After studying this chapter, you should be able to:

♦ Describe the five stages of sleep, the functions of sleep, and the physical changes that occur during sleep.

♦ Compare and contrast the various theories of why people dream.

♦ Describe the role of circadian rhythms in sleep cycles.

♦ Describe four sleep disorders, including their symptoms, effects, and treatments.

♦ Describe the characteristics, theories, and practical uses of hypnosis.

♦ Define meditation, the different types of meditation, and the benefits of meditation.

♦ Define and explain substance abuse and substance dependence, including the seven major symptoms of dependence.

♦ Provide examples and briefly explain the effects of the following substances: depressants, stimulants, narcotic analgesics, and hallucinogens.

As You Read. . . Term Identification

Make flashcards using the following terms as you go. Use the definitions in the margins of this chapter for help. If you write the definitions in your own words, though, you will remember them better!

Absorption
Activation-synthesis hypothesis
Alcohol myopia
Altered states of consciousness
Amphetamines
Blackouts
Circadian rhythms
Concentrative meditation
Consciousness
Crack
Depressants
Disinhibition
Flashbacks
Generalized reality orientation fading
Glove anesthesia
Hallucinogens
Hidden observer
Hypnogogic sleep
Hypnosis
Hypnotic induction
Inhibitory conflict
Insomnia
Latent content
Manifest content

Meditation
Mindfulness meditation
Narcolepsy
Narcotic analgesic
Night terror
Nightmare
Normal consciousness
Opiates
Opening-up meditation
Posthypnotic suggestion
Rapid eye movement (REM) sleep
REM rebound
Sleep
Sleep apnea
Sociocognitive theory
Stimulant
Substance abuse
Substance dependence
Suprachiasmatic nucleus
Tolerance
Trance logic
Trance state
Trance theory
Withdrawal symptoms

As You Read. . . Questions and Exercises

To Sleep, Perchance to Dream

What is **consciousness**? _____
_____
_____

How does **sleep** differ from normal consciousness? _____
_____
_____

	Length of Stage (at Beginning & End of Night)	Physical Characteristics	Brain Activity
Non-REM Stages			
Stage 1			
Stage 2			
Stages 3 & 4			
REM Sleep			

How do **sleep patterns** change over the lifespan? Why?

♦ **Infancy:** _____
_____
_____
_____
_____

♦ **After 40s:** _____
_____
_____
_____

GO SURFING...

...at the following sites and take the online sleep tests:

♦ **Dr. Maas' Power Sleep Site**
http://www.powersleep.org/selftestb.htm

♦ **CNN Health.Com**
http://www.cnn.com/HEALTH/indepth.health/sleeping.conditions/test.html

According to these tests, are you **sleep-deprived**?_____

Do you agree with the results of these tests? Why or why not? _____
_____
_____

How does your **sleep deprivation** (either current or previous) affect you in each of the following areas?

♦ **Cognitive effects:** _____
_____

♦ **Emotional effects:** _____
_____

♦ **Physical effects:** _____
_____
_____

Sleep deprivation has been used by some governments as a method of torture. (For more information about this, search the Human Rights Watch at http://www.hrw.org/.) Based on these situations, as well as studies with rats, if you were not allowed to sleep for a *protracted* length of time (e.g., two weeks), what effects could you expect in each of the following areas?

♦ **Cognitive effects:** _____
_____

♦ **Emotional effects:** _____
_____

♦ **Physical effects:** _____
_____
_____

Why is **sleep** so important? In your own words, summarize the following theories:

♦   **Restorative Theory:** _____

_____

♦   **Evolutionary Theory:** _____

_____

_____

Keep a diary of your dreams for the next few days (or more). Summarize the **manifest content** of one of your dreams here:_____

_____

_____

_____

_____

_____

GO SURFING...

…at one of the following "dream interpretation" sites. Use the dream dictionaries there to interpret your dreams.   Do *not* pay any money to have your dream interpreted online!

♦   **Dream Central's Online Dream Dictionary**
        http://www.sleeps.com/dictionary/dictionary.html
♦   **Sleepy Bear Dream Interpretation Site**
        http://myenvoy.com/sleepybear/
(There are also other sites available; just search for them!)

Now, offer an explanation of the **latent content** of your dream, based on the sites above._____

_____

_____

_____

_____

_____

_____

_____

How else could your **dream** be explained (besides using Freud's ideas of manifest and latent content)?_____

_____

_____

_____

_____

_____

_____

_____

_____

Which **dream theory** does Solms' research support? Explain. _____

_____

_____

_____

_____

Complete the following table, indicating how the following **neurotransmitter** (NT) and **hormone** (H) levels change during sleep and the effects of these changes.

Chemical	Increase or Decrease?	Effects of Change
Acetylcholine (NT)		
Serotonin (NT)		
Norepinephrine (NT)		
Melatonin (H)		

Describe the timing of your **circadian rhythms**: Are you a **lark** or an **owl**? _____

_____

_____

_____

How do you deal with this timing in your everyday life?_____

_____

_____

_____

Why are some people grouchy on Monday mornings? _____

_____

_____

_____

What can they do to keep from being grouchy?_____

_____

_____

_____

_____

For most people, what is the least energetic time of the day? Why?_____

_____

_____

_____

_____

GO SURFING...

...at the following site and take the online **sleep tests** there. (Follow the links at the bottom of the page.)

♦   **National Sleep Dynamics, Inc.**
        http://www.nationalsleep.com

Does this site indicate that you may have a **sleep disorder**? If so, name and describe the disorder.

_____

_____

_____

_____

Do you agree with the results of this test? Why or why not?_____

_____

_____

_____

_____

Can you think of other factors that may influence test results?_____

_____

_____

_____

_____

Looking at Levels

Amanda is embarrassed when her husband, Robin, tells her that she snores. Robin urges Amanda to see the doctor, but she refuses. Because he cannot sleep in the bedroom when she snores, Robin sleeps on the couch in the living room. After 2 months of this, both partners are very grumpy. Finally, Robin issues an ultimatum: Amanda must seek help or he will move out and get his own apartment. Describe the factors at each of the three levels that have contributed to this situation. Draw arrows to indicate how the factors may have interacted.

The Brain	The Person	The Group

GO SURFING...

...at the following site and take the online "Sleep IQ" test and test your knowledge of sleep there:

♦ **National Sleep Foundation**
   http://www.sleepfoundation.org/nsaw/sleepiq99i.html

TRY PRACTICE TEST #1 NOW!
GOOD LUCK!

Hypnosis & Meditation

Hypnosis is a state of mind characterized by:

♦ a focused awareness of _____.
♦ a decreased awareness of _____.

Hypnosis is brought on by **hypnotic induction**, which often involves:

- _____.
- _____.
- _____.

After the induction, a hypnotized person will then enter a **trance state**. What are the two hallmarks of a trance state? Name and define them.

- _____
  _____
  _____

- _____
  _____
  _____

What is a **post-hypnotic suggestion**?_____
_____
_____
_____

How **hypnotizable** do you think you are? Explain your answer._____
_____
_____
_____
_____

There are two theories of hypnosis. Explain each, in your own words.

- **Trance theory:**_____
  _____
  _____
  _____
  _____
  _____

- **Sociocognitive theory:**_____
  _____
  _____
  _____
  _____
  _____
  _____

Which theory of **hypnosis** is supported by neuroimaging data? How? _____
_____
_____
_____

What are some of the benefits of **hypnosis**? List them.

◆ _____
◆ _____
◆ _____
◆ _____
◆ _____
◆ _____
◆ _____
◆ _____

How does **hypnosis** reduce pain? Explain. _____
_____
_____
_____

Have you ever been **hypnotized**? If so, did you experience the results described in this chapter?
_____
_____
_____

On TV and in films, **hypnosis** is often portrayed differently than it is in the textbook. What are these differences? Discuss. _____
_____
_____
_____

Meditation is a state of mind characterized by:

◆ _____.
◆ _____.

How are **hypnosis** and **meditation** similar? _____
_____

How are **hypnosis** and **meditation** different? _____
_____

Describe the following three types of meditation:

◆ **Concentrative meditation:** _____
_____

◆ **Opening-up meditation:** _____
_____

◆   **Mindfulness meditation:** _____

_____

_____

What are some of the benefits of **meditation**? List them.

◆ _____
◆ _____
◆ _____
◆ _____

As the textbook points out, the correlation between **meditation** and these benefits does not imply causation. Can you think of other ways that meditators and non-meditators may differ (that might cause these differences)? Discuss_____

_____

_____

_____

_____

_____

Biologically, what other **state of consciousness** does meditation most resemble? How are the two similar?_____

_____

_____

_____

_____

GO SURFING...

...at the following site and try the meditation suggested there.
◆   **The Skillful Meditation Project**
      http://www.meditationproject.com/Instructions.shtml

What did you experience? Do you think it worked as it was supposed to? Why or why not?

_____

_____

_____

_____

Looking at Levels

After becoming experienced meditators, some people go on retreats with others to deepen their understanding of and their skill at **meditation**. Explain how each of the levels may lead to greater relaxation than does solitary meditation. Indicate how factors at the different levels may interact using arrows.

The Brain	The Person	The Group

TRY PRACTICE TEST #2 NOW!
GOOD LUCK!

Drugs & Alcohol

GO SURFING...

...at the following sites to see if you have any substance dependencies:

♦ **Alcohol Screening.org**
   http://www.alcoholscreening.org/screening/index.asp
♦ **Addiction Treatment Resource Network**
   http://www.efn.org/~pfarmer/

Do these tests reveal that you **abuse substances**?_____

_____

_____

_____

Do you agree with these results? Why or why not?_____
_____
_____
_____

If so, do you abuse substances *chronically*? In other words, do you have a **substance dependence**?_____
_____
_____
_____

The two most important symptoms of substance dependence are tolerance and withdrawal. In your own words, define those terms here:

♦   **Tolerance** = _____
_____
_____

♦   **Withdrawal** = _____
_____
_____

Do you think that many students at your college **binge-drink**?_____
_____
_____

How do you think binge-drinking affects the college (financially, socially, etc.)?_____
_____
_____

What are the effects of **binge-drinking** on the individual? _____
_____
_____

Why is alcohol characterized as a **depressant**?_____
_____
_____

Complete the following table, indicating the physical effects of **alcohol** at different dosages.

Dosage	Physical Effects
Low Doses	
Moderate Doses	
High Doses	

Describe another example of **inhibitory conflict**, other than that described in the text. _____

_____

_____

_____

_____

_____

Describe what would happen if a person with a **high-conflict level** and a **low-conflict level** were challenged to do something dangerous, if they had been drinking.

Low-Conflict	High-Conflict

List and describe the psychological effects of **alcohol**.

♦ _____

♦ _____

♦ _____

♦ _____

♦ _____

Have you ever experienced a **blackout**? Describe what it was like (or, what it would be like).

_____

_____

_____

_____

What kinds of **withdrawal symptoms** could an alcoholic expect?_____

_____

_____

Why are **stimulants** more likely to induce dependence than other drugs? _____

_____

_____

_____

_____

Complete the following form, comparing and contrasting different aspects of using **cocaine powder** versus **crack**.

	Cocaine Powder	Crack
How administered		
Effects		
Dangers		

How does **cocaine** affect neurons, causing the psychological effects that it does?_____

_____

_____

How does **cocaine**, a drug that initially produces pleasure, ultimately lead to the loss of pleasure from other sources (e.g., food and sex). _____

_____

_____

Caffeine and **nicotine** are common stimulants. List their effects in this table.

Caffeine	Nicotine

How do **narcotic analgesics** affect the brain, causing the effects that they do?

◆ _____
   _____
◆ _____
   _____
   _____

What effects does **heroin** have?

◆ _____
◆ _____
◆ _____
◆ _____

Why is it so difficult for a **heroin** addict to "kick the habit"? _____
_____
_____
_____

What effects does **LSD** have on users?

◆ _____
◆ _____
◆ _____
◆ _____
◆ _____

What are the effects of **marijuana** on users?

◆ _____
◆ _____
◆ _____
◆ _____

How do the effects of **marijuana** depend on the social context in which they occur? _____
_____
_____
_____
_____

Looking at Levels

Explain the factors that operated at each of the **levels** to bring about Princess Diana's death. Use arrows to indicate how the events at the different levels may have interacted.

The Brain	The Person	The Group

TRY PRACTICE TEST #3 NOW!
GOOD LUCK!

After You Read . . . Thinking Back

1. You first learned about evolutionary theory in Chapter 1. In this chapter, you read of the evolutionary theory of sleep. What are the two best forms of evidence for evolutionary theories?
    ◆ _____
      _____
    ◆ _____
      _____
      _____

2. What is the biggest problem with testing evolutionary theories? _____
    _____
    _____
    _____

3. In Chapter 1, you learned of the cognitive revolution and subsequent cognitive theories. In this chapter, you read about the social-cognitive theory of hypnosis. What do you think "**socio**cognitive" means? How is this different from "cognitive theories"? _____
    _____
    _____
    _____

4. Based on what you learned of Freud's psychoanalytic theory in Chapter 1, what criticisms can you offer for Freud's dream-interpretation theory? _____
    _____
    _____
    _____

5. What methodological difficulties in studying substance use can you think of? _____
    _____
    _____
    _____

6. In Chapter 4 (Sensation & Perception), you learned about top-down versus bottom-up processing. Compare and contrast these two types of processing. _____
    _____
    _____
    _____

8. How do top-down and bottom-up processes influence:
    ◆ **sleep?** _____
      _____
    ◆ **hypnosis?** _____
      _____
    ◆ **marijuana use?** _____
      _____

After You Read . . . Thinking Ahead

1. Can you think of any psychological disorders that might mimic the effects of sleep deprivation?_____
    _____
    _____
    _____
    _____

2. Given what you know about the functions of sleep, why might babies sleep longer and older people sleep less? (What does this mean about their brain development?)_____
    _____
    _____
    _____
    _____

3. Do you think that substance abuse and/or substance dependence is a psychological disorder? Why or why not?_____
    _____
    _____
    _____
    _____

4. Given this, how would you define "psychological disorder"? Why?_____
    _____
    _____
    _____
    _____

5. Some of the substances described in this chapter can be legally prescribed as treatment for other psychological disorders (e.g., barbiturates can be prescribed to treat insomnia or anxiety). Given the potential for abuse of these substances, how effective do you think drug therapy is in treating psychological disorders?_____
    _____
    _____
    _____
    _____

6. Groups sometimes influence people to abuse substances (as in peer pressure) and sometimes influence people to stop using drugs (as in Alcoholics Anonymous). Why do groups have both kinds of influence? What will determine how an individual is influenced?_____
    _____
    _____
    _____
    _____

After You Read . . . Practice Tests

PRACTICE TEST #1:
SLEEP

Matching Questions

Match the following stages of sleep with their descriptions:

_____ 1.	Stage 1 (p. 174)	A.	Sleep spindles
_____ 2.	Stage 2 (p. 175)	B.	20 – 50% of EEG-recorded brain activity is delta waves
_____ 3.	Stage 3 (p. 175)	C.	Vivid dreaming
_____ 4.	Stage 4 (p. 175)	D.	Hypnogogic sleep
_____ 5.	REM Sleep (p. 175)	E.	Very deep sleep with 50+% delta waves

True/False Questions

Circle TRUE or FALSE for each of the following statements.

1.   TRUE   FALSE   Your "natural" circadian rhythm is exactly 24 hours long. (pp. 182-183)

2.   TRUE   FALSE   Your circadian rhythms are governed at least in part by light. (p. 182)

3.   TRUE   FALSE   Blind people have the same 24-hour cycle as sighted people. (p. 183)

4.   TRUE   FALSE   Some people are "larks" and others are "owls." (p. 183)

5.   TRUE   FALSE   Grouchiness on Monday mornings is because you have to go to class. (p. 183)

6.   TRUE   FALSE   Sleep apnea occurs most often in children. (p. 186)

7.   TRUE   FALSE   Narcolepsy involves sudden attacks of drowiness and/or sleep. (p. 185)

8.   TRUE   FALSE   When rats are deprived of sleep for long enough, they eventually die. (p. 179)

9.   TRUE   FALSE   Night terrors is another term for nightmares. (p. 184)

10.   TRUE   FALSE   When people with narcolepsy fall asleep, they enter REM sleep almost immediately. (p. 185)

Multiple Choice Questions

For each question, circle the best answer from the options given.

1.   Which of the following statements about the stages of sleep is FALSE? (p. 176)
      a.   Everyone proceeds through the five stages of sleep during the night.
      b.   You can be awakened easily during Stage 1 sleep.
      c.   Stage 4 sleep is more frequent as you move into older adulthood.
      d.   Babies spend more time in REM sleep than do older people.

2.   Dreams involving physical activity are possibly due to increased amounts of
      _____ when we sleep. (p. 182)
      a.   Serotonin
      b.   Melatonin
      c.   Acetylcholine
      d.   Norepinephrine

3.   Circadian rhythms are regulated by the: (p. 182)
      a.   Optic nerve.
      b.   Amygdala.
      c.   Brainstem.
      d.   Suprachiasmatic nucleus.

4.   People who share a bed with someone: (p. 177)
      a.   Go to bed at the same time.
      b.   Wake at the same time.
      c.   Don't sleep as well as people who sleep alone.
      d.   Enter REM sleep at the same time.

5.   How would an evolutionary psychologist explain humans' need for sleep? (p. 179)
      a.   It strengthens important neural connections.
      b.   It restores our bodies from the wear and tear of the day.
      c.   It keeps us in bed, at a time when our vision is not very good.
      d.   It increases cortisol levels.

6.   After Kate has a dream in which her teeth fall out, her psychologist tells her that this means that she doesn't feel like she has a voice (or control) of what is happening in her life. Which theory of dreaming does Kate's psychologist most likely believe in? (p. 180)
      a.   Freudian theory
      b.   Evolutionary theory
      c.   Restorative theory
      d.   The activation-synthesis hypothesis.

189

7. Which of the following would you be LEAST likely to experience during hypnogogic sleep? (p. 174)
   a. A gentle falling or floating sensation
   b. Fear
   c. "Seeing" flashing lights
   d. A sudden, violent jerk

8. One night, you go to bed really late because you are studying for your psychology exam. Which of the following can you expect to happen when you do go to sleep? (p. 177)
   a. You will enter REM sleep later than usual.
   b. You will have more deep sleep that night than usual.
   c. More time will be spent in REM sleep.
   d You will dream less than usual.

9. Which of the following would NOT be a recommendation for someone suffering from insomnia? (p. 185)
   a. Don't smoke cigarettes, eat chocolate, or drink anything containing caffeine in the evening.
   b. Put a TV in your bed so it can lull you to sleep.
   c. Keep regular sleep hours.
   d. Consider meditation or progressive muscle relaxation.

10. The 24-hour day: (p. 183)
    a. Is largely maintained through light-dark cycles (which can be either natural or artificial).
    b. Results from external aids, such as clocks.
    c. Is not necessarily humans' "natural" rhythm.
    d. Is all of the above.

11. Night terrors are most common among: (p. 184)
    a. Young boys.
    b. Young girls.
    c. Older adults.
    d. Adolescents.

12. If you had to work swing or graveyard shifts on your jobs, which of the following should you do? (p. 184)
    a. After the shift, try to stay awake until your normal bedtime.
    b. Try to shift your schedule daily.
    c. Try not to stay on shift work for more than three days.
    d. Try not to socialize too much.

13. Researchers have found that individuals with _____ adjust more easily to shift changes in work schedules. (p. 184)
    a. Insomnia
    b. An underactive suprachiasmatic nucleus
    c. Lower levels of brain activity
    d. A greater range of body temperatures in their circadian rhythms

14.   According to Karni and colleagues, the best way to strengthen brain connections made during the day is to: (p. 181)
   a.   Stay awake all night.
   b.   Go to sleep, but have a friend wake you up whenever you enter REM sleep.
   c.   Get a good night's sleep.
   d.   Drink alcohol before going to bed.

15.   Sleep deprivation will cause mood changes after: (p. 178)
   a.   1 night without sleep.
   b.   3 nights without sleep.
   c.   2 weeks without sleep.
   d.   Never; sleep deprivation doesn't affect mood.

PRACTICE TEST #2:
HYPNOSIS & MEDITATION

Matching Questions

Match the correct altered state of consciousness with its description.

_____1.   Hypnosis (p. 188)   A.   Maintaining floating awareness and
                                                         focusing on what is prominent at the moment

_____2.   Opening-up meditation   B.   Yoga is one type of this.
              (p. 195)

_____3.   Concentrative meditation   C.   Focused awareness on vivid experiences
              (p. 195)

_____4.   Mindfulness meditation   D.   Focusing narrowly and then
              (p. 195)   broadening up to merge with the environment

Multiple-Choice Questions

For each question, circle the best answer from the choices given.

1.   According to _____ theory, a hypnotized person is simply acting out the role of
     a hypnotized person, as he or she understands it. (p. 192)
     a.   Sociocognitive theory
     b.   Trance theory
     c.   Generalized reality orientation
     d.   Absorption

2.   Which of the following statements about hypnosis is FALSE? (pp. 189-190)
     a.   A well-trained hypnotist can hypnotize anyone.
     b.   Hypnosis is an altered state of consciousness.
     c.   Some people can become hypnotized even when in a room by themselves.
     d.   The illogical can become logical in a hypnotized state.

3.   In Western cultures, hypnotizability: (p. 189)
     a.   Increases as one ages.
     b.   Peaks in early childhood.
     c.   Peaks in adolescence.
     d.   Decreases across the life span.

4.   A geometric pattern on which a person may focus while meditating is called a: (p. 194)
     a.   Mandala.
     b.   Mantra.
     c.   Matrix.
     d.   Mosaic.

5. The benefits of regular meditation include all of the following except: (p. 196)
   a. Lower tension and anxiety.
   b. Lower levels of stress.
   c. Weight loss.
   d. State of deep restfulness

6. A hypnotist would know that you are in a trace state if: (p. 188)
   a. You tuned out external reality.
   b. You uncritically accepted ideas that you would ordinarily think were impossible.
   c. You had your eyes shut.
   d. A & b, but not necessarily c

7. In comparison to other people, highly hypnotizable people: (p. 190)
   a. Are usually more emotional.
   b. Meditate more frequently.
   c. Are more open to new experiences.
   d. Are shyer.

8. Research by Green & Lynn suggests that hypnosis: (p. 192)
   a. Improves accuracy of memory.
   b. Increases confidence in accuracy of memory.
   c. Improves the amount of material that can be remembered.
   d. Decreases accuracy of memory.

9. In Kosslyn's study, when in a hypnotic trance and told to view a pattern in color (even though the pattern is really in gray), the parts of the brain that process color information were activated. This suggests that: (p. 193)
   a. Hypnosis is primarily routed in the hypnotized person's expectations of the situation.
   b. Hypnosis is a separate brain state.
   c. People have to be very motivated to be hypnotized.
   d. Hypnosis is not an altered state of consciousness.

10. Hypnosis works to reduce pain by: (p. 193)
    a. Inducing relaxation.
    b. Changing how pain is experienced.
    c. Alleviating the fear of pain.
    d. All of the above.

11. Meditation and hypnosis are similar in that they both involve: (p. 194)
    a. Increased awareness of the self.
    b. Decreased awareness of the external environment.
    c. A focused awareness on a particular signal.
    d. Deep breathing.

12. The physical effects of meditation: (p. 196)
   a. Are the same as those produced by hypnosis.
   b. Are the same as those produced by general relaxation techniques.
   c. Are less beneficial than hypnosis.
   d. Are more beneficial than those produced by general relaxation techniques.

13. In terms of brain activity, meditation is most similar to: (p. 196)
   a. REM sleep.
   b. Non-REM sleep.
   c. Hypnosis.
   d. Night terrors.

14. Which of the following would not be typical of a regular, long-term meditator? (p. 196)
   a. Decreased heartrate
   b. Decreased respiration rate
   c. Decreased salivation
   d. Decreased muscle tension

15. The hidden observer: (p. 192)
   a. Dissociates from the self during hypnosis.
   b. Experiences what the entranced part of the self doesn't.
   c. Steps out of the self during meditation.
   d. Is the part of the self that can leave the body during lucid dreaming.

PRACTICE TEST #3:
DRUGS AND ALCOHOL

Matching Questions
Match each substance to its characteristics.

_____ 1.   Alcohol (p. 200)   A.   Can result in sudden death, for even occasional users

_____ 2.   Barbiturates (p. 204)   B.   Damages neurons that produce serotonin

_____ 3.   Cocaine (powder) (p. 204)   C.   Causes hallucinations, sometimes spontaneously

_____ 4.   Crack (p. 205)   D.   Causes decreased awareness and increased relaxation.

_____ 5.   Amphetamines (p. 205)   E.   Legal sutstance that causes alertness and insomnia

_____ 6.   MDMA ("e") (p. 205)   F.   In high doses, can cause effects similar to paranoid schizophrenia

_____ 7.   Caffeine (p. 205)   G.   Causes short-term relaxation and euphoria

_____ 8.   Nicotine (p. 205)   H.   Legally prescribed to aid sleep or reduce anxiety, but lethal if combined with alcohol

_____ 9.   Heroin (p. 206)   I.   Less powerful, but more common, hallucinogen

_____ 10.   LSD (p. 206)   J.   Illegal substance that enhances sense of physical and mental capacity; decreases appetite

_____ 11.   Marijuana (p. 207)   K.   Causes relaxation, irritability, cancer, and emphysema

True/False Questions
Circle TRUE or FALSE for each of the following statements.

1.   TRUE   FALSE   There is an inverse relationship between age at which an individual begins drinking and the likelihood that he will develop an alcohol disorder. (p. 199)

2.   TRUE   FALSE   Men are more likely to binge drink than women. (p. 200)

3.   TRUE   FALSE   Physiologically, alcohol can both depress and stimulate the nervous system. (p. 200)

4.	TRUE	FALSE	It takes about 15 minutes for alcohol to get absorbed in the blood. (p. 200)
5.	TRUE	FALSE	In low-conflict situations, people who have been drinking can typically inhibit their responses. (p. 201)
6.	TRUE	FALSE	A hangover indicates your body is going through withdrawal. (p. 203)
7.	TRUE	FALSE	Cocaine is more likely to induce dependence than any other drug. (p. 204)
8.	TRUE	FALSE	Fifty percent of date rapes happen when women have been drinking. (p. 202)
9.	TRUE	FALSE	LSD use results in increased creativity. (p. 206)
10.	TRUE	FALSE	The most commonly used hallucinogen in the U.S. is LSD. (p. 207)

Multiple-Choice Questions

For each question, circle the best answer from the choices given.

1. Tolerance and withdrawal are the most important symptoms of: (p. 198)
    a. Substance dependence.
    b. Substance abuse.
    c. Substance addiction.
    d. Substance use.

2. If someone is getting progressively less of an effect from her usual dose of a substance, she is experiencing: (p. 198)
    a. Withdrawal.
    b. Addiction.
    c. Dependency.
    d. Tolerance.

3. Alcohol is called a _____ because it _____ CNS activity. (p. 200)
    a. Stimulant; increases
    b. Stimulant; decreases
    c. Depressant; increases
    d. Depressant; decreases

4.   When drunk, a person is more likely to engage in behavior that he would avoid when sober if the behavior is both _____ and _____. (p. 201)
    a.   Strongly desired; strongly prohibited
    b.   Strongly desired; weakly prohibited
    c.   Weakly desired; strongly prohibited
    d.   Weakly desired; weakly prohibited

5.   Cocaine causes an experience of pleasure and euphoria by increasing the amount of available _____ and _____. (p. 204)
    a.   Endorphins; serotonin
    b.   Serotonin; epinephrine
    c.   Dopamine; norepinephrine
    d.   Dopamine; serotonin

6.   Chronic heroin users experience more pain than other people when they are not using heroin because heroin: (p. 206)
    a.   Increases the intensity of pain stimulation.
    b.   Lowers the natural pain thresholds.
    c.   Decreases the body's supply of endorphins.
    d.   All of the above.

7.   An indication that marijuana is not a completely benign drug is the fact that: (p. 207)
    a.   Thousands of people seek professional help each year to stop using it.
    b.   Tolerance to THC occurs rapidly, leading to withdrawal symptoms.
    c.   Its use leads to addiction and possible use of other drugs.
    d.   It causes flashbacks to memories of earlier uses.

8.   Which of the following is *not* a depressant? (p. 199)
    a.   Marijuana
    b.   Valium
    c.   Alcohol
    d.   Barbiturates

9.   Alcohol myopia is defined as: (p. 201)
    a.   A perceptual problem in which a person who has been drinking perceives minor aspects of an experience as more important than they are.
    b.   A neurological problem in which excessive intake of alcohol alters the shape of the eye, resulting in nearsightedness.
    c.   A perceptual problem in which it becomes more difficult for a person who has been drinking to perceive objects that are farther away, particularly in low light.
    d.   A psychological problem in which a person who has been drinking cannot recall events that happen to him in the hours surrounding consumption.

10. Disinhibition refers to the fact that: (p. 200)
    a. When they drink, some people lose their inhibitions about sex.
    b. Depressants activate some neurons that otherwise would not fire.
    c. When they take drugs, some people become more inhibited about revealing details about themselves.
    d. Hallucinogens produce hallucinations.

COMPREHENSIVE PRACTICE TEST

True/False Questions

Circle TRUE or FALSE for each of the following statements.

1.   TRUE   FALSE   If you go to bed hungry, you will probably dream about food. (p. 180)

2.   TRUE   FALSE   You are most likely to remember the dreams that occur during non-REM sleep. (p. 176)

3.   TRUE   FALSE   Dream content is completely random. (p. 180)

4.   TRUE   FALSE   Snoring often accompanies narcolepsy (p. 185)

5.   TRUE   FALSE   Hypnosis as theatrical entertainment is common. (p. 193)

6.   TRUE   FALSE   The effects of hypnosis end as soon as the trance is over. (p. 192)

7.   TRUE   FALSE   Meditation provides the same level of benefit as general relaxation exercises. (p. 196)

8.   TRUE   FALSE   People who are highly hypnotizable have active fantasy lives. (p. 189)

9.   TRUE   FALSE   Dreaming occurs only during REM sleep. (p. 179)

10. TRUE   FALSE   A normal sleep-wake cycle, without light cues, is approximately 24.9 hours. (p. 182)

11. TRUE   FALSE   Meditation is more like REM sleep than any other state of consciousness. (p. 196)

12. TRUE   FALSE   The most important symptom of substance dependence is disruption of work. (p. 198)

13. TRUE   FALSE   Substance dependence results from chronic substance abuse. (p. 198)

14. TRUE   FALSE   Withdrawal symptoms are the uncomfortable effects that occur when the use of the substance is discontinued. (p. 199)

15. TRUE   FALSE   The most commonly used hallucinogen is marijuana. (p. 207).

Multiple-Choice Questions

For each question, circle the best answer from the choices given.

1.   Dreams rarely involve sedentary activities; this may be due to a(n)
      _____ during REM.
      (p. 182)
      a.   Increase in melatonin
      b.   Increase in acetylcholine
      c.   Decrease in acetylcholine
      d.   Increase in serotonin

2.   In Stage 1 sleep, which of the following would be most likely? (p. 175)
      a.   Sleepwalking
      b.   Dreaming
      c.   A feeling of falling
      d.   Muscle paralysis

3.   Over the course of the night, people spend more time in _____ and less time in:
      (p. 176)
      a.   Stage 1; REM sleep.
      b.   Stages 3 & 4; REM sleep.
      c.   Stage 2; Stage 3.
      d.   REM sleep; deep sleep.

4.   A lack of deep, slow-wave sleep may partially explain: (p. 176)
      a.   Why infants' brains develop so quickly.
      b.   Why children have night terrors.
      c.   Why adolescents need more sleep than infants.
      d.   Declines in older adults' health.

5.   If you have a regular sleep cycle and are not troubled by insomnia, studying just before bed:
      (p. 181)
      a.   Is a waste of study time, as you will forget everything while asleep.
      b.   Is a good technique, as REM sleep appears to solidify brain connections.
      c.   Is equally as good as studying at any other time.
      d.   Is not a good idea, as the material studied may disrupt your sleep and cause nightmares.

6.   Becky is very relaxed, has her eyes closed, and has a decreased heart rate. Becky is MOST probably: (p. 196)
      a.   In REM sleep.
      b.   Hypnotized.
      c.   Meditating.
      d.   Any of the above.

7.   Hypnosis can improve athletic performance by: (p. 194)
       a.   Decreasing anxiety.
       b.   Increasing awareness of the external environment.
       c.   Making people insensitive to pain.
       d.   Decreasing physiological awareness.

8.   The genital arousal that occurs during REM sleep: (p. 176)
       a.   Supports Freud's theory of dream interpretation.
       b.   Is unrelated to dream content.
       c.   Reflects a recent lack of sexual activity.
       d.   Supports the activation-synthesis hypothesis.

9.   Ben goes to his doctor complaining of sudden attacks of drowsiness and even sleep,
       sometimes at very unfortunate moments, such as when driving. You would be most likely to
       treat Ben with: (p. 185)
       a.   Sleeping pills.
       b.   Stimulants.
       c.   Recommendations for better sleep hygiene.
       d.   A Continuous Positive Airway Pressure device.

10.   In most cases, people do not act upon their dreams. This is because of: (p. 176)
       a.   Muscle paralysis that occurs during REM.
       b.   Dreams are a mental, not physical exercise.
       c.   Acetylcholine released during sleep inhibits movement.
       d.   The deletion of unnecessary neural connections during dream states.

11.   Sleeping pills work by: (p. 182)
       a.   Increasing production of the hormone melatonin.
       b.   Decreasing production of acetylcholine, which activates the motor and visual areas
              of the brain.
       c.   Blocking production of "wake-up" neurotransmitters serotonin and norepinephrine.
       d.   Activating the suprachiasmatic nucleus (SCN), which regulates circadian rhythms.

12.   A post-hypnotic suggestion: (p. 188)
       a.   Results in specific changes after the hypnotic trance is over.
       b.   Is how a hypnotized person is released by the hypnotic trance.
       c.   Explains trance logic.
       d.   Will only work if a person is very hypnotizable.

13.   The theory that best explains hypnosis is: (p. 192)
       a.   The activation-synthesis hypothesis.
       b.   Freudian theory.
       c.   Evolutionary theory.
       d.   Trance theory.

14. Which of the following conditions does hypnosis NOT effectively treat? (pp. 193-194)
    a. Depression
    b. Pain
    c. Anxiety
    d. Warts

15. Which of the following is NOT a symptom of substance abuse? (p. 198)
    a. Taking more of the substance over time
    b. Using the substance leads to distress in major areas of life
    c. Using the substance occurs in dangerous situations
    d. Using the substance leads to legal problems

16. Alcohol affects the brain by: (p. 200)
    a. Causing some neurons to fire that otherwise wouldn't.
    b. Depressing the nervous system.
    c. Triggering activation of the amygdala, which is involved in aggression.
    d. A & b, but not c

17. Fifty percent of on-campus date rapes occur when men are under the influence of alcohol. The reason for this is probably that: (p. 202)
    a. The amygdala has been activated by the alcohol.
    b. Alcohol impaired men's understanding of women's friendliness.
    c. Alcohol led men to forget women's rejections of their advances.
    d. The frontal lobe, which inhibits responses, is especially affected by alcohol.

18. Cocaine causes a pleasurable feeling by: (p. 204)
    a. Preventing reuptake of dopamine and norepinephrine in the synaptic cleft.
    b. Producing more serotonin.
    c. Causing spontaneous firing of sensory neurons.
    d. Destroying neurons that produce serotonin.

19. Which of the following drugs would be most likely to produce hallucinations? (p. 206)
    a. MDMA (or "e")
    b. Heroin
    c. Opiates
    d. LSD

20. Some narcotic analgesics: (p. 206)
    a. Are derived from poppies.
    b. Are not addictive.
    c. Relieve pain.
    d. Excite the central nervous system.

Essay Questions

Answer the following questions in the space provided.

1.   How would sleep deprivation affect the following activities of your life? Discuss.

     a)   Performance on an exam _____
    _____
    _____
    _____

     b)   Relationship with a roommate _____
    _____
    _____
    _____

     c)   Ability to drive a car _____
    _____
    _____
    _____

     d)   Physical health _____
    _____
    _____
    _____

     e)   Appetite, weight, and temperature _____
    _____
    _____
    _____

2.   Explain some of uses of hypnosis. _____
_____
_____
_____
_____
_____
_____
_____
_____

3.   Can anyone be hypnotized? Discuss._____
_____
_____
_____
_____
_____
_____
_____

4.   Compare and contrast hypnosis and meditation. _____
_____
_____
_____
_____
_____
_____
_____
_____

5.   Compare and contrast substance abuse and substance dependence._____
_____
_____
_____
_____
_____
_____
_____
_____

6.   Why should someone who has been drinking avoid high-conflict situations?_____
_____
_____
_____
_____
_____
_____

When You Are Finished . . . Puzzle It Out

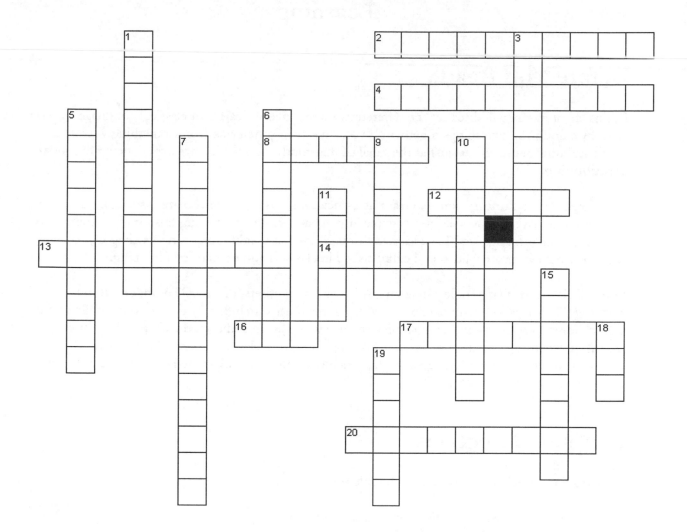

Across

2. Occurs after REM deprivation
4. ASC with deep relaxation
8. Narcotic derived from opium poppy
12. Proposed that dreams are symbolic
13. Most common hallucinogen
14. A major depressant
16. Sleep in which body is paralyzed
17. State of mind with focused awareness
20. Sleep-promoting hormone

Down

1. Another name for Stage 1 sleep
3. Loss of consciousness while drunk
5. Disorder accompanied by snoring
6. More substance needed for same effect
7. Results from hallucinogen use
9. A hypnotically induced ASC
10. Sudden attacks of drowsiness
11. Crystalline form of cocaine
15. Repeated difficulty sleeping
18. Brain part that registers light change
19. Symbolic meaning of dream

Puzzle created with Puzzlemaker at DiscoverySchool.com.

Chapter 6
Learning

Before You Read . . .

In this chapter, you will discover the different ways that people learn. In classical conditioning, you learn by associating two things together. If you have ever gotten sick from something you ate or drank and now get nauseous just at the smell of that food or drink, you are experiencing **classical conditioning**!

In operant conditioning, you also learn by association, but this time you are associating the behavior and its consequence. For example, if you have learned that using this Grade Aid improves your exam performance, you have learned through operant conditioning. In this chapter, you will learn how behaviors are gained and extinguished in classical and operant conditioning.

You will also learn that people can learn just by watching others; this is called **observational learning**. This type of learning explains why parents must watch their language so carefully around their children (lest their children pick up any curse words). In addition, the chapter introduces **cognitive learning**, which is involved in learning complex tasks. Not surprisingly, cognitive learning involves cognitive processes such as memory and reasoning, which are covered in more depth in the next two chapters.

Chapter Objectives

After reading this chapter, you should be able to:

♦   Define classical conditioning and trace its history.

♦   Name some common examples of classical conditioning in daily life.

♦   Define operant conditioning and explain how it occurs.

♦   Name some common examples of classical conditioning in daily life.

♦   For both classical and operant conditioning, explain principles of extinction, spontaneous recovery, generalization, and discrimination.

♦   Explain the brain functions involved in both classical and operant conditioning.

♦   Explain cognitive learning.

♦   Define insight learning.

♦   Explain how watching others can help people learn and why some models are better than others.

♦   Differentiate among the different forms of learning.

As You Read . . . Term Identification

Make flashcards using the following terms as you go. Use the definitions in the margins of this chapter for help. If you write the definitions in your own words, though, you will remember them better!

Acquisition
Avoidance learning
Behavior modification
Biological preparedness
Classical conditioning
Cognitive learning
Conditioned emotional response (CER)
Conditioned response (CR)
Conditioned stimulus (CS)
Conditioning
Continuous reinforcement
Contrapreparedness
Delayed reinforcement
Discrimination
Discriminative stimulus
Extinction
Fixed interval schedule
Fixed ratio schedule
Food aversion
Generalization
Habituation
Immediate reinforcement
Insight learning
Interval schedule
Latent learning
Law of effect

Learning
Negative punishment
Negative reinforcement
Observational learning
Operant conditioning
Partial reinforcement
Phobia
Positive punishment
Positive reinforcement
Primary reinforcer
Ratio schedule
Reinforcement
Reinforcer
Response contingency
Secondary reinforcer
Shaping
Spontaneous recovery
Stimulus discrimination
Stimulus generalization
Successive approximations
Trace conditioning
Unconditioned response (UR)
Unconditioned stimulus (US)
Variable interval schedule
Variable ratio schedule

As You Read . . . Questions and Exercises

Introduction to Learning

How does your text define learning?_____

_____

Which of the following are examples of learning? Circle "YES" or "NO" as appropriate.

1. YES NO The cessation of thumb-sucking by an infant.

2. YES NO The acquisition of language in children.

3. YES NO A computer program generates random opening moves for its first 100 chess games and tabulates the outcomes of those games. Starting with the 101st game, the computer uses those tabulations to influence its choice of opening moves.

4. YES NO A worm is placed in a T maze. The left arm of the maze is brightly lit and dry; the right arm is dim and moist. On the first 10 trials, the worm turns right seven times. On the next 10 trials, the worm turns right all 10 times.

5. YES NO Ethel stays up late the night before the October GRE administration and consumes large quantities of licit and illicit pharmacological agents. Her combined (verbal plus quantitative) score is 410. The night before the December GRE administration, she goes to bed early after a wholesome dinner and a glass of milk. Her score increases to 1210. Is her change in pretest regimen due to learning?

6. YES NO A previously psychotic patient is given Dr. K's patented phrenological surgery and no longer exhibits any psychotic behaviors.

7. YES NO A lanky zinnia plant is pinched back and begins to grow denser foliage and flowers.

8. YES NO MYCIN is a computer program that does a rather good job of diagnosing human infections by consulting a large database of rules it has been given. If we add another rule to the database, has MYCIN learned something?

9. YES NO After pondering over a difficult puzzle for hours, Jane finally figures it out. From that point on, she can solve all similar puzzles in the time it takes her to read them.

10. YES NO After 30 years of smoking two packs a day, Zeb throws away his cigarettes and never smokes again.

Originally published in Rocklin, T. (1987). Defining learning: Two classroom activities. Teaching of Psychology, 14, 228-229. Reprinted with permission of the publisher and author.

Classical Conditioning

Pavlov's Experiments

In Pavlov's initial experiment, in which he paired a tone with the presentation of food, the
_____ was the **unconditioned stimulus**, the _____ was the
unconditioned response; the _____ was the **conditioned stimulus**, and
the _____ was the **conditioned response**.

Practice identifying the US, CS, UR, and CR using these examples.

1. Your professor slams her book down every day when she walks in, so that you now wince
    when you see her walk in the door.
    US:_____ UR:_____ CS:_____ CR:_____

2. Jack always smokes when he is in someone's car at school. When his mother picks him up
    for Fall Break, Jack immediately reaches for a cigarette when he gets in the car (even though
    he doesn't want his mother to know he smokes!).
    US:_____ UR:_____ CS:_____ CR:_____

3. Mandi once got sick after eating Chinese food (because she was allergic to the MSG in it).
    Now, even the smell of Chinese food makes her sick.
    US:_____ UR:_____ CS:_____ CR:_____

4. Marketing researchers have found that men are more likely to buy a car after viewing
    advertisements of attractive women sitting on the car.
    US:_____ UR:_____ CS:_____ CR:_____

5. John successfully quit drinking alcohol by participating in an Antabuse treatment program.
    US:_____ UR:_____ CS:_____ CR:_____

6. Ader and Cohen's rats died after drinking flavored water, even after they were *not* injected
    with an immune-suppressing drug.
    US:_____ UR:_____ CS:_____ CR:_____

7. Marcia was once in a bank robbery in which a robber pulled a gun from his inside coat
    pocket and held it to her face. Now, she jumps every time she sees a man put his hand into
    his inside coat pocket.
    US:_____ UR:_____ CS:_____ CR:_____

8. For her 21st birthday, Teri drank too much tequila and got sick. Now, whenever she sees a
    tequila bottle, she feels nauseous.
    US:_____ UR:_____ CS:_____ CR:_____

9. Every Sunday, Robin visits his mother, who makes him a delicious, 6-course meal. Now, every time he pulls into his mother's driveway, Robin's mouth begins to water.

US:_____ UR:_____ CS:_____ CR:_____

10. Each time she meets with her boss, Michelle gets berated for having done something wrong. Now, whenever she even sees her boss, Michelle flinches.

US:_____ UR:_____ CS:_____ CR:_____

GO SURFING...

...at Fullerton College's interactive demonstration of **classical conditioning**: http://www.uwm.edu/~johnchay/cc.htm. Try conditioning the dog to salivate to a light. Click on each of the boxes to present that stimulus. The lines on the salivation bar represent the frequency of salivating.

In this situation, what is...

♦   the US?_____
♦   the CS?_____
♦   the UR?_____
♦   the CR?_____

What did you do to try to **condition** the dog to salivate to a light? _____
_____
_____

How many **trials** (or pairings) did it take for the dog to salivate before the food was presented? ____

If you stopped presenting the food, and only presented the light, what happened? _____
_____
_____

Now, what happens if you again present the food and the light together?_____
_____
_____

Try doing this a few different times. Is there anything that you can do to make the salivation occur for more trials, even without the food? _____
_____

What is **conditioning**? _____
_____

Here are several different types of **conditioning**. Explain each and note whether or not it is effective.

Type of Conditioning	Explanation	Is it Effective?
Delayed Conditioning		
Trace Conditioning		
Backward Pairing		
Simultaneous Conditioning		

How It Works

What is **avoidance learning?** _____
_____
_____

How was **avoidance learning** discovered? _____
_____
_____

What was the significance of the **Little Albert** study? _____
_____
_____

Some stimuli are easier to **condition** than others.

List some stimuli that organisms seem to be biologically prepared to be conditioned to.	List some stimuli that organisms seem to be contraprepared to be conditioned to.

Why might it be easier to **condition** some stimuli than others? _____
_____
_____

When was **extinction** shown in the interactive demonstration you did earlier?

♦ What did you do to cause the **extinction**? _____
_____

♦ What did the dog do when the behavior had been **extinguished**? _____
_____

When was **spontaneous recovery** shown in the interactive demonstration you did earlier?

♦ What did you do to cause **spontaneous recovery**? _____
_____

♦ What did the dog's behavior look like at this point? _____
_____

How might you demonstrate **stimulus generalization** in a study like the one in the interactive demonstration you did earlier?

♦ What types of stimuli might the dog **generalize** to? _____
_____

♦ What would the dog's behavior look like at this point?_____
_____

Why might dogs (or people) **generalize** stimuli? _____
_____
_____

How might you demonstrate **stimulus discrimination** in a study like the one in the interactive demonstration you did earlier?

♦ What type of stimuli might the dog **discriminate** between?_____
_____

♦ What would the dog's behavior look like at this point?_____
_____

♦ What might you do to help the dog **discriminate** between stimuli?_____
_____

What is **higher-order conditioning?**_____
_____
_____

Describe how **higher-order conditioning** could have been done in the **Little Albert** study?

_____

_____

In your own words, summarize the three pieces of evidence that **cognitive processes** are involved in learning (contrary to what strict behaviorists would say):

- ♦ _____
- ♦ _____
- ♦ _____

There are three distinct brain areas and processes involved in **classical conditioning**. What are they?

Brain Part(s)	Function(s)

In your own words, explain why a **classically conditioned response** will never *really* be extinguished? _____

_____

_____

If this is true, then what is **extinction**?_____

_____

In your own words, explain how the brain is involved in **extinction**? _____

_____

Describe what would have happened to **Little Albert** had his amygdala been removed. What if only the central nucleus of the amygdala had been removed? _____

_____

_____

Applied

In your own words, explain how **classical conditioning** can explain drug overdoses. _____

_____

_____

How is **classical conditioning** used as a therapeutic technique?_____

_____

_____

What is **evaluative conditioning**?_____
_____
_____

Find an example of **evaluative conditioning** in a magazine and attach here:

In your example of **evaluative conditioning**, identify the following components of classical conditioning:

- ◆   US:_____
- ◆   CS:_____
- ◆   UR:_____
- ◆   CR:_____

Have you ever experienced a **taste aversion** to a particular food or drink? If so, explain. (If not, think of a friend's taste aversion and explain that.)_____
_____
_____

In this example, identify the following components of **classical conditioning**:

- ◆   US:_____
- ◆   CS:_____
- ◆   UR:_____
- ◆   CR:_____

In Adar and Cohen's study, identify the following components of **classical conditioning**:

- ◆   US:_____
- ◆   CS:_____
- ◆   UR:_____
- ◆   CR:_____

What was the significance of Adar and Cohen's study?

◆ _____

◆ _____

Explain an example of **classical conditioning** in your own life (other than those listed above).

_____

_____

_____

In this example, identify the following components of **classical conditioning**:

       ◆   US:_____

       ◆   CS:_____

       ◆   UR:_____

       ◆   CR:_____

Looking at Levels

Some chemotherapy patients develop anticipatory nausea from being in the hospital or seeing other stimuli. In this example, identify the following components of **classical conditioning**:

       ◆   US:_____

       ◆   CS:_____

       ◆   UR:_____

       ◆   CR:_____

Explain the factors that operate at **each of the levels** to influence whether or not someone develops anticipatory nausea. Use arrows to show how events at the different levels may interact.

The Brain	The Person	The Group

Do you think you are more **autonomically reactive** than other people? Why or why not?

_____

_____

How might these factors (in the chart above) interact?_____

_____

_____

_____

TRY PRACTICE TEST #1 NOW!
GOOD LUCK!

Operant Conditioning

Discovery and How It Works

Distinguish between **operant** and **classical conditioning**._____
_____
_____
_____

Why does **"operant" conditioning** have its name? _____
_____
_____

What is the **Law of Effect**?_____
_____
_____

How did Thorndike develop the **Law of Effect**?_____
_____
_____
_____

GO SURFING...

...at **Fullerton College**'s interactive demonstration of operant conditioning:
http://www.uwm.edu/~johnchay/oc.htm. This is a computerized model of a **Skinner box**.
Familiarize yourself with all of the different parts of it.

In this model, identify the following components of **operant conditioning**:

◆   the stimulus:_____
◆   the response:_____
◆   the consequence:_____

What happens when you push the button to **reinforce** the pigeon?_____
_____
_____
_____

What do the displayed numbers mean? _____
_____
_____

GO SURFING...

One of the most successful treatments for autism is based on operant conditioning. Search (on www.google.com or another good search engine) for "applied behavioral analysis" and "autism." Here is a good starting link: http://members.tripod.com/RSaffran/aba.html. You can also search by the name "O. Ivar Lovaas," the pioneer of the field. How his childhood influenced him in developing this technique is particularly interesting.

Describe how **applied behavioral analysis** (ABA) is used with autistic children. _____
_____
_____
_____
_____
_____
_____
_____
_____
_____
_____

Principles of Operant Conditioning

The difference between **classical** and **operant conditioning** is exemplified in how responses are described as coming about.

- In classical conditioning, responses are _____, exemplifying that they are usually reflexive and involuntary.
- In operant conditioning, responses are _____, exemplifying that they are usually voluntary.

What would happen if the pigeon (in the interactive model from above) didn't like food pellets?

_____

_____

What is the difference between **reinforcement** and **punishment**?

_____

_____

In the terms **positive reinforcement, positive punishment, negative reinforcement,** and **negative reinforcement,** the words "positive" and "negative" do not refer to whether something is *good* or *bad.* Instead, what do the words mean in this context?

- positive = _____
- negative = _____

Within each cell of this table, write the type of feedback that would result from a combination of that action and that effect. Then, think of an example to illustrate each type of feedback.

Action / Effect	Giving a stimulus.	Removing or withholding a stimulus.
To increase behavior.		
To decrease behavior.		

What type of feedback is involved in these situations: positive reinforcer (PR), positive punisher (PP), negative reinforcer (NR), or negative punisher (NP)?

1. _____   Your professor says that your class' performance on the last exam was so good, she is removing your cumulative final exam.

2. _____   Your boss yells at you because you came late to work.

3. _____   You clean your dorm room before your mother visits so that she won't nag you.

4. _____   Your grades are so bad that the coach takes away your basketball scholarship.

5. _____   Your professor praises your excellent term paper.

6. _____ You have found from past experience that smoking reduces your anxiety, so you light up right before your final exam.

7. _____ Your professor gives you an F because you cheated.

8. _____ You get a bonus from work for going above and beyond the call of duty!

9. _____ Your coach has you run an additional 15 minutes for every pass you miss during practice.

10. _____ Your girlfriend refuses to kiss you because you smoke. (She says you taste like an ashtray!)

11. _____ Your professor has an attendance policy in which you lose four points for each unexcused absence.

12. _____ Your child gives you a hug every time you read her a bedtime story.

Describe three problems with using spankings as a means to control a child's behavior.

♦ _____
♦ _____
♦ _____

If you had children, would you spank them (as a form of **discipline**)? Why or why not?
_____
_____
_____

If you do plan (or do) use spankings as a form of **discipline**, list four things you could do to make them more effective.

♦ _____
♦ _____
♦ _____
♦ _____

Describe at least two alternatives to spankings that you could use to control a child's behavior.

♦ _____

♦ _____

From the list below, circle the **secondary reinforcers**:

Food	**Money**	**Attention**	**Praise**	**Sex**
Promotion	**Good grades**	**Water**	**Pain relief**	**Raises**

Using the principles of **immediate** and **delayed reinforcement**, explain why exercising is so difficult for some people to do. _____
_____
_____
_____

Beyond Basic Reinforcement

Give an original example of **generalization** as it relates to operant conditioning._____
_____
_____
_____

Give an original example of **discrimination** as it relates to operant conditioning._____
_____
_____
_____

Underline the discriminative stimulus in each of the following situations:

♦   Jessica is sure to dress up and put her make-up on when she knows she will be seeing her boyfriend.

♦   Megan's dog, Cosmo, starts wagging his tail and jumping around whenever Megan comes home.

♦   You do all the assigned reading when you know that there will be a quiz.

♦   Jeff is careful to use polite language when his son is present.

GO SURFING…

…at the computerized model of the **Skinner box** that you visited earlier (http://www.uwm.edu/~johnchay/oc.htm).

Shape the pigeon's behavior to get him to peck at the lever. How did you do this?_____
_____
_____

What type of **reinforcement schedule** did you use initially?_____
_____

Why might this be a good schedule to use initially?_____
_____
_____

Next, try using a **fixed ratio schedule** for several minutes. Reinforce the pigeon for every 6th peck.
What happens to the pigeon's other behaviors as you do this?_____
_____
_____

Graph the results of using this **schedule**:

Frequency of Pecking

Time

Now, **extinguish** the behavior. How did you do this? _____
_____
_____

Now, restart the exercise and try using a **variable interval schedule** of reinforcement. How did
you do this?_____
_____

Graph the results of using this **schedule**:

**Frequency
of
Pecking**

Time

Do the same thing using a **fixed interval schedule** of reinforcement. Graph your results below.

**Frequency
of
Pecking**

Time

Finally, try using a **variable ratio schedule** of reinforcement. Graph your results below.

**Frequency
of
Pecking**

Time

After the behavior is well-established using this schedule, try **extinguishing** the pecking behavior. What happens, especially in comparison to extinguishing the pecking following **a fixed ratio schedule**? _____

_____

Now, restart the program. Try using **continuous reinforcement** to encourage the pigeon to slap its wings. What happens, especially in comparison to reinforcing pecking? _____

_____

_____

What does this tell you about the relative frequency of pecking versus flapping in pigeons?

_____

_____

Do you think you could **shape** a more complicated behavior in the pigeon (such as a peck followed by a flap)? If so, how would you do it?_____

_____

_____

Consider pigeons that were not immediately reinforced for their behaviors. (You can try it in the computer model, if you like!) These pigeons had to figure out what caused the food pellet to (eventually) appear. Was it the pecking? Was it because they walked in a circle? Explain how **delayed reinforcement** can help us to understand superstitious behaviors not only among pigeons but among humans as well._____

_____

_____

_____

_____

_____

_____

Which schedule of **reinforcement**. . .

- ♦ is most resistant to extinction? _____
- ♦ causes exhaustion? _____
- ♦ results in slow but consistent responding? _____
- ♦ causes an individual to slow down right after reinforcement? _____

Describe how you could use these same **shaping** techniques to teach your roommate to clean up his room. What **successive approximations** would you reward? What schedule of reinforcement would you use? Explain. _____

_____

_____

_____

_____

_____

_____

GO SURFING...

...at **The Adaptive Mind Center** (http://epsych.msstate.edu/adaptive/index.html) to try another interactive model of **operant conditioning**.

What type of reinforcement schedule is being used in these examples: FR, FI, VR, or VI?

1. _____ Picking up your paycheck at the end of each week

2. _____ Factory worker paid for every three dresses she makes

3. _____ Slot machines at a gambling casino

4. _____ Calling a friend and getting no answer and then continuing to call until you reach her

5. _____ Buying lottery tickets

6. _____ A strawberry picker who gets paid per pints picked

7. _____ Looking at your watch during a lecture until the end of a lecture

8. _____ Mail-checking behavior, assuming that the mailman comes at different times each day

9. _____ Asking people out on dates

10. _____ Checking your e-mail

11. _____ Giving yourself a break from studying after every 30 minutes

12. _____ Getting your favorite cookies (which must bake for exactly seven minutes) from the oven

Learning Brain

Learning by **operant conditioning** involves two phases. Different brain structures and neurotransmitters are involved in each phase. Fill in the following table to indicate which brain parts and neurotransmitters are involved in each phase of the learning process. Use arrows to indicate how events at the different levels may interact.

Brain Parts & Neuro-transmitters / Phase	Involved Brain Parts	Involved Neurotransmitters
#1: Individual learns when to do a certain behavior.		
#2: Individual learns the stimulus-response association (e.g., what the effect of the behavior is).		

List the similarities between **classical** and **operant conditioning**:

◆ _____
◆ _____
◆ _____
◆ _____

Given this, how do we know that **classical** and **operant conditioning** are different? (Or, do we?)
_____
_____

Looking at Levels

If you could alter the behavior of one of your professors, what behavior would you alter and how would you accomplish it? Describe what would happen at the **levels of the brain, person, and group** throughout the process. Use arrows to indicate how events at the different levels may interact.

The Brain	The Person	The Group

What does this say about your role in creating the most beneficial learning environment? Explain.

_____

_____

_____

TRY PRACTICE TEST #2 NOW!
GOOD LUCK!

Cognitive & Social Learning

Cognitive Learning

In what ways **are latent learning** and **observational learning** similar? _____

_____

_____

_____

_____

_____

_____

_____

Give examples from your own experiences of **latent learning**. Is most of what we learn not evident at first? What does the educational setting typically require of students? _____

_____

_____

_____

_____

_____

_____

_____

_____

Insight Learning

GO SURFING...

...at http://www.xsiq.com/content/demonstration/board_psychology2.htm to run an animated version of the Köhler's study. Also, take a look at some real pictures of Köhler's work at: http://elvers.stjoe.udayton.edu/history/history.asp?RURL=http://elvers.stjoe.udayton.edu/history /people/Kohler.html. (Yes, the URL is *very* long!) At the latter site, read some of the commentaries on Köhler's work.

Do you have any other interpretations for **Köhler's** findings, besides that the chimps had **insights**?
_____
_____
_____

Do you think that *all* animals can have **insights,** or is this ability limited to certain species?
_____
_____
_____

Have you ever had an **"aha" moment,** when things finally fell into place for you? If so, explain.
_____
_____
_____

Observational Learning/ Learning from Models

GO SURFING...

...at http://www.emory.edu/EDUCATION/mfp/07BoboDollExperiment.mov to watch a short video clip about **Bandura's** Bobo doll study.

Summarize the clip here:

_____

_____

_____

_____

_____

_____

Think about your role models. For each group listed below, think of at least one behavior that your models engage in. Then, complete the following chart, indicating whether or not you imitate the behavior and list factors that both promote and discourage imitation.

Role Models	Behavior	Do You Imitate This Behavior?	Factors Promoting Imitation	Factors Discouraging Imitation
Your parents				
Your siblings				
Other, older relatives				
Peers				
Your teachers/coaches				
Celebrities				

Looking at Levels

Besides the use of drugs, children and adolescents also imitate a number of **pro-social behaviors** displayed by their parents. Take a step back and look at your own behaviors. Do any of them appear to have derived from imitation of your parents? Explain how, at the **levels of the brain, person, and group**. Use arrows to indicate how events at the different levels may interact.

The Brain	The Person	The Group

TRY PRACTICE TEST #3 NOW!
GOOD LUCK!

Conclusion to Learning

What type of learning is involved in each of the following examples?

1. _____ Nathan was a genius who didn't speak until he was 3. When asked why not, he said, "I didn't have anything important to say until then."

2. _____ You have been attending class all semester, but suddenly one day, you finally understand statistics!

3. _____ You have noticed that your boss is always in a bad mood on Fridays, so you have learned to avoid him on those days.

4. _____ You have watched your roommate all semester and noticed that her study techniques have gotten her good grades. You begin using those techniques yourself.

5. _____ The cafeteria food at your school is awful and you feel sick every time you just walk in the building.

6. _____ Bobby's dad has road rage and frequently curses at other drivers. One time, when he sees an upcoming roadblock, Bobby shouts the same expletives.

7. _____ You are returning to your hometown after a long break, but you find you can still navigate the roads as if you never left.

8. _____ Your professor spits when he gets excited. Unfortunately, you sit in the front row. Now, whenever his voice starts to rise, you keep your head down.

9. _____ You went to church every Sunday with your parents. They thought you didn't pay any attention, until one night you are watching Jeopardy with them and can correctly answer all the questions in the religion category.

10. _____ You have been struggling with how to organize your thesis. One day, while taking a shower, the answer suddenly comes to you.

11. _____ Your boyfriend is so pleased that you have stopped smoking that he gives you a massage each day you don't light up. You love the massages, so you refrain from smoking.

12. _____ Despite your requests to the contrary, your roommate persists in burning aromatherapy candles that aggravate your allergies. Now, you begin coughing and sneezing as soon as you walk in the room, whether or not the candles are lit.

How could you use classical, operant, and/or social learning principles in each of the following situations? (Surf around on the Web if you can't think of any ideas yourself!)

1. After graduation, you take a job as a computer salesperson. Your income depends almost entirely on your sales. (Your base pay is very low.) How could you use learning principles to assist you in generating sales?_____

_____

_____

_____

_____

_____

_____

_____

2.   You are the parent of a four-year-old who STILL isn't potty-trained. How could you use learning principles to encourage him to potty-train?_____

_____
_____
_____
_____
_____
_____
_____

3.   Think of your favorite teacher of all time. How did he or she use learning principles in teaching? _____

_____
_____
_____
_____
_____
_____
_____

4.   After graduation, you get a job as a manager in a restaurant. How could you use your knowledge of learning principles in your management of others?_____

_____
_____
_____
_____
_____
_____
_____

After You Read . . . Thinking Back

1. The Little Albert study is considered a classic study in the field of psychology and has led to many important findings. Yet, it would not be allowed by Institutional Review Boards today. Do you think the field of psychology will be hindered by these ethical restraints? Should ethical standards be revised? Discuss. _____
    _____
    _____
    _____

2. Can you think of situations in which either classically or operantly conditioning an individual or group is unethical? How might individuals in positions of authority get reluctant followers to do what they want them to do, using learning principles?_____
    _____
    _____
    _____

3. Which of the learning theories in this chapter fall into the category of "behaviorism"?
    _____

    How can you remember this, given the content of the theories and the term "<u>behavior</u>ism"?
    _____
    _____

    What were the lasting impacts of behaviorism (from Chapter 1)?_____
    _____
    _____

4. Tolman's studies of **cognitive maps** in rats was one factor that led to the end of the reign of behaviorism (as the predominant school of thought in psychology). Why? _____
    _____
    _____

5. What followed the fall of behaviorism? How would Tolman's studies contribute to this?
    _____
    _____

6. The first phase of operant conditioning involves the hippocampus. What are the other functions of the hippocampus? How are all these functions similar?_____
    _____
    _____

7. In classical conditioning, extinction involves the frontal lobe's active suppression of the amygdala's response. What are the other functions of the frontal lobes? How are all these functions similar?_____
    _____
    _____

After You Read . . . Thinking Ahead

1. Insight is one method of problem-solving. Can you rely on this method? How often does this method work for you? What are some other methods of problem-solving?

   _____

   _____

   _____

   _____

2. Is there anything that you can do to increase the likelihood of having an "aha" moment? Explain._____

   _____

   _____

3. The delay of gratification is one component of "emotional intelligence," which you will study in Chapter 8. Can you think of other skills that might make someone "emotionally intelligent"?_____

   _____

   _____

4. Given what you know about biological preparedness and contrapreparedness, what do you think the most common phobias are?_____

   _____

   _____

5. The least common phobias?_____

   _____

   _____

6. Are there any personal characteristics that might make a person more or less likely to develop a phobia? What might those be?_____

   _____

   _____

   _____

   _____

7. If someone were to have *positive* symptoms of a disorder, what would you think that meant (given what *positive* reinforcement and *positive* punishment are)?_____

   _____

   _____

8. What would you think that *negative* symptoms are?_____

   _____

   _____

After You Read . . . Practice Tests

PRACTICE TEST #1:
CLASSICAL CONDITIONING

Matching Questions

Match the following terms with their definitions:

B 1. Acquisition (p. 214)   A. CS repeatedly presented without US

E x F N 2. Avoidance learning (p. 216)   B. Initial learning

G 3. Biological preparedness   C. CR appearing after extinction
      (p. 218)

H 6 4. Contrapreparedness   D. Not responding to dissimilar stimuli
      (p. 218)

J ___5. Evaluative conditioning (p. 223)   E. Pairing of CS and an unpleasant US
                                                       that leads to later avoidance of the CS

A 6. Extinction (p. 219)   F. CS as a US paired with a new CS

F ___7. Higher-order conditioning (p. 220)   G. Fear of snakes but not babies

C 8. Spontaneous recovery (p. 219)   H. Inability to condition some stimuli

I 9. Stimulus generalization (p. 220)   I. Responding to stimuli similar to CS

D ___10. Stimulus discrimination   J. Using classical conditioning to
      (p. 220)   promote liking of the CS

Multiple-Choice Questions

For each question, circle the best answer from the choices given.

1. Suppose that when you had your wisdom teeth extracted, the procedure was very painful
    and complicated. Now, whenever you pass by the oral surgeon's street, you flinch. Your
    flinching response is a(n): (p. 215)
    a. Unconditioned stimulus.
    b. Backward conditioned response.
    c. Conditioned response.
    d. Example of biological preparedness.

2.	In the previous question, an unpleasant stimulus (pain) was paired with a neutral stimulus (the oral surgeon's office). As a result, you will probably: (p. 216)
	a.	Become depressed.
	b.	Become angry.
	c.	Approach the oral surgeon's office
	d.	Avoid the oral surgeon's office.

3.	The previous question provides an example of: (p. 216)
	a.	Why backward conditioning is ineffective.
	b.	Avoidance learning.
	c.	Contrapreparedness.
	d.	Evaluative conditioning.

4.	According to the principle of contrapreparedness, which of the following stimuli would it probably be most difficult to condition a fear of? (p. 218)
	a.	Rats
	b.	Spiders
	c.	Heights
	d.	Blocks

5.	Which of the following theories is usually used to explain the phenomena of biological preparedness and contrapreparedness? (p. 218)
	a.	Evolutionary
	b.	Psychodynamic
	c.	Humanistic
	d.	Cognitive

6.	Which of the following phenomena has taught us that classical conditioning is a relatively *permanent* form of learning? (p. 219)
	a.	Initial acquisition
	b.	Biological preparedness
	c.	Stimulus generalization
	d.	Spontaneous recovery

7.	If the _____ were removed from the brain, one could not learn to fear through classical conditioning. (p. 221)
	a.	Auditory cortex
	b.	Visual cortex
	c.	Hypothalamus
	d.	Amygdala

8.	The Little Albert study is important because it showed: (p. 217)
	a.	Avoidance learning.
	b.	How unethical past researchers have been.
	c.	How fear can lead to phobias.
	d.	How to extinguish fears.

X 9.   Which of the following is NOT evidence for the fact that cognitive processes are involved in classical conditioning? (p. 221)
         a.   You can condition someone to salivate in response to a mental image of food.
         b.   Backward conditioning is ineffective.
         c.   It is difficult to condition a fear of inanimate objects.
         d.   You can only condition fear to a light if the light provides information about an upcoming event.

X 10.   Classical conditioning is the basis for a treatment technique in which: (p. 222)
         a.   The therapist listens to the patient's thoughts and reflects them back to the patient.
         b.   A person is gradually and repetitively exposed to what she fears.
         c.   A person is provided with positive role models.
         d.   The therapist explores the patient's past, especially her relationship with her mother.

   11.   Suppose that you ring the dinner bell to get your family to come to dinner. You always feed your dog, Apollo, at the same time. So, whenever Apollo hears the dinner bell ring, he begins to drool. Later, your son breaks both of his legs and can't get out of bed without your help. You give him a different bell to ring whenever he needs you. At first, Apollo will probably: (p. 215)
         a.   Ignore your son's bell.
         b.   Drool whenever your son's bell rings.
         c.   Stop drooling whenever the dinner bell rings.
         d.   Drool all the time because he is so confused.

   12.   After awhile, Apollo begins to drool only when the dinner bell rings. This is because he has experienced: (p. 220)
         a.   Stimulus generalization.
         b.   Stimulus discrimination.
         c.   Spontaneous recovery.
         d.   Extinction.

   13.   After his puppy years are over, the vet tells you that Apollo needs to go on a diet because he is gaining too much weight. As a result, you feed him just one meal a day (at breakfast). At dinner time, which is when you ring the dinner bell, he doesn't get to eat. At first, Apollo _____, but then after awhile he: (p. 220)
         a.   Begs for food; experiences spontaneous recovery.
         b.   Drools to the dinner bell; experiences extinction.
         c.   Doesn't drool to the dinner bell; starts drooling again to the dinner bell.
         d.   Experiences discrimination; begins drooling to the dinner bell again.

   14.   After several years, your bell breaks from overuse. You take it into the Bell Shop to have it fixed (after all, its an heirloom), but it takes several months for them to fix it. When you finally get it back, you can expect Apollo to _____ because: (p. 219)
         a.   Drool when it is sounded; he is experiencing spontaneous recovery.
         b.   Not drool when it is sounded; his behavior has already been extinguished.
         c.   Drool when he hears any bell (even the door bell!); he is generalizing.
         d.   Drool when it is sounded; he thinks he isn't on the diet any more.

✗ 15. Researchers have discovered that fast-tempo music generally makes people feel happier. They have also found that when people are happy, they tend to buy more things. As a result, you frequently hear fast-tempo music played in stores. In this case, marketing executives are relying on shoppers to pair the US of _____ with the CS of: (p. 215)
   a. Music; stores.
   b. Stores; happiness.
   c. Happiness; music.
   d. Stores; music.

12/15

PRACTICE TEST #2:
OPERANT CONDITIONING

Fill-In-The-Blank Questions

Complete the following statement by filling in the appropriate words from the following list:

WORD BANK	
Acetylcholine	Hippocampus
Discrimination	Nucleus accumbens
Dopamine	

To learn, we must first decide the appropriate situation in which to make a response, a

process called _____ . This process takes place in the _____

_____, where the neurotransmitter _____ helps us to decide

which stimuli should be grouped together. Next, we learn which consequences follow which

responses, an association that takes place in the _____, which is

behind the amygdala. In this part of the brain, the neurotransmitter _____

_____ seems particularly important. (p. 240)

Multiple Choice Questions

For each question, circle the best answer from the choices given.

1. Negative reinforcement is the _____ of an unpleasant stimulus; negative
   reinforcement _____ the probability of a behavior occurring again. (p. 231)
   a. Presentation; increases
   b. Removal; increases
   c. Presentation; decreases
   d. Removal; decreases

2. Which of the following is NOT a characteristic of effective punishment? (pp. 233-234)
   a. Occurs immediately
   b. Moderately aversive
   c. Consistency
   d. Physical

3. To be most effective, punishment should be accompanied by: (p. 234)
   a. Generalization of pain.
   b. Discrimination among schedules of reinforcement.
   c. Reinforcement of alternative behavior.
   d. Removal of privileges.

4. Bob has learned to be respectful to his parents, as he is reinforced for polite behaviors. He is also respectful to all older individuals, demonstrating the concept of: (p. 236)
   a. Generalization.
   b. Discrimination.
   c. Extinction.
   d. Secondary reinforcement.

5. Bob is not, however, very polite with his friends, demonstrating the concept of: (p. 236)
   a. Generalization.
   b. Extinction.
   c. Discrimination.
   d. Secondary reinforcement.

6. Tara begs for candy every time her mother takes her to the store, a request to which her mother usually gives in. One day, her mother decides no longer to give Tara candy when she begs. What is Tara's likely response? (p. 237)
   a. She will hit her mother.
   b. She will stop begging immediately.
   c. She will beg harder at first, but then eventually stop begging.
   d. She will start crying instead of begging.

7. To teach her daughter to say "Mommy," Clara first rewarded her for putting her lips together to make the "m" sound, then for saying "ma," then for saying "mama," and then for saying "mommy." The earlier behaviors that eventually led to the desired one are called: (p. 238)
   a. Successive approximations.
   b. Simple steps.
   c. Discriminative stimuli.
   d. Partial reinforcers.

8. A quiz every Friday is an example of a _____ schedule of reinforcement. (p. 238)
   a. Fixed interval
   b. Fixed ratio
   c. Variable interval
   d. Variable ratio

9. In Mrs. Orr's classroom, students can earn gold stars by reading books. Once they have enough gold stars, they can shop in the school store, where they can "buy" things such as school pencils and notebooks with their stars. This is an example of: (p. 235)
   a. Negative reinforcement.
   b. A token economy.
   c. Generalization.
   d. The effectiveness of primary reinforcers.

10. Which of the following types of feedback is sometimes called escape conditioning? (p. 232)
    a. Positive reinforcement
    b. Negative reinforcement
    c. Positive punishment
    d. Negative punishment

PRACTICE TEST #3:
COGNITIVE AND SOCIAL LEARNING

True/False Questions
Circle TRUE or FALSE for each of the following statements.

1.   TRUE   FALSE   Köhler discovered that chimps have cognitive maps. (p. 243)

2.   TRUE   FALSE   One of Bandura's most famous studies involved Bobo dolls. (p. 247)

3.   TRUE   FALSE   Children will imitate all adults. (p. 248)

4.   TRUE   FALSE   The process of observational learning is involved in learning social norms. (p. 248)

5.   TRUE   FALSE   Tolman's work with rats demonstrated that cognitive processes are at work in learning. (p. 243)

Multiple-Choice Questions
For each question, circle the best answer from the choices given.

1.   Which of the following is NOT a form of cognitive learning? (p. 243)
      a.   Salivating when you think of a lemon
      b.   Learning how to drive a car
      c.   Memorizing the names of your classmates
      d.   Evaluating the differences among the choices in this question

2.   Tolman's rats developed _____ to be able to use later when they were motivated to find their way around the maze. (p. 244)
      a.   Insight
      b.   Cognitive maps
      c.   Neural networks
      d.   Conditioned responses

3.   Latent learning refers to: (p. 244)
      a.   Learning information later in life.
      b.   Learning information by observing someone else.
      c.   Acquiring information through memorization.
      d.   Learning but not displaying the learned behavior immediately.

4.   The study of learning focuses on the _____ of information; in contrast, the study of memory focuses on the _____ of information. (p. 244)
      a.   Retention; acquisition
      b.   Acquisition; retention
      c.   Generalization; discrimination
      d.   Discrimination; generalization

5. Robin has been struggling for a week with how to calculate standard deviations. While he is taking a shower one day, the answer suddenly comes to him. This is called: (p. 244)
   a. Latent learning.
   b. Insight.
   c. Observational learning.
   d. Cognitive learning.

6. Learning that is not dependent on reinforcement, occurs in a social context, and involves voluntary behaviors is called: (p. 246)
   a. Latent learning.
   b. Observational learning.
   c. Classical conditioning.
   d. Insight learning.

7. Albert Bandura is the psychologist who developed: (p. 246)
   a. Social learning theory.
   b. Classical conditioning.
   c. Cognitive mapping.
   d. The latent hypothesis.

8. A child who observes hypocritical behavior, in which an adult says "Do as I say, not as I do," will: (p. 246)
   a. Do as the adult says, not as the adult does.
   b. Say what the adult says, but do what he does.
   c. Disregard the model all together and do what he wants to do.
   d. Become confused and upset by the discrepancy in word and deed.

9. Which of the following is not a characteristic of a model to which a person is more likely to attend? (p. 248)
   a. Kind
   b. Expert in the field
   c. High status
   d. Socially powerful

10. Researchers have found that adolescents will model their parents' use of drugs if: (p. 249)
    a. Their parents were honest with them about their use.
    b. The drugs are "soft" (marijuana), not "hard" (e.g., cocaine).
    c. Their friends are also using drugs.
    d. They have a positive relationship with their parents.

COMPREHENSIVE PRACTICE TEST

True/False Questions
Circle TRUE or FALSE for each of the following statements.

1.   TRUE   FALSE   The unconditioned response to the unconditioned stimulus is usually a reflex. (p. 215)

2.   TRUE   FALSE   Any phobia can be classically conditioned. (p. 218)

3.   TRUE   FALSE   Once classical conditioning has occurred, the stimulus-response connection never completely vanishes. (p. 219)

4.   TRUE   FALSE   Food aversions require only one pairing of the CS and US. (p. 223)

5.   TRUE   FALSE   Negative reinforcement and punishment are the same concepts. (p. 233)

6.   TRUE   FALSE   A partial reinforcement schedule is more resistant to extinction. (p. 238)

7.   TRUE   FALSE   Classical and operant conditioning are really the same concept. (pp. 241-242)

8.   TRUE   FALSE   Children who observe hypocrisy model hypocrisy. (p. 246)

9.   TRUE   FALSE   Cognitive maps demonstrate the effectiveness of insight learning. (p. 244)

10. TRUE   FALSE   Children's ability to delay reinforcement predicts later social competence. (p. 235)

Multiple-Choice Questions
For each question, circle the best answer from the choices given.

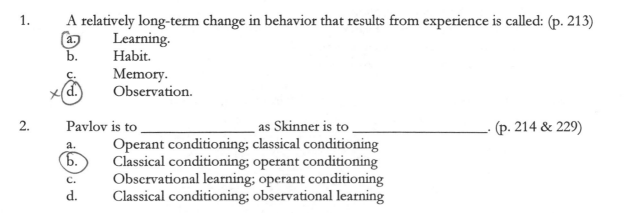

1.   A relatively long-term change in behavior that results from experience is called: (p. 213)
     a.   Learning.
     b.   Habit.
     c.   Memory.
     d.   Observation.

2.   Pavlov is to _____ as Skinner is to _____. (p. 214 & 229)
     a.   Operant conditioning; classical conditioning
     b.   Classical conditioning; operant conditioning
     c.   Observational learning; operant conditioning
     d.   Classical conditioning; observational learning

243

3. Avoidance learning occurs when a(n) _____is paired with a conditioned stimulus and the organism tries to avoid the CS. (p. 216)
    a. Neutral stimulus
    b. Conditioned emotional response
    c. Reinforcement
    (d.) Unpleasant US

4. It is easier to condition a fear of spiders than of flowers because of: (p. 218)
    a. Conditioned emotional responses.
    (b.) Biological preparedness.
    c. Latent learning.
    d. Generalization.

5. When Quinn learns to write on paper, but not on walls, he has: (p. 236)
    a. Learned to generalize.
    (b.) Learned to discriminate.
    c. Experienced extinction.
    d. Spontaneously recovered his writing.

6. In classical conditioning, extinction involves: (p. 219)
    a. Completely undoing the stimulus-response connection.
    (b.) Layering new learning over old learning.
    c. Forgetting a stimulus-response connection.
    d. Not rewarding a behavior any more.

7. Running for shelter when a slight drizzle threatens rain is an example of : (p. 231)
    (a.) Positive reinforcement.
    b. Extinction.
    (c.) Negative reinforcement.
    d. Discrimination.

8. At the beginning of the semester, your professor gave extra credit points for class participation. After a few weeks, however, she stopped doing this. You noticed that class participation then dropped off, due to _____. However, the first day back to school after your week-long Fall break, the class was once again participating, due to: (p. 237)
    a. Discrimination; generalization.
    (b.) Extinction; spontaneous recovery.
    c. Classical conditioning; latent learning.
    d. Discrimination; spontaneous recovery.

9. Food is an example of a _____ reinforcer. (p. 234)
    (a.) Primary
    (b.) Positive
    c. Secondary
    d. Negative

10. Researchers found that children who were able to delay gratification: (p. 235)
   a. Were more socially competent as adolescents.
   b. Had more friends.
   c. Received more positive reinforcement from their parents.
   d. Were from higher social classes.

11. In comparison to a fixed interval schedule, individuals on a fixed ratio will respond: (p. 239)
   a. Slower and more consistently.
   b. Faster, with a lull right after reinforcement.
   c. Slower and more inconsistently.
   d. Faster, with no pauses in rate of responding.

12. The _____ schedule yields the highest rate of responding. (p. 239)
   a. Fixed interval
   b. Variable interval
   c. Fixed ratio
   d. Variable ratio

13. Operant conditioning relies on the dopamine-based "reward system" found in the: (p. 241)
   a. Frontal lobes.
   b. Nucleus accumbens.
   c. Hypothalamus.
   d. Pituitary gland.

14. When researchers block dopamine receptors, animals: (p. 240)
   A. Fail to respond to reinforcement.
   B. Respond more quickly to reinforcement.
   C. Cannot learn which stimuli should be grouped together.
   D. Become aggressive toward other animals.

15. Jeremy just couldn't understand how to "do" geometry proofs. One day, after months of trying, Jeremy was riding his bike when suddenly it all became clear—he had found the key for doing proofs! Jeremy's experience is an example of: (p. 244)
   a. Latent learning.
   b. Observational learning.
   c. Insight learning.
   d. Classical conditioning.

16. Researchers found that adolescents who had good relationships with their drug-using parents: (p. 249)
   a. Tried to get their parents to stop using drugs.
   b. Also used drugs.
   c. Hid their own drugs from their parents.
   d. Avoided drug use.

17. Suppose that you wanted to use operant conditioning to teach your child to use the potty. To do this as quickly as possible (because diapers are *so* expensive), which reinforcement schedule should you use at first? (p. 238)
    a. Continuous
    b. Fixed interval
    c. Fixed ratio
    d. Variable interval

18. Backward pairing in classical conditioning is ineffective because: (p. 215)
    a. Punishment is less effective than reinforcement.
    b. The US doesn't warn the individual of the CS.
    c. Interval schedules are not as effective as ratio schedules.
    d. It will lead to a phobia.

19. Classical and operant conditioning: (p. 242)
    a. Are really the same thing.
    b. Are different because one involves association, the other doesn't.
    c. Are different, as demonstrated by the fact that they involve different brain mechanisms.
    d. Are similar in that they are both governed by the Law of Effect.

20. If you want someone to engage in a complex behavior, you should: (p. 238)
    a. Use a variable schedule of reinforcement.
    b. Use punishment, rather than reinforcement.
    c. Be patient; they are probably experiencing latent learning and will demonstrate the behavior later.
    d. Shape their behavior.

Essay Questions
Answer each of the following questions in the space provided.

1. A positive response to a placebo has typically been attributed to "mind over matter," or the individual's belief that he/she will get better. How has research in the area of classical conditioning shed light on another possible explanation? Discuss.

_____

_____

_____

_____

_____

_____

_____

_____

_____

2.   What characteristics of "live" action shows (e.g., *Cops* and *Real TV*) may lead a child to imitate the violence depicted? What characteristics are less likely to cause them to do so?

_____

_____

_____

_____

_____

_____

3.   If you had to give advice to parents who are trying to "teach" their infant to sleep through the night (assuming the child is old enough), what would you tell them to do and what should they expect?

_____

_____

_____

_____

_____

_____

_____

_____

_____

4.   Explain how operant conditioning, latent learning, and observational learning all interact when a child learns to have a temper tantrum after watching a friend do the same.

_____

_____

_____

_____

_____

_____

_____

_____

_____

5.   Your text clearly explains why physical punishment is a relatively ineffective way of modifying behavior. What role does culture play in the issue of physically disciplining children? As families from other cultures move to the United States, do we have the right to impose our values about discipline on them? How can we balance the knowledge we have about discipline with sensitivity to other cultures?

_____

_____

_____

_____

_____

_____

_____

_____

6. Can classical and operant conditioning be latent? Why or why not? If they <u>can</u> be latent, what does that say for the argument that such learning takes place without cognition?

_____

_____

_____

_____

_____

_____

_____

_____

When You Are Finished . . . Puzzle It Out

Across

5. Type of reinforcer, such as food
8. Watson's famous subject
11. Reinforcing successive approximations
12. Time-based reinforcement schedule
14. Non-continuous reinforcement
16. Secondary-reinforcement based economy
18. Type of punishment, such as spanking
19. Ineffective pairing
20. Developed the Law of Effect

Down

1. Irrational Fear
2. A non-medicine that acts like one
3. Thorndike's cat box
4. Discovered classical conditioning
6. An "aha" experience
7. Learning not immediately observable
9. Increases likelihood of behavior
10. Name of Kohler's chimp
13. Tolman's rats had these in their heads
15. Developed a box for pigeons
17. Dog's salivation to food

Puzzle created with Puzzlemaker at DiscoverySchool.com.

Chapter 7
Memory: Living With Yesterday

Before You Read . . .

Do you think of yourself as having a good memory or a bad memory? In fact, as you will learn in this chapter, memory is not one unit or process. Rather, memory consists of multiple memory stores and processes. For example, there are three types of memory stores: sensory memory, short-term memory, and long-term memory (of which there are several different types). To move information into the memory system and then from one store to the next, a person must use different strategies, including encoding and retrieving information.

Memory is not just about remembering, but about forgetting, and there are many different reasons why people forget information. In addition to losing information, we can also have false memories and suffer from amnesia. What about repressed memories? Are they real? The chapter attempts to shed some light on this most controversial topic in psychology.

Finally, the chapter ends with information you can use in all your classes: how to improve your memory.

Chapter Objectives

After reading this chapter, you should be able to:

♦   Differentiate between and describe the three different memory stores: sensory memory, short-term memory, and long-term memory.

♦   Describe the different stores within LTM, including modality-specific stores, semantic and episodic memory, and explicit and implicit memory.

♦   Explain the concept of working memory and its components.

♦   Discuss the genetic foundations of memory.

♦   Explain how memories are made, stored, and retrieved.

♦   Discuss how memory can be disrupted, including false memories, forgetting, amnesia, and repression.

♦   Provide examples of how memory can be improved, both at storage and retrieval.

As You Read . . . Term Identification

Make flashcards using the following terms as you go. Use the definitions in the margins of this chapter for help. If you write the definitions in your own words, though, you will remember them better!

Amnesia	Flashbulb memory	Recency effect
Anterograde amnesia	Forgetting curve	Recognition
Breadth of processing	Habit	Rehearsal
Central executive	Hypermnesia	Repetition priming
Chunk	Implicit memory	Repressed memories
Code	Incidental learning	Retrieval
Consolidation	Intentional learning	Retroactive interference
Cues	Interference	Retrograde amnesia
Decay	Long-term memory (LTM)	Semantic memory
Depth of processing	Long-term potentiation (LTP)	Sensory memory (SM)
Elaborative encoding	Memory store	Short-term memory (STM)
Encoding	Mnemonic devices	Source amnesia
Encoding failure	Modality-specific memory stores	State-dependent retrieval
Episodic memory	Proactive memory	Storage
Explicit memory	Reality monitoring	Transfer appropriate processing
False memories	Recall	Working memory (WM)

As You Read . . . Questions and Exercises

Storing Information

In the following table, compare and contrast the differences between **sensory**, **short-term** and **long-term memory**.

	Sensory Memory	Short-Term Memory	Long-Term Memory
What does it hold?			
How much does it hold?			
How long does it hold information?			
Does it have sub-components? If so, what are they?			

For the following events below, indicate whether **sensory**, **short-term**, or **long-term memory** is being activated:

Event	Type of Memory
Trying to remember the names of the states and their capitals.	
Believing you hear your name during a loud and busy conference.	
Trying to remember a phone number long enough to dial it.	
"Committing" the phone number to memory.	
Fleeting visual images as you watch a movie.	
Looking at an object for a few seconds before sketching it.	

Long-Term Memory

Draw a picture of the **memory curve** and indicate where the **primacy effect** and **recency effect** are evident.

Draw a diagram, showing how all the different types of memories fit together. (Your drawing should end up looking like an upside down tree.) Include the following terms:

Memory
Explicit memory
Modality-specific memories
Long-term memory
Implicit memory
Working memory
Sensory store
Priming
Episodic memory

Articulatory loop
Short-term memory
Central executive
Habits
Semantic memory
Autobiographical memory
Iconic memory
Echoic memory
Visuospatial sketchpad

Identify the following experiences as **semantic** or **episodic memories**. If the experience is an episodic memory, identify whether or not it is **autobiographical**.

Experience	Type of Memory
Your 16th birthday party	
What you had for breakfast this morning	
The largest country in the world	
The difference between dogs and cats	
The smell of your grandmother's baking	
The first president of the United States	
The meaning of the word "psychology"	
The image of the World Trade Center collapsing	
The square root of 36	
The death of Princess Diana	

Identify the following memories as being either **explicit** or **implicit**.

Memory	Implicit/Explicit
Riding a bike	
Spelling the word "psychology"	
The names of the 50 states	
Tying your shoe	
Your first kiss	
Walking	

Working Memory

How is **working memory** different from **short-term memory**? _____
_____
_____
_____

Provide three examples from your own life of when you use your **working memory**.

♦ _____
♦ _____
♦ _____

Genetic Foundations of Memory

What are **"knockout mice"**? _____
_____
_____
_____

What do **"knockout mice"** tell us about the biological basis for memory? _____
_____
_____
_____

Looking at Levels

Given the negative effects of stress on the **hippocampus**, explain why it is crucial to keep your anxiety level down when studying for and taking an exam, using each of the three levels. Use arrows to indicate how events at the three levels may interact.

The Brain	The Person	The Group

TRY PRACTICE TEST #1 NOW!
GOOD LUCK!

Encoding and Retrieving Information From Memory

Making Memories

Using the following concepts, explain how you would teach someone to study for an exam in this class: **consolidation, breadth of processing, depth of processing, transfer appropriate processing, elaborative encoding.** _____

_____

_____

_____

_____

_____

_____

_____

In your own words, distinguish between **intentional learning** and **incidental learning**, providing an example of each from your own experiences. _____

_____

_____

_____

_____

_____

_____

Describe, in as much detail as you can, how you remember learning about the World Trade Center bombings on September 11, 2001. _____

_____

_____

_____

_____

_____

_____

_____

_____

_____

Were any other people with you at the time you heard of it? If so, who?_____

_____

CALL...

...the people who were present when you first learned of the bombings and record their memories for hearing about the World Trade Center bombings. _____

_____
_____
_____
_____
_____
_____
_____
_____
_____
_____

How does your recall compare to their recall? What does the research say about the accuracy (or inaccuracy) of **flashbulb memories**?_____

_____
_____
_____
_____
_____
_____
_____
_____
_____
_____

The Act of Remembering: Reconstructing Buried Cities

How is remembering like **reconstructing** buried cities? Why do Kosslyn and Rosenberg use this analogy?_____

_____
_____
_____
_____
_____

Distinguish between **recognition** and **recall**. Do you do better on essay tests or multiple choice tests? What does this tell you about your own memory abilities?_____

_____
_____
_____
_____
_____
_____

How can you use what you now know about **cues** and **state-dependent retrieval** to help you study for an exam?_____

_____

_____

_____

_____

_____

_____

Looking at Levels

Do you categorize and organize information when trying to remember lists? Why or why not? Are there factors at the level of brain, person, or group that lead you to use or not use such **organizational strategies**? Use arrows to indicate how these factors may interact.

The Brain	The Person	The Group

TRY PRACTICE TEST #2 NOW!
GOOD LUCK!

Fact, Fiction, and Forgetting: When Memory Goes Wrong

False Memories

When you did the "sweet" experiment in the textbook, did you have any **false recalls**?_____

_____

Why does this happen?_____

_____

_____

_____

_____

Give an example from your own life of a time when you have had difficulty with the following:

♦ **Reality monitoring:** _____

_____

♦ **Source amnesia:** _____

_____

Forgetting

Identify the likely sources of forgetting below, choosing from **encoding failure, decay, retroactive interference**, and **proactive interference**.

Experience	Type of Forgetting
Susan met numerous people at a party, but when she bumps into them the next week, she can't remember their names.	
Having just moved last month and memorized her new address, Kristy can't remember her previous address.	
Sam can't remember if he passed a drug store on the way home from his new job.	
James called his new girlfriend by his old girlfriend's name.	
60-year-old Frank can't remember what his 2nd grade teacher looked like.	

Amnesia

Distinguish between **anterograde** and **retrograde amnesia.** _____

_____
_____
_____
_____
_____

Do you have any memories of your childhood before the age of three? Given that memory before this age is pretty poor, what do you think accounts for your memories? _____

_____
_____
_____
_____
_____

Repressed Memories

Explain how events with highly charged emotional content (e.g., abuse) can be forgotten, when such **emotional tone** usually enhances memory. _____
_____
_____
_____
_____
_____

Looking at Levels

How might **false memories** of abuse be constructed? Consider what you learned earlier about false memories. _____
_____
_____
_____
_____
_____

Can you think of a time when someone told you that something was true, when you had originally thought it was false? What do you think now? Is it possible that you were just biased to believe it is true when it is not? How did your relationship with that person affect your belief? _____
_____
_____
_____
_____
_____

TRY PRACTICE TEST #3 NOW!
GOOD LUCK!

Improving Memory: Tricks and Tools

Storing Information Effectively

Using **interactive images**, remember ten items on a grocery list: apples, milk, tissues, hotdogs, cereal, bananas, juice, pasta, green beans, and rice. Study the list for about one minute, then cover it up and write as many items as you can remember in the space below.

How many could you remember? _____

Now, use the **method of loci** to remember this list: asparagus, paper towels, dog food, hamburger, bread, syrup, olives, cookies, peaches, and peanut butter. Again, study the list for about one minute, then cover it up and write as many items as you can remember in the space below.

How many could you remember? _____

Which method worked best above? Did you experience **interference** in trying to learn the lists? If so, what type of interference did you experience?_____
_____
_____

Improving Memory Retrieval

Can you remember what the five methods suggested to enhance **retrieval** were? Use what you have learned in this section to memorize the five methods. List your mnemonic devices below:

♦_____

♦_____

♦_____

♦_____

♦_____

Looking at Levels

How might **hypnosis**, at the levels of the brain, person, and group, lead an individual to strongly believe in a **false memory**?   Use arrows to indicate how events at the different levels may interact.

The Brain	The Person	The Group

What implications does this have for the use of **hypnosis** in therapy?_____
_____
_____
_____
_____
_____
_____
_____

TRY PRACTICE TEST #4 NOW!
GOOD LUCK!

After You Read . . . Thinking Back

1. In Chapter 1, you considered the impact of the Cognitive Revolution. Certainly, memory research has benefited from the Cognitive Revolution. However, some of the key studies in memory also contributed to the Cognitive Revolution. Name two important people and/or studies in memory and explain how they impacted the Cognitive Revolution._____
    _____
    _____
    _____
    _____
    _____
    _____

2. In Chapter 2, you learned about different kinds of psychological studies, including correlational, quasi-experimental, and experimental studies. What methods lend themselves particularly well to memory studies? Why?_____
    _____
    _____
    _____
    _____
    _____
    _____

3. In Chapter 4, you learned about top-down and bottom-up processing. How does top-down processing affect memory? _____
    _____
    _____
    _____
    _____
    _____
    _____

4. How does bottom-up processing affect memory? _____
    _____
    _____
    _____
    _____
    _____

5. What is the difference between learning, as described in Chapter 6, and memory? Or, is there one? Discuss._____
    _____
    _____
    _____
    _____

After You Read . . . Thinking Ahead

1. What memory strengths, if any, do you think might facilitate problem-solving abilities?
    Why? _____
    _____
    _____
    _____
    _____
    _____

2. Is memory a component of intelligence? If so, which aspect(s) of memory? _____
    _____
    _____
    _____
    _____
    _____

3. Do you think that your memories affect your emotions? If so, how? _____
    _____
    _____
    _____
    _____
    _____
    _____

4. Can you think of any reasons that people might not have first memories before the age of
    approximately 3 or 4? Why? _____
    _____
    _____
    _____
    _____
    _____

5. How might memory skills affect a person's stress level (or, vice versa)? Discuss. _____
    _____
    _____
    _____
    _____

6. How do memories affect how we perceive other people? Discuss. _____
    _____
    _____
    _____
    _____
    _____

After You Read . . . Practice Tests

PRACTICE TEST #1:
STORING INFORMATION

True/False Questions
Circle TRUE or FALSE for each of the following statements.

1. TRUE   FALSE   Most people find verbal memories easier to recall than visual memories. (p. 260)

2. TRUE   FALSE   Visual and auditory memories are stored in different parts of the brain. (p. 260)

3. TRUE   FALSE   Your memory for terms in this text is an example of semantic memory. (p. 260)

4. TRUE   FALSE   Your left frontal lobe is activated when you recall episodic memories. (p. 260)

5. TRUE   FALSE   Habits are a type of memory.   (p. 262)

6. TRUE   FALSE   Working memory includes iconic memory. (p. 265)

7. TRUE   FALSE   Most people find visual memory easier to recall than verbal memory. (p. 265)

8. TRUE   FALSE   The primacy and recency effects demonstrate that short-term memory and long-term memory are different. (p. 258)

9. TRUE   FALSE   Priming is a form of semantic memory. (p. 263)

10. TRUE   FALSE   People can become conscious of explicit memory, but not implicit memory. (p. 262)

Multiple-Choice Questions
For each question, circle the best answer from the choices given.

1. According to the long-term potentiation view, the types of memories that are stored depend on: (p. 266)
    a. How the incoming information is perceived.
    b. Which connections among neurons are strengthened.
    c. Whether the memory is implicit or explicit.
    d. How hard a person tried to remember them.

2. A "fleeting memory" that fades almost immediately after the stimulus has passed is best described as a(n) _____ memory. (p. 257)
   a. Flashbulb
   b. Short-term
   c. Sensory
   d. Long-term

3. Carl forgot to bring the written list of grocery items to the store, and when he arrived home, he found that he had remembered the first five items, but few of the others, demonstrating the _____ effect. (p. 258)
   a. Primacy
   b. Ebbinghaus
   c. Recency
   d. Reversal

4. The primacy effect provides evidence for _____ memory. (p. 259)
   a. Iconic
   b. Short-term
   c. Echoic
   d. Long-term

5. The concept of working memory is like an updated version of _____ memory. (p. 265)
   a. Sensory
   b. Recency
   c. Short-term
   d. Long-term

6. The easiest modality-specific memory for <u>most</u> people to recall is a _____ memory. (p. 260)
   a. Visual
   b. Olfactory
   c. Verbal
   d. Short-term

7. The meanings of words are part of your_____ memory. (p. 260)
   a. Implicit
   b. Semantic
   c. Long-term
   d. Sensory

8. Conditioned responses and habits are _____ memories. (p. 262)
   a. Modality-specific
   b. Episodic
   c. Semantic
   d. Implicit

9.   Adrienne and Rob are fighting. She says, "You aren't listening to me," after which he says, "Sure, I am. You just said…" and repeats her previous sentence verbatim. This is probably because Rob is holding that information in his _____ memory. (p. 257)
    a.   Iconic
    b.   Echoic
    c.   Semantic
    d.   Working

10.   Six-year-old Michelle has just finished watching the movie *Bambi* when her mother tells her to write a thank-you letter to her grandparents. Michelle accidentally writes "Dear Grandma and Grandpa" as "Deer Grandma and Grandpa." This is probably because: (p. 263)
    a.   She has amnesia.
    b.   She doesn't yet know how to spell "dear."
    c.   She has been primed for the word "deer."
    d.   The word "deer" is still in her long-term memory.

PRACTICE TEST #2:
ENCODING AND RETRIEVING INFORMATION FROM MEMORY

Multiple-Choice Questions
For each question, circle the best answer from the choices given.

1. According to the dual coding hypothesis, _____ will be easy to remember because they can be encoded _____. (p. 278)
    a. Words; semantically and episodically
    b. Pictures; visually and verbally
    c. Words; visually and verbally
    d. Pictures; semantically and episodically

2. When trying to memorize the faces of the new students in his class, the professor's _____ was activated. (p. 260)
    a. Frontal lobe
    b. Right temporal lobe
    c. Occipital lobe
    d. Left temporal lobe

3. Something will be remembered better if it has been stored _____ rather than _____. (p. 261)
    a. Explicitly; implicitly
    b. Dynamically; structurally
    c. Implicitly; explicitly
    d. Structurally; dynamically

4. *Depth of processing* refers to the number and complexity of _____ used to process something. (p. 271)
    a. Connections to other information
    b. Retrieval cues
    c. Operations
    d. Forms of encoding

5. Which of the following study techniques demonstrates the greatest depth of processing? (p. 271)
    a. Reading the textbook
    b. Recopying your notes
    c. Thinking of examples for key ideas
    d. Reading your notes aloud to a friend

6.   To study for the GRE's, Sandra took many practice tests that were similar in content and format, utilizing the concept of _____ to help her remember the material. (p. 271)
        a.   Chunking
        b.   Transfer appropriate processing
        c.   Primacy effect
        d.   Long-term potentiation

7.   Learning without intention is called _____ learning. (p. 273)
        a.   Unintentional
        b.   Imaginal
        c.   Incidental
        d.   Inherent

8.   During emotionally charged events, activity in the _____ influences the hippocampus, which in turn enhances memory. (p. 274)
        a.   Frontal lobe
        b.   Amygdala
        c.   Occipital lobe
        d.   Reticular activating system

9.   Multiple-choice tests require _____ rather than _____. (p. 276)
        a.   Recognition; recall
        b.   Implicit memory; explicit memory
        c.   Recall; recognition
        d.   Explicit memory; implicit memory

10.   State and mood appear to be _____ retrieval cues. (p. 279)
        a.   Excellent
        b.   Explicit
        c.   Somewhat weak
        d.   Implicit

11.   The advantage of converting memories into a structural form is that it: (p. 292)
        a.   No longer needs to be continually activated.
        b.   Is particularly vivid.
        c.   Can be retrieved at will.
        d.   Is stored in the hippocampus.

12.   Which of the following statements about flashbulb memories is FALSE? (p. 274)
        a.   Flashbulb memories are particularly vivid.
        b.   People are usually very confident of their flashbulb memories.
        c.   Flashbulb memories involve greater activation of the amygdala.
        d.   Flashbulb memories do not contain errors.

13. The tip-of-the-tongue phenomenon illustrates that: (p. 275)
    a.   It is easier to recognize information than to recall it.
    b.   It is easier to recall information than to recognize it.
    c.   People store information in fragments.
    d.   Good retrieval cues can help people remember anything they have previously stored.

14. Kyle always studies in the same classroom as he takes most of his tests. Kyle is using the principle of: (p. 279)
    a.   The von Restorf effect.
    b.   Dual coding.
    c.   Hypermnesia.
    d.   Encoding specificity hypothesis.

15. Sir Frederic Bartlett had students read a Native American legend, *The War of the Ghosts*, and were then asked to retell it. Over time: (p. 275)
    a.   Students experienced hypermnesia.
    b.   Students' confidence in their memory for the story decreased.
    c.   Students' memory for the story changed very little.
    d.   Students reorganized events in the story.

16. Suppose that you are studying for your next psychology exam. Which of the following factors would be most influential in whether you can remember the material later? (p. 270)
    a.   How hard you studied for your exam
    b.   How much you wanted to do well
    c.   How much you organized new information into your existing knowledge
    d.   How emotionally charged the information was

17. Elaborative encoding will improve your _____ because it organizes and integrates information into what you already know. (p. 270)
    a.   Depth of processing
    b.   Breadth of processing
    c.   Reality monitoring
    d.   Dynamic memory

18. Tom is arrested and charged with burglary. Which of the following best characterizes what type of line-up Tom would want to have? (p. 277)
    a.   If Tom is innocent, he would want a simultaneous line-up.
    b.   If Tom is innocent, he would want a sequential line-up.
    c.   If Tom is guilty, he would want a simultaneous line-up.
    d.   If Tom is guilty, he would want a small line-up.

19. Tori is taking a test and just cannot remember the right answer for one of the essay questions. Which of the following would you advise Tori to do? (p. 279)
    a.   Guess.
    b.   Think about all possible retrieval cues, such as where in her book the information was.
    c.   Try not to think about it so much; she is probably trying too hard.
    d.   None of the above.

20. Alexa is given the following list of words to remember: rape, burglary, book, arson, terrorism. Which word(s) would you think that Alexa would be most likely to forget? (p. 273)
    a.   Rape
    b.   Burglary
    c.   Book
    d.   Arson

PRACTICE TEST #3:
FACT, FICTION AND FORGETTING

True/False Questions
Circle TRUE or FALSE for each of the following statements.

1.   TRUE   FALSE   We do not always remember what actually happens to us. (p. 273)

2.   TRUE   FALSE   Most people will discount their own false memories when told that they are false. (p. 281)

3.   TRUE   FALSE   Some false memories are easier to create than others. (p. 282)

4.   TRUE   FALSE   Misleading questions erase actual memories. (p. 282)

5.   TRUE   FALSE   The recall of false memories activates different areas of the brain than does the activation of actual memories. (p. 283)

6.   TRUE   FALSE   Reality monitoring can help us to distinguish false from actual memories. (p. 284)

7.   TRUE   FALSE   People with damage to the frontal lobe sometimes have extreme source amnesia. (p. 284)

8.   TRUE   FALSE   Retroactive interference disrupts memory for things that are learned earlier. (p. 286)

9.   TRUE   FALSE   Penfield's studies showed that people retain all memories forever. (p. 285)

10. TRUE   FALSE   Infantile amnesia is common. (p. 287)

Multiple-Choice Questions
For each question, circle the best answer from the choices given.

1.   Research suggests that when misleading information is presented, it: (p. 282)
     a.   Replaces the original, correct information.
     b.   Makes it more difficult to access the original, correct information.
     c.   Makes the original memory stronger.
     d.   Creates a new memory which merges the original and misleading information

2. To be able to distinguish real from imagined stimuli, individuals should use _____ when encoding information. (p. 284)
    a. State-dependent retrieval
    b. Consolidation
    c. Rehearsal
    d. Reality monitoring

3. Evidence for decay theory comes from: (p. 285)
    a. Studies of sea slugs showing that neural connections are lost over time.
    b. Penfield's studies, in which he stimulated parts of the brain during brain surgery.
    c. Studies showing that retrieval cues can accidentally trigger the wrong memory.
    d. Studies showing that some memories are never encoded.

4. Interference can occur because: (p. 286)
    a. The brain has limited capacity to store information.
    b. We don't want to remember certain events.
    c. We are distracted by extraneous factors when encoding information.
    d. Retrieval cues for various memories are often similar.

5. _____ amnesia disrupts previous memories but doesn't prevent the learning of new facts. (p. 286)
    a. Episodic
    b. Anterograde
    c. Retrograde
    d. Semantic

6. Anterograde amnesia affects all _____ memories. (p. 287)
    a. Implicit
    b. False
    c. Explicit
    d. Source

7. Daniel Gilbert (1991) found that people are biased to remember that statements are: (p. 289)
    a. True.
    b. Made by reputable individuals.
    c. False.
    d. Dependent upon the context.

8. Hypnosis: (p. 293)
    a. Almost always enhances memory and confidence in recollections.
    b. Usually enhances memory but not confidence in recollections.
    c. Usually enhances confidence in recollections but not actual memories.
    d. Enhances neither memory not confidence in recollections.

9. Schacter suggests that the reason for repressed memories of abuse is that: (p. 288)
    a. Therapists implant false memories.
    b. It is as if the person were "someone else" during the abuse and thus, has few retrieval cues for accessing the memory until later.
    c. Infantile amnesia.
    d. People who repress memories are more suggestible in general than other people.

10. Martha is unable to form new memories, but can remember her past perfectly. Martha probably has: (p. 286)
    a. Alzheimer's Disease.
    b. Anterograde amnesia.
    c. Retrograde amnesia.
    d. Damage to her amygdala.

PRACTICE TEST #4:
IMPROVING MEMORY

Multiple-Choice Questions

For each question, circle the best answer from the choices given.

1.   Which of the following methods was discovered by the ancient Greek orator, Simonides? (p. 290)
     a.   Interactive images
     b.   Method of loci
     c.   Pegword system
     d.   Hierarchical organization

2.   In the mnemonic technique involving a list of rhymes, such as *"One is a bun"* etc., the bun is called the: (p. 291)
     a.   Interactive image.
     b.   Pegword.
     c.   Initialism.
     d.   Loci.

3.   The key to using mnemonic devices is that: (p. 290)
     a.   The person spends lots of time trying to develop it.
     b.   The number of times a person repeats it to himself.
     c.   The amount of effort a person spends on it.
     d.   That people organize integrate the knowledge with their existing knowledge.

4.   The fact that most people remember that *F.B.I.* stands for Federal Bureau of Investigation makes F.B.I. a(n): (p. 292)
     a.   Pegword.
     b.   Initialism.
     c.   Modality-specific memory.
     d.   Acronym.

5.   In order to remember Dr. Oakley's name, Maureen imagines Dr. Oakley swinging from oak leaves. Which mnemonic device is Maureen using? (p. 290)
     a.   Method of loci
     b.   Forming a story
     c.   Interactive images
     d.   Hierarchical organization

6.   The key difference between people who can accurately remember a lot of information and those who can't seems to be: (p. 290)
     a.   What genes people have inherited.
     b.   What strategies and tricks are used when storing and retrieving information.
     c.   How much effort is put into trying to recall the information.
     d.   How much effort is put into storing the information.

7.   Mnemonic devices: (p. 290)
     a.   Give people short-cuts for remembering information, so that the information does not waste a lot of space in working memory.
     b.   Provide an effort-free way to remember material.
     c.   Provide a visual way to remember information.
     d.   Help people make connections between information to-be-remembered and what is already known.

8.   In most cases, hypnosis has the effect of: (p. 294)
     a.   Improving people's confidence in their memories.
     b.   Improving people's accuracy in their memories.
     c.   Improving the quantity of people's memories.
     d.   Decreasing the vividness of people's memories.

9.   Which of the following is NOT part of Fisher's method of interview techniques, which is frequently used by detectives? (p. 292-293)
     a.   Focus on the task at hand.
     b.   Mentally reinstate the environment in which the information was learned.
     c.   If you can't remember immediately, it is gone and you should just give up.
     d.   Try to think of characteristics of the information you are trying to remember.

10. Which of the following is NOT one of the principles of improving memory retrieval? (p. 293)
     a.   Recall is better if a person mentally reinstates the environment in which information was learned.
     b.   To remember well, try shutting out distractions.
     c.   Arrange the world in a way that provides external cues.
     d.   The more times a person tries to recall something, the less likely he will be to recall it.

COMPREHENSIVE PRACTICE TEST

True/False Questions

Circle TRUE or FALSE for each of the following statements.

1.   TRUE   FALSE   Sensory memory happens automatically, without effort. (p. 255)

2.   TRUE   FALSE   Information in short-term memory can last for up to a day. (p. 257)

3.   TRUE   FALSE   Incidental learning can be as effective as intentional learning. (p. 273)

4.   TRUE   FALSE   Flashbulb memories are always more accurate than other memories. (p. 274)

5.   TRUE   FALSE   Misleading questions can lead to false memories. (p. 282)

6.   TRUE   FALSE   The interference theory has been largely supported by evidence. (p. 286)

7.   TRUE   FALSE   Anterograde amnesia leaves consolidated memories intact. (p. 286)

8.   TRUE   FALSE   The most effective mnemonic device is the use of interactive images. (p. 290)

Multiple-Choice Questions

For each question, circle the best answer from the choices given.

1.   The type of memory that holds information for the shortest period of time is _____ memory. (p. 256)
   a.   Short-term
   b.   Sensory
   c.   Long-term
   d.   Working

2.   The visual form of sensory memory is called _____ memory. (p. 256)
   a.   Iconic
   b.   Working
   c.   Echoic
   d.   Sensory

277

3.   You can hold information in short-term memory by: (p. 257)
     a.   Consolidation.
     b.   Priming.
     c.   Rehearsal.
     d.   Overlearning.

4.   Which of the following is NOT part of working memory? (p. 265)
     a.   Visuospatial sketchpad
     b.   Articulatory loop
     c.   Central executive
     d.   Auditory transfer

5.   Verbal and visual memories are *explicit* if the words or images: (p. 261)
     a.   Can be called to mind.
     b.   Have been processed through working memory.
     c.   Are integrated in a coherent fashion.
     d.   Are autobiographical.

6.   A *habit* is a type of _____ memory. (p. 262)
     a.   Explicit
     b.   Episodic
     c.   Implicit
     d.   Semantic

7.   Which of the following could most likely be explained by damage to the hippocampus? (p. 263)
     a.   H.M.'s habit of unfolding his walker
     b.   Steve's inability to form new memories
     c.   Clara's inability to access old, episodic memories
     d.   Jonah's infantile amnesia

8.   Portions of the _____ lobes are particularly active when people encode new information. (p. 260)
     a.   Occipital
     b.   Frontal
     c.   Temporal
     d.   Parietal

9.   Taking the practice tests in this Grade Aid will help you on your exams in this class, particularly if the exams are multiple-choice. This is because of: (p. 271)
     a.   Associative priming.
     b.   Elaborative encoding.
     c.   Repetition priming.
     d.   Transfer appropriate processing.

10. Students who "audit" a class—take it without credit—often do not take notes or study, but learn nonetheless. In fact, they often learn as much as students who actually *try* to learn. This most closely reflects: (p. 273)
    a. Unintentional learning.
    b. Transfer appropriate processing.
    c.) Incidental learning.
    d. Associative priming.

11. An unusually vivid and accurate memory of a dramatic event is called a: (p. 274)
    a.) Flashbulb memory.
    b. Declarative memory.
    c. Flashlight memory.
    d. Semantic memory.

12. Improved memory for emotionally charged events can be attributed to: (p. 274)
    a. An increase in people's confidence for these memories.
    b.) Increased activity in the amygdala.
    c. Increased activity in the hypothalamus.
    d. People trying harder to learn this information.

13. Most of us suffer from a type of _____ amnesia in which we cannot remember our early childhood experiences. (p. 286)
    a. Retroactive
    b. Anterograde
    c.) Infantile
    d. Repressed

14. Perhaps the most controversial issue in memory research today is whether or not: (p. 288)
    a. Flashbulb memories are accurate.
    b.) Information we forget is actually still in our memory somewhere.
    c. Repressed memories exist.
    d. False memories can be constructed.

15. "ROY G BIV" is how many people remember the colors of the rainbow. This use of letters, which spell out a name, is an example of a(n): (p. 292)
    a.) Association.
    b. Method of loci.
    c. Pegword.
    d.) Initialism.

16. Long-term potentiation refers to: (p. 266)
    a.) The strengthening of the connection between the sending and receiving neuron.
    b. A person's maximum possible memory capability.
    c. The fact that memories are never truly lost, as shown in Penfield's studies.
    d. The genetic component of memory.

17. The tip-of-the-tongue phenomenon demonstrates that: (p. 275)
    a. Recall is generally easier than recognition.
    b. Memories are stored in fragments.
    c. It is easy to forget information that is neutral.
    d. Information should be well-integrated into semantic networks to be remembered.

18. Episodic and semantic memories are: (p. 264)
    a. Explicit.
    b. Implicit.
    c. Procedural.
    d. Autobiographical.

19. After being in a car accident in which her head hit the windshield, Carly was no longer able to form new memories. Carly was probably suffering from: (p. 287)
    a. Retroactive interference.
    b. Source amnesia.
    c. Anterograde amnesia.
    d. Retrograde amnesia.

20. Working memory is different from short-term memory in that it: (p. 267)
    a. Uses different neural patterns.
    b. Working memory also includes processes, as well as stores.
    c. Is more affected by genetics than short-term memory.
    d. All of the above.

Essay Questions
Answer each of the questions in the space provided.

1. Is short-term memory really different from long-term memory?_____
   _____
   _____
   _____
   _____
   _____
   _____
   _____
   _____

2. How is a habit also a memory? _____
   _____
   _____
   _____
   _____
   _____

3. "I understood everything you said. I just don't understand why I didn't do better on the test!" This is something college professors hear all the time. Why *don't* students always remember class material when taking an exam? _____

    _____

    _____

    _____

    _____

    _____

    _____

    _____

    _____

    _____

4. Are repressed memories real? _____

    _____

    _____

    _____

    _____

    _____

    _____

    _____

    _____

    _____

5. On page 292, your authors state that "It barely matters how much you *try* to learn something; almost all that really matters is how well you integrate and organize the material." What implications does this statement have for your own academic success? Have you ever tried hard to remember something but found that you couldn't? Was the inability to recall due to faulty integration and organization? Did reading this chapter help you to recognize ways in which you could possibly enhance your own learning and memory? How?

    _____

    _____

    _____

    _____

    _____

    _____

    _____

    _____

    _____

    _____

6. What implications do false memories play in eyewitness testimony? Should eyewitness testimony be allowed in court? What precautions should be taken in allowing eyewitness testimony?_____

_____
_____
_____
_____
_____
_____
_____
_____
_____

7. Imagine you arc a judge hearing a case of a woman who alleges her father abused her when she was two years old. She has recently remembered the event, while undergoing psychotherapy. What questions would you want to ask the woman and her therapist? Would you allow the repressed memory evidence in the courtroom? Why or why not?

_____
_____
_____
_____
_____
_____
_____
_____
_____
_____

8. What in your life is the most difficult event for you to forget? Why? What is the most difficult event to remember? Do you have an actual memory for the event, or is the memory constructed for you? How do you know?_____

_____
_____
_____
_____
_____
_____
_____
_____

9. People will often say, "I have a bad *memory*." Knowing what you do know, about how many different kinds of memories there are, why is this probably an inaccurate statement? Explain._____

_____
_____
_____
_____
_____
_____

10. Why do you forget information that you need (such as information needed for exams)?

_____
_____
_____
_____
_____
_____
_____
_____
_____
_____

When You Are Finished...Puzzle It Out

Across

2. Devices that improve memory
4. Unusually vivid and accurate memory
6. Established the forgetting curve
7. Visual sensory memory
10. Amnesia disrupting previous information
12. Also called procedural memories
13. Theory that memory degrades over time
14. Repeating information over and over
15. Also called declarative
17. Unit of memory
18. Form of broad encoding

Down

1. Memories of general facts
2. Discovered by Simonides
3. Learning without trying
5. Amnesia for childhood events
8. Mental representations
9. Matching encoded information to environmental stimuli
11. Memory that is lost if inactive
16. Stimuli that help people remember

Puzzle created with Puzzlemaker at DiscoverySchool.com.

Chapter 8
Language and Thinking

Before You Read. . .

When and how did you learn to speak? Why is your best friend a Spanish major yet you can't even roll your *r*'s? This chapter presents an overview of language and thinking. Language has many components, including sounds, word meanings, grammar, and implied meanings. Each of these components contributes to our abilities to produce and understand language. The chapter also explores bilingualism.

Moving from language to thought, the chapter next covers the foundations of thought before turning to problem solving, logic, and reasoning. After reading this chapter, maybe you'll be a more logical and effective problem-solver!

Chapter Objectives

After reading this chapter, you should be able to:

♦   Name the essential characteristics of all languages.

♦   Explain how first and second languages are learned and used.

♦   Explain if language molds our thoughts.

♦   Describe how we think with mental images.

♦   Explain the idea of concepts and the different levels of concepts.

♦   Describe the methods used to solve problems.

♦   Understand whether people reason logically.

♦   Explain why we commit reasoning errors.

As You Read. . .Term Identification

Make flashcards using the following terms as you go. Use the definitions in the margins of this chapter for help. If you write the definitions in your own words, though, you will remember them better!

Affirming the consequent
Algorithm
Aphasia
Artificial intelligence (AI)
Availability heuristic
Base-rate rule
Basic level
Broca's aphasia
Category
Child-directed speech (CDS)
Cognitive engineering
Concept
Confirmation bias
Critical period
Deducative reasoning
Deliberate practice
Empiricism
Functional fixedness
Grammar
Heuristic
Incubation
Inductive reasoning
Insight
Language acquisition device (LAD)
Language comprehension
Language production
Linguistic relativity hypothesis
Logic

Mental images
Mental model
Mental set
Morpheme
Nativism
Neural network
Nonverbal communication
Overextension
Overregularization error
Phoneme
Phonology
Pragmatics
Problem
Propositional representation
Prototype
Representation problem
Representativeness heuristic
Schema
Semantics
Sensitive period
Specific Language impairment
Strategy
Syntax
Telegraphic speech
Typicality
Underextension
Wernicke's aphasia

As You Read. . . Questions and Exercises

Language: More Than Meets the Ear

The Essentials: What Makes Language Language?

Language is best understood as having four aspects: **phonology**, **syntax**, **semantics**, and **pragmatics**. Indicate below which function is illustrated:

Example	Function
Grammar produces this aspect of language	
Represented by morphemes	
Helps us to understand jokes and metaphors	
The difference between "cat" and bat"	
Can't program a computer to do this (at least, so far!)	
A sentences needs a noun and verb phrase	
The difference between "read" and "reading"	
The basic building blocks of speech	

In this sentence, identify a **phoneme**, the **syntax**, a **morpheme**, the **semantic meaning** of the words, and the **pragmatic meaning** of the entire phrase.

"People in glass houses should not throw stones."

Phoneme: _____

Syntax: _____

Morpheme: _____

Semantic meaning: _____

Pragmatic meaning: _____

GO SURFING...

...at the following sites, to learn more about **aphasia**:

♦   http://www.nidcd.nih.gov/health/voice/aphasia.asp
♦   http://serendip.brynmawr.edu/bb/neuro/neuro99/web1/Xiong.html
♦   http://nanonline.org/nandistance/mtbi/ClinNeuro/aphasia.html#broca
♦   http://www.aphasia.org/shirley_says.html
♦   http://www.nidcd.nih.gov/health/voice/aphasia.asp

For each of the following types of **aphasia**, specify the symptoms and the area of brain damage.

	Symptoms (Give an Example)	Area of Brain Damage
Broca's aphasia		
Wernicke's aphasia		

Which type of **aphasia** do you think it would be worse to have? Why?_____
_____
_____
_____
_____
_____

How many **morphemes** are in the word *transcontinental*? What are they? What do they mean?

_____
_____
_____
_____
_____

Write a sentence that has meaning, but is **syntactically incorrect**: _____
_____

Write a sentence that is **syntactically correct**, but has no meaning:_____
_____

Suppose that you were a lawyer, questioning a child witness. How could you use your knowledge of children's skills in pragmatics to obtain the best testimony?_____
_____
_____
_____

How are each of the **hemispheres** involved in **pragmatics**?

Left	Right

In your own words, explain how **speech production** and **comprehension** draw on the same brain mechanisms in each of the following four areas:

♦   **Phonology:** _____
    _____

♦   **Syntax:**_____
    _____

♦   **Semantics:**_____
    _____

♦   **Pragmatics:**_____
    _____

Language Development: Out of the Mouths of Babes

If you had a child, how would you most likely talk to your baby?_____

What are the characteristics of this form of language?

- ♦ _____
- ♦ _____
- ♦ _____

In some ways, infants have better language skills than adults. Name and describe one such way.

_____

_____

_____

Name the **language skills** that develop at each of the following ages:

Language Comprehension

- ♦ **2-3 months:** _____
- ♦ **6 months:** _____
- ♦ **8 months:** _____
- ♦ **13 months:** _____
- ♦ **14 months:** _____

Language Production

- ♦ **6 months:** _____
- ♦ **12 months:** _____
- ♦ **14 months:** _____
- ♦ **18 months:** _____
- ♦ **24 months:** _____
- ♦ **6 years:** _____

Provide a new example (not from the textbook) of an **overextension:** _____

_____

_____

Provide a new example (not from the textbook) of an **underextension:** _____

_____

_____

CALL...

...your parents and ask what your first sentence was. How does this match the research on **telegraphic speech**? Discuss. _____
_____
_____

Provide a new example (not from the textbook) of **overregularization:**_____
_____
_____

GO SURFING...

...at http://www.feralchildren.com/ to find out more about Victor, Genie, and the other feral children.

Based on cases of feral children, some researchers argue that there is a **critical period** for learning language. What is a **critical period**? _____
_____
_____

How is a **critical period** different from a **sensitive period**? _____
_____
_____

What are the difficulties in concluding that there is a **critical** or **sensitive period** from cases of feral children such as Victor and Genie? _____
_____
_____
_____
_____

Other Ways to Communicate: Are They Language?

Which of the four characteristics of language (**phonology**, **syntax**, **semantics**, and **pragmatics**) does nonverbal communication not have? Why?_____
_____
_____

GO SURFING…

…at http://www.koko.org/ to see one famous primate, Koko, learning to "talk." Based on what you see there, do you believe that nonhuman primates can use language? Why or why not?

_____
_____
_____
_____
_____

Bilingualism: A Window of Opportunity?

Have you taken a course in some foreign language in high school or college? What aspects of the **language** were the hardest to learn? The **vocabulary**? The **grammar**? **Reading** or **writing**? Given what you have learned in this chapter, explain why you may have (or may not have) had difficulty learning a **second language**. _____
_____
_____
_____
_____
_____
_____
_____

Looking at Levels

Explain why—at the **levels of the brain, person, and group—language** is a uniquely *human* trait. Draw arrows to show how factors at these levels may interact in creating language.

The Brain	The Person	The Group

TRY PRACTICE TEST #1 NOW!
GOOD LUCK!

Means of Thought: Words, Images, Concepts

Words: Inner Speech and Spoken Thoughts

What are the 3 problems with asserting that **thinking** is just talking to yourself?

- ♦ _____
- ♦ _____
- ♦ _____

What is the evidence that **language** shapes **thought**?

- ♦ _____
  _____
  _____
- ♦ _____
  _____
  _____

What is the evidence that **language** does not shape **thought**?_____
_____
_____
_____

Mental Imagery: Perception Without Sensation

In your own words, describe the three properties of **mental space:**

- ♦ _____
- ♦ _____
- ♦ _____

Try the exercises described in the textbook. Does your experience demonstrate these 3 effects?
_____

How can we explain the following facts about **visual images**:

- ♦ **Spatial extent:**_____
  _____

- ♦ **Limits on spatial extent:** _____
  _____

- ♦ **Grain:** _____
  _____
  _____

Concepts: Neither Images nor Words

How are **concepts** different from words or images? For each of the following ideas, indicate whether you think of a word, an image, or neither (a concept):

Idea	Word/Image/Concept
Book	
Angry	
Freedom	
Hungry	
Automobile	
Excitement	

Why was Aristotle's definition of the features of a **concept** (necessary and sufficient) inaccurate? For the following **concepts**, see if you can come up with **necessary and sufficient features**:

Concept	Necessary feature	Sufficient feature
Bird		
Friend		
Depression		
Hunger		

Name a **prototype** and a **non-prototype** to illustrate each of the following **concepts**:

Concept	Prototype	Non-prototype
Bird		
Mammal		
Furniture		
Fruit		

For the following **basic level** words, describe a related **concept** that is more **general** and more **specific**.

Word	More General	More Specific
Apple		
Car		
House		
Angry		
Computer		

How does the **brain** store **concepts**? _____

_____

_____

For the following **schemas**, list one **necessary** and one **optional characteristic**.

Schema	Necessary characteristic	Optional characteristic
Classroom		
Parent		
Airplane		
Beverage		
Tree		

Looking at Levels

Consider the **prototype** of a drinker (self-assured, attractive, and mature). Do you feel these characteristics match those of drinkers at your college? Do you think your answer depends upon your own drinking patterns? _____

_____

_____

_____

_____

TRY PRACTICE TEST #2 NOW!
GOOD LUCK!

Problem Solving

How to Solve Problems: More Than Inspiration

What difficulties can arise during the **representation** of a problem that can make it difficult to solve the problem? _____
_____
_____
_____

Name one instance in which you use an **algorithm** and describe when you use it.
_____
_____
_____

Name one instance in which you use a **heuristic** and describe when you use it.
_____
_____
_____

Can you remember any time that you have used **analogical reasoning** to solve a problem? If so, describe._____
_____
_____
_____

Can you ever remember having a flash of **insight learning** into a problem? If so, describe.
_____
_____
_____

What can you do to increase the probability that you will have an **insight**? Explain._____
_____
_____
_____

Expertise: Why Hard Work Pays Off

On what topic are you an **expert**? _____ How does your **expertise** in this area help you in **solving problems** in this area? _____
_____
_____
_____

How did you become an **expert** on this topic? How does this match the research literature on how **expertise** develops?_____

_____

_____

_____

Artificial Intelligence

How are **neural networks** similar to how the brain works?_____

_____

_____

_____

Overcoming Obstacles to Problem Solving

Name and briefly describe five things that you can do to overcome obstacles to **problem solving**:

♦ _____

♦ _____

♦ _____

♦ _____

♦ _____

GO SURFING...

...at one of the following sites and try some of the **logic** puzzles there:
♦   http://www.thakur.demon.nl/
♦   http://einstein.et.tudelft.nl/~arlet/puzzles/logic.html
♦   http://puzzles.karplus.org/

What **obstacles** did you face? How did you overcome them? (Or, did you?)_____

_____

_____

_____

Looking at Levels

How could **cognitive engineering** help software engineers determine how to write more useful software? Use arrows to indicate how factors at the **different levels** may interact to influence the usefulness of software.

The Brain	The Person	The Group

TRY PRACTICE TEST #3 NOW!
GOOD LUCK!

Logic, Reasoning, and Decision Making

Are People Logical?

Identify the type of reasoning, **deductive** or **inductive**, in the following situations:

Situation	Type of Reasoning
In her new town, Susan met three people, all of whom were rude to her. She therefore assumed that all people in the new town would be rude.	
All aliens have an antenna. An antenna allows aliens to communicate with the mothership. All aliens can communicate with the mothership.	
Frank bought a car that turned out to be a lemon. He told his friends not to buy a car from that dealer, as all of the cars on the lot were sure to be lemons.	
When the pressure drops, it rains. When it rains, the plants grow. When the pressure drops, the plants grow.	

Identify the type of error, **affirming the consequent** or **confirmation bias**, below:

Situation	Error
All babies are bald. Jim is bald. Jim must be a baby!	
Lara is convinced that she is psychic because yesterday she picked up the phone to call a friend just as her friend called her!	
Ignoring her dissatisfaction, poor coworker relationships, and demanding boss, Paula convinced herself that she loved her job because she was well-paid.	
If it rains today, people will carry umbrellas. People are carrying umbrellas, so it must be raining!	

How does the way the problem is **framed** define the decision to be made, the alternative possible outcomes, and the criteria for a good decision? _____
_____
_____
_____

Identify what type of **error** is made in each of the following situations:

Situation	Error
Vince's neighbor is a quiet, reserved unmarried woman. When asked to guess whether she is a nurse or a librarian, Vince guesses that she must be a librarian.	
More people are victims of homicide than die of stomach cancer every year.	
Oscar was up all night working on his paper, the same one that a week ago he assumed he would have a lot of time to finish!	

Heuristics and Biases: Cognitive Illusions?

People do not always use the **rules of logic**, but instead sometimes rely on sets of heuristics. These can result in wrong conclusions.

Define each of the following **heuristics** and explain how it may result in errors.

Heuristic	Definition	How May It Result in Errors?
Representativeness		
Availability		

Emotions and Decision Making: Having a Hunch

What is the evidence that **emotions** can facilitate **decision making**? _____
_____
_____
_____
_____
_____
_____

Looking at Levels

How could doctors use an analysis of pain at the **levels of the brain, person, and group** (and their interactions) to provide better patient care? Discuss._____
_____
_____
_____
_____
_____
_____

TRY PRACTICE TEST #4 NOW!
GOOD LUCK!

After You Read . . . Thinking Back

1. How do you think myelination of different brain parts (discussed in Chapter 3) affects individuals' language and thinking?_____

    _____

    _____

    _____

    _____

2. How do you think the paradigm shift from behaviorism to cognitive psychology (as discussed in Chapter 1) influenced the study of thinking?_____

    _____

    _____

    _____

    _____

    _____

3. Do you think that there are particular difficulties with the research methodology used to study thinking, as opposed to some other topics in psychology? _____

    _____

    _____

    _____

    _____

    _____

4. This chapter discusses some of the obstacles in problem solving. What steps of the information processing theory (presented in Chapter 7) do these obstacles represent?_____

    _____

    _____

    _____

    _____

    _____

5. The importance of imagery was demonstrated in Tolman's study of cognitive maps. What did Tolman find? _____

    _____

    _____

    _____

    _____

    _____

6. How might being left-handed versus right-handed influence language acquisition and disruption (following brain damage, for example)?_____

    _____

    _____

    _____

    _____

After You Read . . . Thinking Ahead

1. Can you think of other abilities that may have critical or sensitive periods? What are they?
    Explain. _____
    _____
    _____
    _____
    _____
    _____

2. What nonverbal cues do you know? For example, what cues do people use to indicate
    their romantic interest in each other?_____
    _____
    _____
    _____
    _____
    _____

3. At what age do you think children can form concepts? Why?_____
    _____
    _____
    _____
    _____
    _____

4. Do you think that language, problem solving, and/or mental imagery play an important role
    in intelligence? Why or why not?_____
    _____
    _____
    _____
    _____
    _____

5. Can you think of group interactions that might help or hurt problem solving? Explain.
    _____
    _____
    _____
    _____
    _____

6. Can thinking provide a motivation for some people? Do you know anyone like this?
    Discuss._____
    _____
    _____
    _____
    _____
    _____

After You Read . . . Practice Tests

PRACTICE TEST #1:
LANGUAGE

True/False Questions
Circle TRUE or FALSE for each of the following statements.

1.   TRUE   FALSE   Broca's aphasia causes problems with comprehending language. (p. 303)

2.   TRUE   FALSE   Semantics refers to the meaning of a sentence. (p. 304)

3.   TRUE   FALSE   Children can usually understand words before they can produce them. (p. 310)

4.   TRUE   FALSE   If a person is bilingual, brain damage will affect both languages in the same way. (p. 316)

5.   TRUE   FALSE   Pragmatics involves being able to read the underlying meaning of a sentence. (p. 306)

6.   TRUE   FALSE   Different languages use different numbers of phonemes. (p. 301)

7.   TRUE   FALSE   The case of Genie suggests that there may be a sensitive time for learning language. (p. 313)

8.   TRUE   FALSE   It is easier for an adult to recover from aphasia than for a child. (p. 314)

9.   TRUE   FALSE   English uses approximately 45 phonemes. (p. 301)

10.   TRUE   FALSE   People store propositions, rather than the literal meanings of sentences. (p. 306)

Multiple-Choice Questions
For each question, circle the best answer from the choices given.

1.   The basic building blocks of speech sound are called: (p. 301)
      a.   Vowels.
      b.   Phonemes.
      c.   Consonants.
      d.   Pragmemes.

2.   In comparison to the English language, French: (p. 302)
       a.   Is more difficult to speak.
       b.   Has fewer phonemes.
       c.   Is more "cultured."
       d.   Doesn't stress syllables.

3.   B. F. Skinner believed that language was: (p. 309)
       a.   Inborn.
       b.   Biologically-based.
       c.   Learned.
       d.   Unmodifiable.

4.   Nativists, like Chomsky, believe that language is: (p. 309)
       a.   Learned.
       b.   Inborn.
       c.   Imitated.
       d.   Related to intelligence.

5.   The smallest unit of meaning in a language is represented by a: (p. 304)
       a.   Phoneme.
       b.   Word.
       c.   Morpheme.
       d.   Syllable.

6.   The implied meaning of an utterance is called: (p. 306)
       a.   Pragmatics.
       b.   Syntax.
       c.   Semantics.
       d.   Morphology.

7.   Patients with damage to the right hemisphere cannot understand: (p. 307)
       a.   Verbs.
       b.   Questions.
       c.   Sentences.
       d.   Jokes.

8.   At the zoo, Mariah says to her mother, "Did you see the mouses?" This is an example of: (p. 312)
       a.   Overextension.
       b.   Underextension.
       c.   Overregularization.
       d.   Telegraphic speech.

9. Which of the following provides evidence that people have an innate ability to understand at least some aspects of language? (p. 309)
    a. The fact that child-directed speech is found in many cultures.
    b. The fact that the structure of the brain changes at approximately the same time as children acquire language.
    c. The fact that the words that children acquire first differ according to the children's cultures.
    d. The fact that virtually all human beings come to speak a language.

10. One way that we know that sign language is truly a language is that: (p. 315)
    a. Brain damage disrupts it in similar ways as it would damage the language of hearing people.
    b. There are multiple versions of sign language.
    c. Even deaf babies babble.
    d. It can be taught.

PRACTICE TEST #2:
MEANS OF THOUGHT

True/False Questions

Circle TRUE or FALSE for each of the following statements.

1. TRUE   FALSE   Language and images are the only means by which we think. (pp. 318-319)

2. TRUE   FALSE   Thinking is just "talking to oneself." (p. 319)

3. TRUE   FALSE   The most common form of mental imagery is visual. (p. 319)

4. TRUE   FALSE   The Dani, who have only two words for color ("light" and "dark"), do not perceive different shades of color. (p. 319)

5. TRUE   FALSE   The written structure of a language may affect how people think. (p. 320)

Multiple-Choice Questions

For each question, circle the best answer from the choices given.

1. The Dani of New Guinea, who use only two words for color ("dark" and "light") perceive: (p. 319)
    a.   Only black and white.
    b.   More shades of colors than people who do not emphasize "dark" and "light."
    c.   The same variations and shades of colors as people who use more labels.
    d.   Striking colors, but not muted pastels.

2. According to _____, thinking is shaped by the particular language we speak. (p. 319)
    a.   The language acquisition device
    b.   The linguistic relativity hypothesis
    c.   The critical period theory
    d.   John B. Watson

3. The most common form of mental imagery is: (p. 320)
    a.   Auditory.
    b.   Olfactory.
    c.   Visual.
    d.   Somatosensory.

4.   The reason that it will take longer to mentally scan the walls of a big room than to mentally scan the walls of a small room is because of the _____ property of "mental space." (p. 320)
    a.   Grain
    b.   Limited size
    c.   Spatial extent
    d.   Topographical organization

5.   Which of the following would be a prototype of a chair? (p. 325)
    a.   Bar stool
    b.   Rocking chair
    c.   Dining-room chair
    d.   Lawn chair

6.   Which of the following words is likely to be at the basic level for objects? (p. 325)
    a.   Furniture
    b.   Chair
    c.   Easy chair
    d.   Household items

7.   Which of the following is the least likely to be included in the schema for a elementary-school classroom? (p. 326)
    a.   Books
    b.   Student desks
    c.   Blackboard
    d.   Carpet

8.   The brain appears to organize concepts into two general classes: (p. 326)
    a.   Familiar and unfamiliar things.
    b.   Living and manufactured objects.
    c.   Colored and noncolored objects.
    d.   Things and people.

9.   Which of the following would be most difficult to visualize? (p. 323)
    a.   A close relative's face
    b.   A chocolate-chip cookie
    c.   Love
    d.   A clock

10.   The relationship between concepts, words, and images is: (p. 324)
    a.   They are the same thing.
    b.   Words and images are different types of concepts.
    c.   Words and images are methods of expressing concepts.
    d.   a & b

PRACTICE TEST #3:
PROBLEM SOLVING

Fill-in-the-Blank Questions

Complete the following paragraph by filling in the blanks with the following words:

WORD BANK	
Algorithm	Insight
Analogy	Representation
Heuristic	Strategies
Incubation	

The first step to solving any problem is figuring out how to approach it; this challenge is called the

_____ problem. There are two _____, or approaches to solving

problems. The first is a(n) _____, a methodical, step-by-step approach that often

results in the right answer but is slow and laborious. The second approach, using a(n) _____

_____, is quicker but more prone to error. Sometimes you will have a(n)

_____, when the solution comes to them rather suddenly. This is especially likely to

happen after a period of _____. At other times, you must use a(n)

_____, comparing features of the novel problem to a problem you have already solved. (p.

327-332)

Multiple-Choice Questions

For each question, circle the best answer from the choices given.

1. Which of the following would experts be more likely than novices to do? (p. 333)
    a. Organize their knowledge around fundamental principles.
    b. Rely on more vague ideas.
    c. Be less flexible in problem solving.
    d. Rely on insights for problem solving.

2. If you want to be 100% certain that you get the correct answer, you should use: (p. 330)
    a. An analogy.
    b. A heuristic.
    c. An algorithm.
    d. A strategy.

3. The representation problem involves determining: (p. 328)
    a. How to best visualize the problem.
    b. How to best formulate the nature of the problem.
    c. How to determine the criteria for a good decision.
    d. What type of strategy to use.

4.   If you want to have an answer quickly, you should probably use a(n): (p. 330)
      a.   Insight.
      b.   Heuristic.
      c.   Strategy.
      d.   Algorithm.

5.   When Michelle's house floods, she uses all the towels that she has. With more water still on
      the floor, she initially doesn't know how to sop it up. Finally, her son suggests that she use
      sheets and bedspreads. Michelle's son is showing that he has no problem with: (p. 329)
      a.   Using algorithms.
      b.   Becoming functionally fixated.
      c.   Problem-solving.
      d.   Helping out around the house.

6.   One reason that people probably experience functional fixation is: (p. 329)
      a.   They are not good problem-solvers.
      b.   They are using a heuristic, not an algorithm.
      c.   It takes extra brain activity to switch between different types of performance.
      d.   It takes practice to do this.

7.   Expertise in a given field typically takes _____ to achieve. (p. 333)
      a.   6 months
      b.   1 year
      c.   5 years
      d.   10 years

8.   Neural networks are like the human brain in that: (p. 335)
      a.   They have small units that are connected together.
      b.   They have processes that work at the same time.
      c.   They can generalize to novel examples.
      d.   All of the above.

9.   Which of the following is the primary determinant in becoming an expert? (p. 334)
      a.   Talent
      b.   Intelligence
      c.   Deliberate practice
      d.   Social skills

10.   If you get stuck solving a problem, which of the following might be helpful to try? (p. 336)
      a.   Walk away from the problem for awhile.
      b.   Be willing to consider other possible outcomes.
      c.   Don't forget what the problem is.
      d.   All of the above.

PRACTICE TEST #4:
LOGIC, REASONING AND DECISION MAKING

Multiple-Choice Questions

For each question, circle the best answer from the choices given.

1. The process of applying the principles of correct reasoning to reach a decision or evaluate the truth of a claim is called: (p. 337)
    a.   Deductive reasoning.
    b.   Affirming the consequent.
    c.   Inductive reasoning.
    d.   Logic.

2. Which of the following does <u>not</u> matter in logic? (p. 337)
    a.   Content
    b.   Conclusion
    c.   Premises
    d.   Form

3. People often make the error of _____ by assuming that a specific cause is present because a particular result has occurred. (p. 337)
    a.   Deductive reasoning
    b.   Affirming the consequent
    c.   Inductive reasoning
    d.   Affirming the premises

4. Jeremy *really* wants to buy a new Corvette, so he attends a Corvette Lovers Convention and asks the Corvette owners there if they are happy with their cars. Jeremy is making a mistake by: (p. 338)
    a.   Affirming the consequent.
    b.   Using the confirmation bias.
    c.   Denying the premise.
    d.   Buying an expensive car.

5. Reasoning that moves from a particular case to a generalization is called: (p. 338)
    a.   Deductive reasoning.
    b.   Affirming the consequent.
    c.   Inductive reasoning.
    d.   Narrowing the stimulus field.

6.	If you drove two Volkswagon Beetles and each time there was a mechanical error, you might decide that all Volkswagons are faulty cars. You have used _____ to come to your conclusion. (p. 337)
	a.	Inductive reasoning
	b.	Confirmation bias
	c.	Deductive reasoning
	d.	Affirmation bias

7.	The _____ heuristic assumes that the more similar something is to a prototype stored in memory, the more likely the entity belongs to the category of the prototype. (p. 340)
	a.	Inductive
	b.	Availability
	c.	Deductive
	d.	Representativeness

8.	The representativeness heuristic often fails to take into consideration: (p. 340)
	a.	Base rates.
	b.	Consequences.
	c.	Premises.
	d.	Prototypes.

9.	The _____ might explain why people tend to remember airplane crashes, but not car crashes. (p. 341)
	a.	Prototype hypothesis
	b.	Availability heuristic
	c.	Planning fallacy
	d.	Representativeness heuristic

10.	How you frame a decision will affect: (p. 339)
	a.	The criteria for a good decision.
	b.	The possible outcomes.
	c.	The decision to be made.
	d.	All of the above.

COMPREHENSIVE PRACTICE TEST

True-False Questions

Circle TRUE or FALSE for each of the following statements.

1.   TRUE   FALSE   Because a dog can whine when hungry, it uses language. (p. 301)

2.   TRUE   FALSE   Most language abilities depend primarily on the left hemisphere. (p. 306)

3.   TRUE   FALSE   It is relatively easy to learn the grammar of a second language. (p. 316)

4.   TRUE   FALSE   Language is the basis of thinking. (p. 318)

5.   TRUE   FALSE   A kiwi fruit is a good prototype of a "fruit." (p. 325)

6.   TRUE   FALSE   The most accurate problem solving method is the algorithm. (p. 330)

7.   TRUE   FALSE   Emotion always hurts problem-solving abilities. (p. 342)

8.   TRUE   FALSE   People who are experts on a certain skill rarely have to practice. (p. 334)

9.   TRUE   FALSE   Computer neural networks roughly model the way the brain works. (p. 335)

10.   TRUE   FALSE   Visual imagery relies on many of the same brain parts that are used in visual perception. (p. 322)

Multiple-Choice Questions

For each question, circle the best answer from the choices given.

1.   "Sandwich ate boy all the" is an example of incorrect: (p. 302)
   a.   Morphology.
   b.   Syntax.
   c.   Phonology.
   d.   Logic.

2. When Jane asked her two-year-old son "Could you hand me the salt?" he replied, "Yes," clearly not understanding the _____ of her statement. (p. 306)
    a. Morphology
    b. Pragmatics
    c. Phonology
    d. Syntax

3. Which of the following aspects of a second language would be easiest to learn? (p. 317)
    a. Grammar
    b. Sound patterns
    c. Vocabulary
    d. All would be equally difficult to learn.

4. People consistently name objects at the _____ level. (p. 325)
    a. Prototypical
    b. Conceptual
    c. Ordinary
    d. Basic

5. In Blanton's (1997) study of prototypes for drinking, he found that adolescents who had more positive prototypes: (p. 327)
    a. Reported drinking more.
    b. Reported drinking less.
    c. Had more stable family systems.
    d. Considered themselves different from other drinkers.

6. Maria can't find the rice in the store, and doesn't know where to look, so she starts in the first aisle and looks on all shelves before moving to the next. Maria is using a(n) _____ to find the rice. (p. 330)
    a. Heuristic
    b. Function
    c. Algorithm
    d. Representation

7. The quickest way to solve a problem is by using a(n): (p. 330)
    a. Algorithm.
    b. Prototype.
    c. Heuristic.
    d. Schema.

8. When people seek information that will confirm a rule but do not seek information that might refute it, they are: (p. 338)
    a. Denying the inevitable.
    b. Deciding the alternative.
    c. Affirming the consequent.
    d. Using the confirmation bias.

9. Following a car accident, Cathy could only speak in "empty speech," which didn't make much sense. Further, she didn't appear able to understand much of other people's speech. Cathy is probably suffering from: (pp. 303-304)
    a. Broca's aphasia.
    b. Wernicke's aphasia.
    c. Brain damage in the left frontal lobe.
    d. Brain damage to the right frontal lobe.

10. The ability to understand metaphor depends on: (p. 306)
    a. Semantics.
    b. Pragmatics.
    c. Syntax.
    d. Morphology.

11. Which of the following is NOT a key characteristic of child-directed speech (CDS)? (p. 309)
    a. Sentences are shorter.
    b. Enunciation is more careful.
    c. Pitch is low.
    d. There are clear pauses between phrases.

12. Which of the following is an example of telegraphic speech? (pp. 311-312)
    a. "Mommy, I put my shoe on."
    b. "Mommy, put shoe on please."
    c. "I put shoe on."
    d. "Shoe on."

13. Deaf children are similar to hearing children in that: (p. 309)
    a. They begin babbling at around six months of age.
    b. They pay more attention to child-directed speech than other forms of speech.
    c. Brain damage disrupts their sign language the same way it would hearing speakers' spoken language.
    d. All of the above.

14. Intuition is: (p. 342)
    a. A myth; it doesn't exist.
    b. Based on implicit memories.
    c. Based in the medial frontal cortex.
    d. B & C

15. Which of the following provides evidence that there may be a sensitive period for learning language? (p. 313)
    a. The fact that child-directed speech is common to most cultures
    b. The case of Genie
    c. The fact that animals cannot learn true "languages"
    d. The fact that the first words that children learn depend on their cultures

16. One night, John goes to a bar. He meets a really nice woman whose name is "Susan Smith." They exchange phone numbers, but he loses her number before he gets home. An algorithm for solving this problem would be: (p. 330)
    a. To call every "Smith" in the phone book and ask to speak with "Susan," until he reaches her.
    b. To go to the same bar next week and hope that she shows up again.
    c. To go to the same bar next week and ask patrons if they know Susan Smith's phone number.
    d. To wait for her to call him.

17. If you are stuck in solving a problem, which of the following might help you come up with the answer? (pp. 335-336)
    a. Make sure you really understand the problem.
    b. Walk away from the problem for awhile.
    c. See if you can come up with multiple ways of solving the problem.
    d. All of the above might help.

18. Some reasoning errors can be overcome by: (p. 338)
    a. Setting up mental models.
    b. Affirming the consequent.
    c. Using the representativeness heuristic.
    d. Using the availability heuristic.

19. Gigeranzer says that people fail to use the base-rate rule because: (p. 340)
    a. They do not have a cognitive illusion.
    b. They have trouble understanding descriptions of proportions.
    c. They cannot apply the rule in unfamiliar situations.
    d. It is a heuristic and people prefer to use algorithms.

20. Skin-conductance tests demonstrate that: (p. 342)
    a. Emotions may facilitate reasoning.
    b. The ventral medial frontal lobes appear to be involved in forming hunches.
    c. Hunches appear to be based on implicit memories.
    d. All of the above.

Essay Questions

Answer each of the following questions in the space provided.

1. Is thought simply talking to ourselves? Why or why not? _____
   _____
   _____
   _____
   _____
   _____
   _____

2. Do people reason logically? _____
_____
_____
_____
_____
_____
_____

3. Researchers state that true language must have phonology, syntax, semantics, and pragmatics. Do you agree? Is this how you had defined language before having read this chapter? Have your thoughts about the communication of other species (e.g., dolphins and apes) changed after reading this chapter? What is the difference between language and communication?_____
_____
_____
_____
_____
_____
_____

4. You may know someone who you believe "has no common sense." What is meant by this phrase? How would you define "common sense"? Is it related to problem solving or logical thinking? Do people with "no common sense" make more errors of logic and reasoning?
_____
_____
_____
_____
_____
_____

5. Consider children raised in Spanish-speaking homes in America. Frequently, they are not exposed to English until they go to school, and then they often act as interpreters for their parents and grandparents (at doctors' offices and other places). The parents in these homes insist on maintaining their cultural background and resist learning and teaching English to their children. Given what you have learned about bilingualism, do you agree or disagree with the parents of these children? _____
_____
_____
_____
_____
_____
_____

6.   Why do people make errors of logic and reasoning? Would some real-life decisions be better made by a computer? Consider the Challenger disaster, the decision to enter into conflict with another country, and the decisions to marry, divorce, or have children. Which types of situations would best be handled by an emotionless but accurate computer decision-making program? _____

_____

_____

_____

_____

_____

_____

7.   Consider the controls in your car, from their size to their placement. How might cognitive engineers have influenced these characteristics? _____

_____

_____

_____

_____

_____

_____

8.   If an infant is not exposed to language before a certain period of development, will she develop any language? How do we know? _____

_____

_____

_____

_____

_____

_____

9.   Explain why it is so difficult for infants to learn to understand and produce language.

_____

_____

_____

_____

_____

_____

10.   Discuss the pros and cons of using heuristics and algorithms. Under what circumstances would you want to use each strategy? _____

_____

_____

_____

_____

_____

_____

When You Are Finished . . . Puzzle It Out

Across

2. Number of years needed to gain expertise
7. Has won every chess game played
8. Applying correct reasoning
9. Number of morphemes in "reread"
10. New way to look at problem
12. Hypothesized the LAD
13. Obstacle to overcome to reach goal
14. Says language comes from learning
18. Guarantees solution to problem
19. Earliest, simplest sentence
20. Meaning of a word or sentence

Down

1. Rule of thumb
3. Only time learning is possible
4. Aphasia based in left frontal lobe
5. People viewing language as innate
6. Most typical example of a category
11. Basic building block of speech
15. Improved thinking after a break
16. Another name for "motherese"
17. Grammatical structure of sentence

Puzzle created with Puzzlemaker at DiscoverySchool.com.

Chapter 9
Intelligence

Before You Read . . .

Have you ever taken an IQ test? What did those results mean, exactly? In fact, those are not simple questions to answer. IQ stands for intelligence quotient, which is a measurement of intelligence. Yet, the definition of intelligence continues to be debated. The common view is that it is "the ability to solve problems well and to understand and learn complex materials." However, other researchers have introduced new ideas about intelligence, including emotional intelligence and multiple intelligences.

Next, you will learn what makes some people smart. Do smarter people have bigger heads, faster processing abilities, better memories, or just better DNA? Clearly, genetics play a role in intelligence, but so does the environment. Both factors also play a role in determining the intelligence and functioning level of people who are mentally retarded, gifted, and creative.

Chapter Objectives

After studying this chapter, you should be able to:

♦   Compare and contrast different theories of intelligence.

♦   Identify and explain how intelligence is measured.

♦   Describe what IQ tests are, how they are scored, and what they say about a person's future.

♦   Discuss what makes people intelligent.

♦   Discuss heritability and the problems with heritability studies.

♦   Describe research on group differences in intelligence.

♦   Explain and summarize research on mental retardation and giftedness.

♦   Describe creativity and why some people are more creative than others.

♦   Discuss the success of efforts to enhance intelligence and creativity.

As You Read . . . Term Identification

Make flashcards using the following terms as you go. Use the definitions in the margins of this chapter for help. If you write the definitions in your own words, though, you will remember them better!

Adoption studies
Analytic intelligence
Autism
Bodily-kinesthetic intelligence
Brainstorming
Convergent thinking
Creative cognition
Creative intelligence
Creativity
Crystallized intelligence
Existential intelligence
Divergent thinking
Down Syndrome
Emotional intelligence
Factor analysis
Fetal alcohol syndrome
Fluid intelligence
Flynn effect
Fragile X Syndrome
General factor (g)
Gifted
Heritability
Intelligence
Intelligence quotient (IQ)
Interpersonal intelligence
Intrapersonal intelligence
Islands of excellence
Linguistic intelligence
Logical-mathematical intelligence
Mentally retarded

Microenvironment
Musical intelligence
Naturalist intelligence
Normal curve
Norming
Population
Practical intelligence
Profile of intelligences
Primary mental abilities
Prodigies
Project Head Start
Psychometric approach
Raven's Progressive Matrices
Reaction range
Reliable
Savants
Spatial intelligence
Specific factors (s)
Standard deviation
Standardized sample
Stanford-Binet (Revised) Intelligence Test
Stereotype threat
Test bias
Theory of multiple intelligences
Valid
Wechsler Adult Intelligence Scale (WAIS)
Wechsler Intelligence Scale for Children (WISC)
Williams Syndrome

As You Read . . . Questions and Exercises

Is There More Than One Way to Be Smart?

Measuring Intelligence: What is IQ?

Who is the smartest person you know? Describe him or her. _____
_____
_____
_____

What makes that person so **intelligent**?_____
_____
_____
_____
_____

Based on the above, what is your definition of **intelligence**?_____
_____
_____
_____
_____

Which theory of **intelligence** is most similar to yours? _____
_____
_____
_____
_____

Which theory of **intelligence** is most different from yours? _____
_____
_____
_____
_____

Who started **intelligence tests** and why?_____
_____
_____
_____
_____

What was **Wechsler**'s major complaint about the **Stanford-Binet Test of Intelligence**? How did
he design his IQ tests to overcome this limitation?_____
_____
_____

How were **IQ tests** originally scored? What was the problem with that method?_____
_____
_____
_____
_____

How are **intelligence tests** scored now? Why?_____
_____
_____
_____
_____

Name and describe a test or measurement that is not **reliable**. _____
_____
_____
_____
_____

Name and describe a test or measurement that is not **valid** for a certain purpose. _____
_____
_____
_____
_____

Draw a **normal curve** below.
- Indicate the mean and mark off standard deviations, as appropriate.
- In a different color ink, indicate the range of IQ scores of typical college students.

If **IQ** and **job success** are positively correlated, why can't we say that intelligence leads to success or that it causes one to be successful?_____
_____
_____
_____
_____

Intelligence: One Ability or Many?

GO SURFING...

...at the following sites and take the IQ tests there:
- http://www.iqtest.com/ (traditional psychometric test)
- http://www.utne.com/interact/test_iq.html (emotional intelligence test)
- http://www.acsu.buffalo.edu/~rom2/center/new_page_2.htm (multiple intelligences test)

What were your scores on these tests?_____
_____

Which test do you think best represents your **intelligence**? Why? _____
_____
_____
_____
_____

What other variables might have influenced your score, besides your **intelligence**? _____
_____
_____
_____
_____

In the **normal curve** you drew (on the previous page), mark an X indicating where you fall, using the score from the traditional psychometric test you took above.

Imagine that you were a social studies teacher and were trying to teach students about the Revolutionary War. How could you teach this so that students with each of the following intellectual strengths could best grasp the material?

- **Linguistic:** _____
_____
_____

- **Spatial:** _____
_____
_____

◆   **Musical:** _____
_____

◆   **Logical-mathematical:** _____
_____

◆   **Bodily-kinesthetic:** _____
_____

◆   **Intrapersonal:** _____
_____

◆   **Interpersonal:** _____
_____

◆   **Naturalist:** _____
_____

◆   **Existentialist:** _____
_____
_____

Do you agree that **Gardner's theory** is one of **intelligence** (or with his critics, who claim that some of these are talents, not intelligences)? Explain. _____
_____
_____
_____
_____

Write a question (on intelligence) that would test each of the following types of intelligence (from **Sternberg's theory**.

◆   **Analytic:**_____
_____

◆   **Practical:** _____
_____

◆   **Creative:** _____
_____
_____

Can you think of someone who may or may not be highly **intelligent** (using a traditional definition), but who is very **emotionally intelligent**? Describe him or her. How successful has this person been? Why?_____
_____
_____
_____

In your own words, what are **fluid** and **crystallized intelligence**?

◆   **Fluid:** _____
_____
_____

◆   **Crystallized:** _____
_____
_____

Why do you think **fluid intelligence** tends to diminish as one ages, but **crystallized intelligence** does not? _____
_____
_____
_____
_____

Do you think that people can improve their **crystallized** and/or **fluid intelligence**? If so, how?
_____
_____
_____
_____

Name 3 types of careers in which you think **crystallized intelligence** would be vital. Briefly explain why it would be so important in each.

◆   _____
_____
_____

◆   _____
_____
_____

◆   _____
_____
_____

Name three types of careers in which you think **fluid intelligence** would be vital. Briefly explain why it would be so important in each.

◆   _____
_____
_____

◆   _____
_____
_____

◆   _____
_____
_____

Do you think most of your school tests measure **fluid** or **crystallized intelligence** better? _____
_____
_____
_____
_____

After having taken **intelligence tests**, how do you feel about using IQ tests for school placement?
_____
_____
_____
_____

Suppose that parents had their child take an **IQ test** for the purpose of determining whether the child should be placed in a Gifted & Talented class. Analyze the effects of this decision at each of the three levels.

♦   **Level of the Brain:** _____
_____

♦   **Level of the Person:** _____
_____

♦   **Level of the Group:** _____
_____

Boosting IQ

Define the **Flynn Effect**. What are the possible explanations for this effect? _____
_____
_____
_____
_____
_____

Do you think that you are more intelligent than your parents or your grandparents? What theory of the cause of the **Flynn effect** does your answer support? Explain. _____
_____
_____
_____
_____
_____

Suppose that your state becomes concerned about the poor performance of low-income students in elementary school. They hire you as a consultant to develop an **enrichment program**. What would be the key components of your program? Why? _____

_____

_____

_____

_____

_____

_____

_____

_____

_____

_____

_____

_____

_____

Given that most enrichment programs do not show long-term gains in intelligence, do you think that the government should continue to support such programs? Are they worth using taxpayer dollars for? Why or why not?_____

_____

_____

_____

_____

_____

_____

_____

_____

_____

Looking at Levels

At **each level**, list some of the factors that may affect a person's performance on an intelligence test. Draw arrows to indicate the interactions between events at the different levels.

The Brain	The Person	The Group

TRY PRACTICE TEST #1 NOW!
GOOD LUCK!

What Makes Us Smart: Nature & Nurture

The Machinery of Intelligence

What are the roles of **brain size**, **speed of processing**, and **working memory** in intelligence? Summarize the findings of research that has investigated each of these possibilities.

Characteristic	Evidence Supporting	Evidence Refuting	Conclusion
Bigger brains			
Faster processing			
Better working memory			

For each pair below, circle the one that would have more similar **IQs**:

Fraternal twins raised together	vs.	Identical twins reared apart
Child and adoptive mother	vs.	Child and biological mother
Fraternal twins raised apart	vs.	Child and biological mother
Siblings raised apart	vs.	Siblings raised together
Child and adoptive mother	vs.	Siblings raised apart
Fraternal twins raised together	vs.	Siblings raised together

The usual estimate of the **heritability** of intelligence is .50. What does this mean? _____
_____
_____
_____
_____

What are the four problems with interpreting **heritability scores**? Explain.

◆ _____
_____
_____

◆ _____
_____
_____

◆ _____
_____
_____

◆ _____
_____
_____

What is the evidence for a **genetic contribution** to intelligence?_____
_____
_____
_____
_____
_____
_____

What is the evidence for an **environmental contribution** to intelligence?_____
_____
_____
_____
_____
_____

What is a **reaction range** and how does it help explain genetic and environmental contributions to intelligence?_____
_____
_____
_____
_____

How wide or narrow do you think your **reaction range** is? Why? _____
_____
_____
_____
_____

Based on this, where within your **range** do you think you fall? Why? _____
_____
_____
_____
_____

Group Differences in Intelligence

Why don't heritability estimates tell us anything about **group differences** in intelligence?_____
_____
_____
_____
_____
_____
_____

Three theories for explaining **racial differences** in IQ have been proposed. For each of the
following theories, describe the evidence that supports or refutes it.

Theory	Evidence Supporting	Evidence Refuting
Test bias		
Socioeconomic status		
Microenvironment		

GO SURFING...

...at http://www.highiqsociety.org/ and take the **Culture-Fair IQ tests** there.

How was this test different than the **traditional IQ test** you took earlier? (Or, was it?) _____
_____
_____
_____
_____

Do you think this test was **culture-fair**? Why or why not? _____
_____
_____
_____
_____

How do men and women's intellectual strengths differ?_____
_____
_____
_____
_____

What is the evidence that these differences are **biologically determined**? _____
_____
_____
_____
_____

What is the evidence that these differences are **environmentally determined**?_____
_____
_____
_____
_____

Some research findings indicate that biology affects **gender differences** in intelligence; other findings, indicate that the environment affects these differences. How can both sets of research findings be accurate? Explain._____
_____
_____
_____
_____

Looking at Levels

Explain how believing that **racial differences** in intelligence are biologically determined might affect each of the **three levels**.

♦   **Level of the Brain:** _____
_____
_____
_____

♦   **Level of the Person:** _____
_____
_____
_____

♦   **Level of the Group:** _____
_____
_____
_____

How might events at the different levels interact?_____
_____
_____
_____
_____
_____

TRY PRACTICE TEST #2 NOW!
GOOD LUCK!

Diversity in Intelligence

Mental Retardation

What are the three criteria for **mental retardation**?

♦   _____
♦   _____
♦   _____

Return to the **normal curve** you drew earlier in this chapter. In a different colored ink, mark the borderline for mental retardation. Also mark the average IQ for people with mental retardation.

Have you ever known anyone with **mental retardation**? If so, describe his or her level of functioning. _____
_____
_____
_____

Suppose that you had a child with **Down syndrome**. What could you do to maximize his or her functioning?_____

_____

_____

_____

_____

The Gifted

What does it mean to be "**gifted**"?_____

_____

_____

_____

_____

What are the possible "prices" of **giftedness**?_____

_____

_____

_____

_____

Why do you think there might be these "prices"?_____

_____

_____

_____

_____

Creative Smarts

What is the two-stage process of **creativity**? Name and briefly describe each of the stages.

♦_____
♦_____

Use the shapes below. Combine them (using rotation, size adjustment, etc.) and make as many objects as you can. Then, try to interpret what you created.

333

How difficult was this? What part was difficult? _____
_____
_____
_____
_____

Now, give yourself exactly two minutes to think of as many uses for a brick as you can. List them here:

Now, divide the total number by two. The answer is your **creativity** score: _____.
(The average score is four; eight is a very high score.)

Do you think these tests are good measures of **creativity**? Why or why not? _____
_____
_____
_____
_____

Here is a checklist of some of the special abilities that **creative** people appear to have. Check all of those abilities that you think describe you.

_____	1.	the ability to generate many solutions
_____	2.	the ability to choose among solutions well
_____	3.	the ability to keep options open
_____	4.	the ability to keep from making snap decisions about the likely outcome of an effort
_____	5.	the ability to see problems from multiple vantage points
_____	6.	the ability to be flexible
_____	7.	the ability to reorganize information
_____	8.	the ability to think in terms of analogies
_____	9.	high intelligence
_____	10.	wide interests
_____	11.	not liking traditional dogmas
_____	12.	high self-esteem
_____	13.	fondness for hard work
_____	14.	high motivation and persistence
_____	15.	being driven to create

Do you think of yourself as **creative**? Why or why not? _____
_____
_____
_____
_____

What environmental factors do you think contributed to your **creativity**?_____
_____
_____
_____
_____

What can you do to enhance your **creativity**? _____
_____
_____
_____
_____

Describe the limitations of **brainstorming** in **creativity**. How might these limitations be
overcome?_____
_____
_____
_____

Describe the factors that contributed to the success and/or failures of the "**termites**," at each of the
different **levels**.
- ◆   **Level of the Brain:** _____
    _____
    _____

- ◆   **Level of the Person:** _____
    _____
    _____

- ◆   **Level of the Group:** _____
    _____
    _____

How might events at these different levels interact?_____
_____
_____
_____
_____

TRY PRACTICE TEST #3 NOW!
GOOD LUCK!

After You Read . . . Thinking Back

1. What type of studies are adoption studies (e.g., experiments, correlational studies, quasi-experiments)? What are the advantages and disadvantages of this type of study? How is that reflected in adoption studies on intelligence?_____

    _____

    _____

    _____

    _____

    _____

2. Your textbook points out that there is a positive correlation between brain size and intelligence. Draw a scatterplot of a positive correlation. Be sure to label both axes.

3. Why can causal conclusions not be drawn from correlational studies? Explain._____

    _____

    _____

    _____

    _____

    _____

4. Do you think that people with high IQs might differ from people with low IQs in terms of learning? If so, what type of learning (classical, operant, social, cognitive)? How? What evidence supports your opinion? _____

    _____

    _____

    _____

    _____

    _____

5. Your text discussed the relationship between intelligence and working memory. Can you think of any other aspects of memory (either storage or processing components) that you think might be related to intelligence? Defend your answer._____

    _____

    _____

    _____

    _____

    _____

After You Read . . . Thinking Ahead

1. How do people with high intelligence differ from others, with regard to motivation? Why might this be? _____

    _____

    _____

    _____

    _____

    _____

    _____

2. What could parents do to encourage this type of motivation?_____

    _____

    _____

    _____

    _____

    _____

    _____

3. What do you think the first signs of giftedness might be? Why?_____

    _____

    _____

    _____

    _____

    _____

    _____

4. Are there particular points in the lifespan during which being gifted might be particularly difficult? Why? _____

    _____

    _____

    _____

    _____

    _____

    _____

5. How do groups react to people who are retarded or gifted? Why do you think this is? How does this affect the person?

    _____

    _____

    _____

    _____

    _____

    _____

After You Read . . . Practice Tests

PRACTICE TEST #1:
IS THERE MORE THAN ONE WAY TO BE SMART?

Matching Questions

Match the following theorists with their theories of intelligence.

_____	1.	Spearman (p. 353)	A.	Emotional intelligence
_____	2.	Thurstone (p. 354)	B.	Analytic, practical, and creative
_____	3.	Cattell & Horn (p. 354)	C.	*g* and *s*
_____	4.	Gardner (p. 355)	D.	Primary mental abilities
_____	5.	Sternberg (p. 357)	E.	Crystallized and fluid
_____	6.	Goleman (p. 358)	F.	Multiple intelligences

Multiple-Choice Questions

For each question, circle the best answer from the choices given.

1. The first intelligence test was devised to identify: (p. 348)
    a. Military recruits who would make suitable officers.
    b. Immigrants who might "water down" the gene pool.
    c. Children in French schools who might need extra help.
    d. Gifted children who might contribute in a positive way to society.

2. The most widely used intelligence tests in the United States today are the: (p. 349)
    a. Stanford-Binet scales.
    b. Terman scales.
    c. Wechsler scales.
    d. Kaufman scales.

3. An average IQ score is: (p. 351)
    a. 10.
    b. 20.
    c. 50.
    d. 100.

4.   Tests that are _____ yield consistent scores over time. (p. 351)
   a.   Reliable
   b.   Valid
   c.   Normed
   d.   Standardized

5.   Which of the following are correlated with high intelligence? (p. 352)
   a.   High GPAs
   b.   Job success
   c.   Stable marriages
   d.   All of the above

6.   Becoming an expert in an area boosts one's _____ intelligence. (p. 354)
   a.   Crystallized
   b.   Fluid
   c.   Verbal
   d.   Nonverbal

7.   As people age, their _____ intelligence tends to diminish. (p. 355)
   a.   Verbal
   b.   Nonverbal
   c.   Crystallized
   d.   Fluid

8.   When faced with a novel situation, it would be best to have _____ intelligence. (p. 354)
   a.   Crystallized
   b.   Fluid
   c.   Native
   d.   Acquired

9.   Almost always, IQ scores across a population fall along a(n): (p. 351)
   a.   Normal curve.
   b.   Abnormal curve.
   c.   Skewed distribution.
   d.   Standard deviation.

10.   According to Sternberg and his colleagues, measures of _____ intelligence are the best predictors of how well someone will do on the job. (p. 357)
   a.   Standard
   b.   Analytic
   c.   Interpersonal
   d.   Practical

11. People with high emotional intelligence: (pp. 358-359)
    a. Are self-motivating.
    b. Understand their own emotions.
    c. Recognize others' emotions.
    d. All of the above.

12. Most studies of programs such as Head Start indicate that such programs: (p. 360)
    a. Are generally ineffective.
    b. Demonstrate short-term but not long-term increases in IQ.
    c. Demonstrate both short-term and long-term increases in IQ.
    d. Are effective only for children from higher socioeconomic classes.

13. Sarah Hughes, 2002 Olympic gold-medal winner in figure skating, is probably high on which of Gardner's nine forms of intelligence? (p. 356)
    a. Intrapersonal
    b. Interpersonal
    c. Naturalist
    d. Bodily-kinesthetic

14. In the original Binet intelligence test, a bright child was one whose mental age was _____ his chronological age. (p. 349)
    a. Lower than
    b. The same as
    c. Higher than
    d. Comparable to

15. Because the subtest scores on intelligence tests are all positively correlated, but to different degrees, Spearman argued that intelligence involves: (p. 353)
    a. The g-factor.
    b. The a-factor.
    c. The s-factors.
    d. Both a & c.

PRACTICE TEST #2:
WHAT MAKES US SMART

True/False Questions

Circle TRUE or FALSE for each of the following statements.

1.   TRUE   FALSE   Men are smarter than women. (p. 373)

2.   TRUE   FALSE   Women have better verbal skills than men. (p. 373)

3.   TRUE   FALSE   Evolutionary explanations for gender differences in IQ have received tremendous support. (p. 373)

4.   TRUE   FALSE   A woman's spatial ability depends upon her monthly cycle of hormones. (p. 374)

5.   TRUE   FALSE   There is a positive correlation between amount of testosterone and spatial ability. (pp. 373-374)

6.   TRUE   FALSE   The cerebral hemispheres in women are more sharply specialized than in men. (p. 374)

Multiple-Choice Questions

For each question, circle the best answer from the choices given.

1.   In general, the greater the reaction range: (p. 370)
    a.   The more evident the effects of genetics.
    b.   The more evident the effects of the environment.
    c.   The less important genetics and environment.
    d.   The more intelligent an individual is.

2.   Males tend to be better than females at tasks requiring: (p. 373)
    a.   Crystallized intelligence.
    b.   Fluid intelligence.
    c.   Verbal reasoning.
    d.   Spatial reasoning.

3.   Better spatial ability appears to be related to: (p. 374)
    a.   Excess testosterone (the more the better).
    b.   Less testosterone (the less the better).
    c.   Average amounts of testosterone (not too much or too little).
    d.   Fluctuating amounts of testosterone throughout the day.

4. The highest correlation between IQ and speed of processing occurs in tasks for _____ difficulty. (p. 364)
   a. Low
   b. High
   c. Moderate
   d. Varying

5. Damage to the _____ lobes will disrupt fluid intelligence. (p. 365)
   a. Occipital
   b. Frontal
   c. Parietal
   d. Temporal

6. Approximately _____ of the variation in IQ is due to inherited characteristics. (p. 367)
   a. 10%
   b. 25%
   c. 50%
   d. 75%

7. The environment you create by your presence is called the: (p. 368)
   a. Self-environment.
   b. Microenvironment.
   c. Minienvironment.
   d. Microcosm.

8. As people age, genetic influences: (p. 369)
   a. Become more apparent.
   b. Become less apparent.
   c. Interact more with the environment.
   d. Are more objective.

9. Which of the following findings suggests that the environment has an influence on intelligence? (p. 368)
   a. Biologically unrelated siblings show no IQ correlations as adults.
   b. More enriched environments can raise IQ scores.
   c. Identical twins have more similar IQs than fraternal twins.
   d. All of the above.

10. According to your textbook, the high correlations between the IQ scores of identical twins separated at birth: (p. 367)
    a. Is clear evidence that IQ is largely heritable.
    b. Needs to be interpreted cautiously.
    c. Is clear evidence that IQ is largely environmental.
    d. Suggests that intelligence is influenced both by heredity and the environment.

PRACTICE TEST #3:
DIVERSITY IN INTELLIGENCE

Matching Questions

Match the following types of mental retardation with their definitions

_____ 1.   Williams syndrome (p. 376)   A.   Repeating genetic material on X chromosome

_____ 2.   Down syndrome (p. 377)   B.   Environmentally caused

_____ 3.   Fragile X syndrome (p. 377)   C.   Extra material on the 21st chromosome

_____ 4.   Autism (p. 377)   D.   Large vocabularies and knowledge of facts

_____ 5.   Fetal alcohol syndrome   E.   Accompanied by self-involvement and socially
               (p. 377)   bizarre behavior

True/False Questions

Circle TRUE or FALSE for each of the following statements.

1.   TRUE   FALSE   Creative people are good at divergent thinking, but not at
                                    convergent thinking. (p. 380)

2.   TRUE   FALSE   Creativity is highly heritable. (p. 381)

3.   TRUE   FALSE   Creative individuals tend to have high IQs. (p. 381)

4.   TRUE   FALSE   Social recognition increases creativity. (p. 382)

5.   TRUE   FALSE   Creative people are more likely to have mental disorders.
                                    (pp. 381-382)

Multiple-Choice Questions

For each question, circle the best answer from the choices given.

1.   People with an IQ score of _____ or lower are traditionally considered to be mentally
       retarded. (p. 376)
       a.   100
       b.   80
       c.   70
       d.   50

2.   People with Williams syndrome are retarded but also: (p. 376)
    a.   Have large vocabularies and detailed knowledge of facts.
    b.   Have strong mathematical skills.
    c.   Have exceptional spatial reasoning skills.
    d.   All of the above.

3.   The most common form of mental retardation is: (p. 377)
    a.   Williams syndrome.
    b.   Down syndrome.
    c.   fetal alcohol syndrome.
    d.   autism.

4.   With each succeeding generation, retardation due to _____ becomes worse. (p. 377)
    a.   Down syndrome
    b.   Williams syndrome
    c.   fetal alcohol syndrome
    d.   Fragile X syndrome

5.   Which of the following causes of mental retardation affects boys more than girls? (p. 377)
    a.   Down syndrome
    b.   Williams syndrome
    c.   Fragile X syndrome
    d.   Autism

6.   Ceci (1990, 1996) found that highly intelligent children would not succeed if they didn't have: (p. 384)
    a.   Adequate schooling.
    b.   A mentor.
    c.   Motivation.
    d.   Social skills.

7.   Most research on giftedness involves people who have IQs above: (p. 378)
    a.   100.
    b.   135.
    c.   150.
    d.   200.

8.   Creativity is primarily determined by: (p. 381)
    a.   Genetic factors.
    b.   Environmental factors.
    c.   The interaction of genes and the environment.
    d.   A genetically determined reaction range.

9. The process in which a group of people throw out any ideas that come to mind, without evaluation or criticism, is called: (p. 382)
   a. Groupthink.
   b. Brainstorming.
   c. Creative cognition.
   d. Modifying attributes.

10. Gifted children usually grow up to: (p. 379)
    a. Become distinguished adults.
    b. Be ordinary people.
    c. Be mentally ill.
    d. Be jailed.

11. Prodigies and savants are similar in that they both have: (p. 376 & 379)
    a. High IQ scores.
    b. Low IQ scores.
    c. Islands of retardation.
    d. Islands of excellence.

12. Charlotte has a large vocabulary and detailed knowledge about space. However, she doesn't understand all of the facts she has. Charlotte probably: (p. 376)
    a. Is a savant.
    b. Has Williams syndrome.
    c. Has autism.
    d. Has fragile X syndrome.

13. Which of the following characteristics is NOT typical of creative people? (p. 379)
    a. Making snap decisions
    b. Having high intelligence
    c. Liking to work hard
    d. Having high self-esteem

14. The rate of mild mental retardation appears to: (p. 376)
    a. Be increasing.
    b. Be decreasing.
    c. Be holding steady.
    d. Vary from year to year.

15. In addition to having mental retardation, people with autism are likely to: (p. 377)
    a. Be very creative.
    b. Rock back and forth.
    c. Talk non-stop.
    d. Be paranoid.

COMPREHENSIVE PRACTICE TEST

True/False Questions

Circle TRUE or FALSE for each of the following statements.

1.   TRUE   FALSE   Heritability can explain group differences in intelligence. (p. 370)

2.   TRUE   FALSE   IQ scores are the best predictors of job success. (p. 384)

3.   TRUE   FALSE   Wechsler believed that there was too much emphasis on math skills on IQ tests. (p. 349)

4.   TRUE   FALSE   Men score higher than women on emotional intelligence tests. (p. 359)

5.   TRUE   FALSE   In the Western world, IQ scores have been increasing about 3 points every 10 years. (p. 359)

6.   TRUE   FALSE   Enrichment programs that teach people how to reorganize their thinking are more likely to increase IQ than are other programs. (p. 361)

7.   TRUE   FALSE   Brain size and intelligence are positively correlated. (p. 363)

8.   TRUE   FALSE   People with high IQs take longer in executing their decisions than do people with low IQs. (p. 364)

9.   TRUE   FALSE   Research indicates that testing bias is responsible for group differences in intelligence. (p. 372)

10. TRUE   FALSE   Down syndrome is more likely to happen in children of older mothers. (p. 377)

Multiple-Choice Questions

For each question, circle the best answer from the choices given.

1.   Jeannie is in her 70s. She finds that whereas she can reason about familiar situations well, she has trouble solving new types of problems. Jeannie has good _____ intelligence but poor _____ intelligence. (p. 354)
     a.   Crystallized; fluid
     b.   Fluid; crystallized
     c.   Analytical; practical
     d.   Practical; analytical

2. Which of the following is NOT one of Gardner's forms of multiple intelligence? (p. 355-356)
    a. Intrapersonal
    b. Emotional
    c. Bodily
    d. Logical-mathematical

3. Mikhail was his high school's valedictorian and had perfect SAT scores. However, he has a great deal of trouble in college because he can't seem to figure out the registration process or how to manage the campus buses. In terms of Sternberg's theory of multiple intelligences, Mikhail has great _____ but is lacking in _____ intelligence. (p. 357)
    a. Analytical; creative
    b. Analytical; practical
    c. Practical; analytical
    d. Practical; creative

4. Although Anjuli did not have the highest GPA of the students applying for the job of peer advisor, she was hired because her interview went so well. The interviewer felt that she had good insight into her own strengths and weaknesses, as well as those of other people. Anjuli probably has a high level of _____ intelligence. (p. 358)
    a. Practical
    b. Existential
    c. Emotional
    d. Analytical

5. A person's reaction range is: (p. 370)
    a. Determined by his genes.
    b. Determined by his environment.
    c. Determined by an interaction of genes and the environment.
    d. Determined by the proportion of shared to unshared environment.

6. The reason within-group differences cannot be generalized to between-group differences is that: (p. 370)
    a. Within-group differences are larger.
    b. Within-group differences are smaller.
    c. The individuals within a group may be influenced by different factors.
    d. The groups may be affected by different factors overall.

7. As environmental factors have gotten more similar, the average IQ difference between African Americans and White Americans: (p. 372)
    a. Has remained the same.
    b. Has actually widened.
    c. Has gotten smaller.
    d. Is still produced by biased testing.

8. According to the Flynn effect, average American IQ scores are: (p. 359)
   a. Increasing.
   b. Decreasing.
   c. Remaining the same.
   d. Increasing only for certain groups.

9. To be considered retarded, someone must have an IQ below _____; to be considered gifted, someone must have an IQ above: (pp. 376-377)
   a. 60; 150.
   b. 70; 120.
   c. 60; 135.
   d. 70; 135.

10. Retardation occurs in the majority of people who have which psychological disorder? (p. 377)
    a. Autism
    b. Schizophrenia
    c. Bipolar disorder
    d. Dysthymia

11. Which form of retardation involves genetic abnormalities, but is not inherited? (p. 377)
    a. Fragile X syndrome
    b. Down syndrome
    c. Autism
    d. Fetal alcohol syndrome

12. Compared to children of average intelligence, how would the social skills of gifted children be described? (p. 379)
    a. Equal
    b. Better
    c. Worse
    d. It depends on the IQ level.

13. The most widely supported model of creative thinking involves _____ stages. (p. 380)
    a. 2
    b. 3
    c. 4
    d. 5

14. Doing a logical proof involves _____ thinking; thinking of all the different ways in which you could pack to go on vacation involves _____ thinking. (pp. 380-381)
    a. Implicit; explicit
    b. Explicit; implicit
    c. Divergent; convergent
    d. Convergent; divergent

15. Creative people are: (p. 381)
    a. More flexible in their thinking.
    b. Motivated by extrinsic rewards.
    c. Less likely to be hardworking.
    d. More highly educated.

Essay Questions

Answer each of the following questions in the space provided.

1. If you were designing your own test of intelligence, what would it look like? Explain.

_____

_____

_____

_____

_____

_____

_____

_____

2. Is intelligence a single characteristic or a complex set of characteristics?

_____

_____

_____

_____

_____

_____

3. Clinical psychologists are sometimes asked to test children to assess their intelligence level, for placement in gifted programs. Often, they are asked to test the children after the children failed to meet the cutoff for the program based on their performance on a similar test in school. What would you say to a parent who approached a psychologist, asking to be re-tested? _____

_____

_____

_____

_____

_____

_____

_____

_____

4. Which of Gardner's types of intelligence are emphasized, rewarded, and nurtured in our culture? Why? Do you feel that American schools should do more to nurture the other types of intelligence? Which ones? Why?_____

_____

_____

_____

_____

_____

_____

_____

5. Your text discusses way to "boost" intelligence. Do you think there are also ways to boost <u>emotional</u> intelligence? How? Which do you think is more important – "book smarts" or emotional intelligence? Why?_____

_____

_____

_____

_____

_____

_____

_____

_____

6. What aspects of brain function underlie intelligence?_____

_____

_____

_____

_____

_____

7. How do the environment and genetics contribute to intelligence? _____

_____

_____

_____

_____

8. How can we interpret group differences in IQ? _____

_____

_____

_____

_____

9.   If you were asked to develop a "culture-fair" test of intelligence, what types of items would you include? Why? Could you develop a test that is culture fair not only for all races and socioeconomic groups in the United States, but also for people of other cultures (even third world)?_____

_____

10.   What is the relationship between intelligence and memory? Discuss._____

_____

11.   Do you believe that IQ tests measure how smart you are? Please explain._____

_____

12.   Do you think that intelligence needs to be measured at all? Why or why not? _____

_____

13.   If you could only have crystallized or fluid intelligence, but not both, which one would you choose? Why?_____

_____

14. Compare and contrast the methodologies used by Thurstone (and other psychometric researchers) and those used by Gardner. _____

_____

_____

_____

_____

_____

15. What are the characteristics of a creative individual? Discuss._____

_____

_____

_____

_____

_____

16. What is creativity? _____

_____

_____

_____

_____

_____

17. Why are some people more creative than others?_____

_____

_____

_____

_____

_____

18. How can creativity be enhanced? _____

_____

_____

_____

_____

_____

When You Are Finished: Puzzle It Out

Across

2. Boys do better on this type of task
4. Said there was one *g* and multiple *s*'s
11. Hormone implicated in spatial ability
12. People who have IQs of 135+
15. Type of studies used to study genetic roles
17. Ability to produce original, quality things
19. Score on an intelligence test
20. Cattell's problem-solving type of intelligence

Down

1. Upward trend in IQ over time
3. Said there are 8-9 intelligences
5. Environment created by person
6. Technique used to analyze IQ data
7. Most frequently used adult intelligence test
8. Purported cause of group IQ differences, not supported
9. Math genius with otherwise normal intelligence
10. Said there are 3 types of intelligence
13. Found seven primary mental abilities
14. Primary cause of mental retardation
16. Developed first IQ test
18. Name for Terman's gifted subjects

Puzzle created with Puzzlemaker at DiscoverySchool.com.

Chapter 10
Emotion and Motivation: Feeling and Striving

Before You Read . . .

How are you feeling right now: Happy? Excited? Bored? Angry? Why do you feel that way? In this chapter, you will gain an overview of emotion, ranging from basic emotions to more complex ones. You will also learn several theories of the causes of emotion, and the evidence that supports or refutes them. Of special interest will be the role of cognition in emotion. Two particular emotions, fear and happiness, are explored in detail.

Cultural norms, body language, and lie detection are part of the story. The chapter then moves to motivation, the needs and wants of humans and animals. The concepts of drives and incentives, being pushed and pulled toward certain events, are explained, as are the different needs of people. The needs for achievement and cognition are explained in greater detail. Lastly, the motivations of eating and sex are set out in separate sections, with the reasons why we eat and have sex discussed. Overeating and sexual orientation are covered in some detail.

Chapter Objectives

After reading this chapter, you will be able to:

♦ Name the different emotions.

♦ Understand what causes emotion.

♦ Explain how culture affects our emotional lives.

♦ Name the sources of motivation.

♦ Explain the differences between "needs" and wants" and how culture affects them.

♦ Explain the nature of sexual response.

♦ Understand what determines whether we are attracted to the same or opposite sex.

♦ Define "normal sexual behavior" and explain how culture affects our standards of normality.

As You Read . . . Term Identification

Make flashcards using the following terms as you go. Use the definitions in the margins of this chapter for help. If you write the definitions in your own words, though, you will remember them better!

Androgens	Heterosexual	Motivation
Basic emotions	Homeostatis	Needs
Bisexual	Homosexual	Need for achievement
Collectivist culture	Implicit motives	Nondeprived reward
Deprived reward	Incentives	Polygraph
Display rules	Individualist culture	Set point
Drives	Instincts	Sexual response cycle
Emotions	Learned helplessness	Transvestites
Estrogens	Metabolism	Wants
Facial feedback hypothesis	Misattribution of arousal	

As You Read . . . Questions and Exercises

Emotion: I Feel, Therefore I Am

Types of Emotions

Before reading this section, list below the various <u>distinct</u> **emotions** you believe individuals have.

_____
_____
_____
_____

What did **Ekman & Friesen** (1971) find when they showed the Caucasian facial expressions of emotion to members of a New Guinea tribe?_____
_____
_____
_____
_____
_____
_____
_____

What are the six **basic emotions** as outlined by Ekman (1984)?

- ♦ _____
- ♦ _____
- ♦ _____
- ♦ _____
- ♦ _____
- ♦ _____

Does your list above differ at all from Ekman's? How so? _____
_____
_____
_____
_____

Define **approach** and **withdrawal emotions**. What parts of the brain do these emotions activate?

Approach: _____
_____
_____

Withdrawal: _____
_____
_____

Complete the following paragraph, which contrasts the various theories of emotion.

The earliest theory of emotion, put forth by _____ and _____ argued that emotions arise *after* your body reacts – that different emotions cause different sets of bodily reactions. In 1929, Cannon and Bard argued that _____ and _____ occur in tandem, arising at the same time. In other words, arousal is arousal! The _____ theory, on the other hand, holds that we interpret situations differently, which gives rise to different emotions. But Joseph LeDoux (1996) argued that interpretation takes place only for emotions such as _____, not for other emotions such as _____, since these emotions arise from different parts of the brain.

Since the leading **theories of emotion** have been posited, evidence has been found to cast doubt on their veracity. For each of the theories below, indicate what evidence serves to refute it:

Theory	Evidence to refute
James-Lange	
Cannon-Bard	
Cognitive interpretation	

What is the **facial feedback hypothesis**? How can you use this in your daily life?_____
_____
_____
_____

What are the four important findings about **fear** that researchers have discovered?

♦ _____
_____
_____

♦ _____
_____
_____

♦ _____
_____

♦ _____
_____
_____

How do these four findings about **fear** support the following theories?

Theory	Support
James-Lange	
Cannon-Bard	
Cognitive	
LeDoux	

List the factors involved in **happiness** among Americans.

At the Level of the Group:

♦ _____
♦ _____
♦ _____
♦ _____

At the Level of the Person:

♦ _____
♦ _____

At the Level of the Brain:

♦ _____
♦ _____

Expressing Emotion: Letting It All Hang Out?

For the following situations, define what **display rules** are present:

Situation	Display Rules
A bar	
A funeral	
A classroom	
Thanksgiving dinner at home	
A football game	

Name some of the factors that make some people better able to read **nonverbal communication** than others:

♦ _____

♦ _____

♦ _____

How is **body language** involved in unwanted sexual encounters? Explain. _____

_____

_____

_____

_____

_____

_____

Can people **control their emotions**? Why is this important? _____

_____

_____

_____

_____

_____

_____

GO SURFING...

...at the following sites and take one of the road rage tests there:
♦   http://webhome.idirect.com/~kehamilt/rage.htm
♦   http://www.aaafoundation.org/quizzes/index.cfm?button=aggressive
♦   http://www.werner.com/home.cfm?page=roadRage.cfm
♦   http://li.commuter.com/articles/0107/cover.php
♦   http://www.roadrageiq.org/home.asp

What do these tests say about you? Do you **"let it all hang out"** on the road?_____

_____

_____

_____

If so, what are some ways that you could try to control your **road rage** in the future?_____

_____

_____

_____

Looking at Levels

People with antisocial personality disorder, by definition, feel no remorse for crimes they commit. What effect would this characteristic have on the use of **lie detector tests** for these individuals?

_____
_____
_____
_____
_____
_____
_____
_____
_____
_____

TRY PRACTICE TEST #1 NOW!
GOOD LUCK!

Motivation and Reward: Feeling Good

Getting Motivated: Sources and Theories of Motivation

Describe the focus of the following **theories of motivation**:

Theory	Focus
Instinct theory	
Evolutionary theory	
Drive theory	
Arousal theory	

What is the **drive** that motivates you to:

♦   Drink alcohol? _____
♦   Go to a party? _____
♦   Eat chocolate? _____
♦   Study for a test? _____

360

Graph and explain the **Yerkes-Dodson law**.

_____
_____
_____
_____

GO SURFING...

...to discover how much arousal you need in your life. Take the following test, at the following site:

♦   **Sensation Seeking Scale**
     http://www.bbc.co.uk/science/humanbody/mind/sensation/

What do the results of this scale say about your **need for arousal**? How do you see this need in your everyday life? How can you modify your life to meet the level of your needs for arousal?

_____
_____
_____
_____
_____
_____

Which of the following are **drive-related motivations**, and which are **incentive-related**?

Sex	drive-related	**OR**	incentive-related
Food	drive-related	**OR**	incentive-related
Praise	drive-related	**OR**	incentive-related
Money	drive-related	**OR**	incentive-related
Water	drive-related	**OR**	incentive-related

361

GO SURFING…

…to discover what the different scales say about your motivations:

♦   **Work and Family Orientation Questionnaire**
    http://www.rrcc-online.com/~psych/WorknFamQuest.htm
♦   **Desirability of Control Scale**
    http://www.rrcc-online.com/~psych/DesConScale.htm
♦   **Entrepreneur Test**
    http://www.liraz.com/webquiz.htm
♦   **Need for Cognition Scale**
    http://www.prenhall.com/divisions/hss/app/social/chap7_2.html#

Based on the results of these tests, what do you think **motivates** you? What doesn't? _____
_____
_____

The following is a list of **needs** as proposed by researchers. Given your results on the surveys above, rank-order them in terms of importance to you (i.e., "1" would indicate the need that is most important to you):

The need to be competent   _____
The need to be autonomous   _____
The need to have social approval   _____
The need to be dominant   _____
The need for affiliation   _____
The need to be powerful   _____
The need for closure   _____
The need to understand   _____
The need to maintain self-esteem   _____
The need to find the world
    benevolent   _____

Do you agree with the priorities established by this list or not? _____
_____
_____
_____
_____

How can you use knowledge of your **motivations** in everyday life?_____

_____

_____

_____

_____

List the seven needs as outlined by **Maslow**, from lowest to highest:

- ♦ _____
- ♦ _____
- ♦ _____
- ♦ _____
- ♦ _____
- ♦ _____
- ♦ _____

What evidence do we have that casts doubt on **Maslow's theory**? _____

_____

_____

_____

_____

_____

_____

_____

_____

People in **individualist cultures** have stronger needs for _____, but
they also _____.

Looking at Levels

How can **learned helplessness** explain why a woman would stay with her abusive husband, at the
levels of the brain, person, and group? Draw arrows to indicate how these events may interact.

The Brain	The Person	The Group

TRY PRACTICE TEST #2 NOW!
GOOD LUCK!

Hunger and Eating: Not Just About Fueling the Body

Eating Behavior: The Hungry Mind in the Hungry Body

There are two distinct brain systems involved in eating:

♦ **One system leads you to feel a need to eat.**
This feeling arises when your brain senses that one of two types of food molecules is too low:

 ♦ _____ or

 ♦ _____ .

♦ **The other system leads you to feel full.**
This feeling arises because of signals sent by the _____ in the _____ to the _____ of the brain.

What role does the **ventromedial hypothalamus** play in eating behaviors? _____
_____
_____
_____
_____

What role does learning play in **eating behaviors**? _____
_____
_____
_____

What effect do the following factors have on the size and/or timing of your **appetite**?

Factor	Effect
Opioids	
Changes in flavor, texture, color, shape of food	
Presence of other people	
Insulin	
Culture	
Memory	
The clock/time of day	

Overeating: When Enough is Not Enough

Using the words **set point** and **metabolism** explain why dieting can actually lead to eventual increases in weight rather than to decreases. _____

_____

_____

_____

_____

GO SURFING...

...to discover to find your current and ideal body mass index. Visit one of the following sites:
♦   **National Heart, Lung and Blood Institute**
        http://nhlbisupport.com/bmi/bmicalc.htm
♦   **Total Health Dynamics**
        http://www.totalhealthdynamics.com/bodymass.htm

The maximum recommended BMI is 24.9. What is your BMI? _____

Use the charts on the website to calculate how many pounds you would have to gain or lose to reach a BMI of 24.9. How many? _____

What is the best way that you could gain or lose this weight? _____

_____

_____

_____

_____

_____

For each reason given below, provide the various explanations for **obesity**:

Reason	Explanation
Psychodynamic Theory	
Serotonin	
Ob Gene	
"Fidget Factor"	
Environmental Factors	
Range-of-reaction	

Looking at Levels

Have you ever been on a **diet** or been close to someone on a diet? How did the diet appear to affect you or the individual, at the **levels of the brain, person, and group**? Use arrows to indicate how events at the different levels may have interacted.

The Brain	The Person	The Group

TRY PRACTICE TEST #3 NOW!
GOOD LUCK!

Sex: Not Just About Having Babies

Sexual Behavior: A Many-Splendored Thing

Would you volunteer to be in a **study of sexual behavior**? Why or why not? _____
_____
_____
_____
_____

How are **volunteers in sexual behavior studies** different from non-volunteers?_____
_____
_____
_____
_____

What does this mean for the **validity** of the studies? _____
_____
_____
_____
_____

Fill in the arrows, indicating a comprehensive description of the **sexual response cycle**.

```
┌──────────────┐        ┌──────────────┐        ┌──────────────┐
│              │   →    │              │   →    │              │
│              │        │              │        │              │
└──────────────┘        └──────────────┘        └──────────────┘
                                                        │
                                                        ↓
                                                ┌──────────────┐
                                                │              │
                                                │              │
                                                └──────────────┘
                                                        │
                                                        ↓
                                                ┌──────────────┐
                                                │              │
                                                │              │
                                                └──────────────┘
                                                        │
                                                        ↓
                                                ┌──────────────┐
                                                │              │
                                                │              │
                                                └──────────────┘
```

Hormones are controlled by the _____, which in turn is controlled by the _____. Hormones are secreted into the bloodstream by the _____ .

Testosterone is one male hormone. The male hormones, _____, have the following effects:

♦ _____

♦ _____

Female hormones, or _____, cause many characteristics including:

◆ _____
◆ _____

What type of **hormone(s)** do you have in your body?_____
_____

Women's **sex hormones** change over the course of their menstrual cycles. This has the following effects:

◆ _____
   _____

◆ _____
   _____

◆ _____
   _____

◆ _____
   _____

What **stimuli** turn men on the most?_____
What **stimuli** turn women on the most? _____

Describe the different **motives** that people have for having sex, including the two dimensions described by Cooper and colleagues. _____
_____
_____
_____

The evolutionary theory suggests that men should be more interested in short-term sex and less particular about mates; females, who are typically very invested in nurturing and raising children, should have opposite preferences.

Sexual Orientation: More Than a Choice

What is the evidence that **sexual orientation** has a biological basis?

◆ _____
   _____

◆ _____
   _____

◆ _____
   _____

What evidence is there that the environment may play a role in **sexual orientation**?

◆ _____
 _____
◆ _____
 _____
 _____
 _____

What's Normal?

What **cultural norms** govern sexuality in the United States today? _____
_____
_____
_____
_____

Can you think of any behaviors that would be considered **abnormal** in today's society? Why would they be considered abnormal? _____
_____
_____
_____
_____
_____
_____

What we once called *impotence* is now called _____, and what we once called *frigidity* is now called _____.

Looking at Levels

Describe why homophobic men might be **sexually aroused** by homosexual films, at the levels of the brain, the person, and the group. Draw arrows to indicate how events at the different levels may interact.

The Brain	The Person	The Group

TRY PRACTICE TEST #4 NOW!
GOOD LUCK!

After You Read . . . Thinking Back

1. In Chapter 2, you learned about how people sense and perceive. How do you think people's emotions affect what they sense and perceive?_____
    _____
    _____
    _____
    _____

2. How is classical conditioning involved in emotions? _____
    _____
    _____
    _____
    _____

3. How does emotion affect memory? _____
    _____
    _____
    _____
    _____

4. Does memory also affect emotion? If so, how?_____
    _____
    _____
    _____
    _____

5. Is there a relationship between intelligence scores and motivation? If so, what types of motivation? _____
    _____
    _____
    _____
    _____

6. How is learning involved in motivation? _____
    _____
    _____
    _____
    _____

7. What other aspects of emotions, besides control of them, are involved in emotional intelligence? _____
    _____
    _____
    _____
    _____

After You Read . . . Thinking Ahead

1. How do you think children might develop emotional control?_____
   _____
   _____
   _____
   _____

2. How do you think they develop knowledge of display rules? _____
   _____
   _____
   _____
   _____

3. Do you think emotions affect health? If so, in a positive or negative way? _____
   _____
   _____
   _____
   _____

4. How do you know when emotions are normal versus when they have become a disorder
   (e.g., depression)?_____
   _____
   _____
   _____
   _____

5. How might knowing whether or not cognition precedes emotion assist a therapist in treating
   a psychological disorder? _____
   _____
   _____
   _____
   _____

6. How do our social groups influence our happiness?_____
   _____
   _____
   _____
   _____

7. What can parents do to motivate children without pressuring them? _____
   _____
   _____
   _____
   _____

After You Read . . . Practice Tests

PRACTICE TEST #1:
EMOTION: I FEEL, THEREFORE I AM

True/False Questions
Circle TRUE or FALSE for each of the following statements.

1. TRUE   FALSE   Money can buy happiness. (p. 400)

2. TRUE   FALSE   Cultural enrichment makes everyone happy. (p. 400)

3. TRUE   FALSE   Westerners focus on external evaluation as a source of happiness. (p. 401)

4. TRUE   FALSE   Married people are happier than unmarried people. (p. 401)

5. TRUE   FALSE   In Western countries, assertive people are happier than unassertive people. (p. 401)

6. TRUE   FALSE   Surprise is one of the six basic emotions. (p. 392)

7. TRUE   FALSE   It is impossible to hate and love someone at the same time. (p. 393)

8. TRUE   FALSE   Once you learn to fear an object, you may always fear it. (p. 398)

9. TRUE   FALSE   The amygdala responds only to negative emotions. (p. 399)

10. TRUE   FALSE   Emotions can be associated with single brain parts, although the parts differ for each emotion. (p. 399)

Multiple-Choice Questions
For each question, circle the best answer from the choices given.

1. Which of the following is <u>not</u> a basic emotion, according to Ekman? (p. 392)
    a. Love
    b. Happiness
    c. Fear
    d. Surprise

2. People with more activation in their left frontal lobe tend to be _____ in comparison to people with more activation in their right frontal lobe. (p. 401)
   a. More guilt-ridden
   b. More negative generally
   c. More likely to have intense rage episodes
   d. Happier

3. According to William James and Carl Lange: (p. 394)
   a. Bodily reactions cause emotions to arise.
   b. Emotions happen first, causing us to act in certain ways.
   c. Bodily reactions and emotions occur simultaneously.
   d. We *think* about the situation before we experience emotions.

4. The Cannon-Bard theory of emotion holds that: (p. 395)
   a. Bodily reactions cause emotions to arise.
   b. Emotions happen first, causing us to act in certain ways.
   c. Bodily reactions and emotions occur simultaneously.
   d. We *think* about the situation before we experience emotions.

5. Joseph LeDoux argued that: (p. 395)
   a. Bodily reactions cause emotions to arise.
   b. Emotions happen first, causing us to act in certain ways.
   c. Cognition always precedes the experience of emotion.
   d. Cognition precedes some emotions, but not all.

6. The fact that many emotions are accompanied by distinct patterns of physiological arousal casts doubt on the _____ theory of emotion. (p. 396)
   a. James-Lange
   b. Cognitive
   c. Cannon-Bard
   d. LeDoux

7. According to the facial feedback hypothesis, people who walk around with frowns on their faces: (p. 396)
   a. Make others feel unhappy.
   b. Are *making* themselves unhappy.
   c. Are clinically depressed.
   d. Are more stressed than others.

8. Westerners focus on _____ when asked about the sources of happiness. (p. 401)
   a. Money and prestige
   b. Achievement and internal evaluation
   c. Interpersonal interactions
   d. Intelligence and external evaluation

9.	Which of the following American people is most likely to be happy? (p. 401)
	a.	Martha, who is married
	b.	Paul, who is poor
	c.	Nancy, who is nonassertive
	d.	Ollie, who is overweight

10.	Which of the following statements about gender differences in emotional expression is FALSE? (p. 403)
	a.	Women are more expressive than men.
	b.	Men are more expansive than women.
	c.	Women can register nonverbal signs of happiness better than men.
	d.	Women can register nonverbal signs of anger better than men.

PRACTICE TEST #2:
MOTIVATION AND REWARD

Multiple-Choice Questions

For each question, circle the best answer from the choices given.

1. A(n) _____ is an inherited tendency to produce organized and unalterable responses to particular stimuli. (p. 407)
   a. Insight
   b. Motive
   c. Inclination
   d. Instinct

2. Which of the following could not be easily explained by Maslow's theory: (p. 413)
   a. The fact that Stephania harbored Jews during World War II, despite the enormous personal risk to herself.
   b. The fact that 16-year-old Chris spent more time trying to fit in to the high school scene than learning his lessons.
   c. The fact that Jean divorced her emotionally abusive husband, despite their many similar intellectual interests and the fact that he cognitively stimulated her.
   d. The fact that Irving, who lived in the inner city, joined a gang to feel protected, even though he knew he was jeopardizing his future.

3. The process of maintaining a steady physiological state is called: (p. 408)
   a. Drive maintenance.
   b. Heterostasis.
   c. Homeostasis.
   d. Motive maintenance.

4. The Yerkes-Dodson law states that: (p. 409)
   a. We perform best when we are at an intermediate level of arousal.
   b. We perform best when we are at a high level of arousal.
   c. We perform best when we are at a low level of arousal.
   d. The optimal level of arousal for performance depends upon the individual.

5. An activity that is desirable for its own sake is said to be: (p. 410)
   a. Extrinsically motivating.
   b. Imminently motivating.
   c. Intrinsically motivating.
   d. Expectantly motivating.

6. When people are happily anticipating an event, what part of their brains are activated? (p. 410)
   a. Pituitary gland
   b. Hypothalamus
   c. Frontal lobes
   d. Hippocampus

7. People who have a high need for achievement attribute their successes to _____, and their failures to: (p. 412)
    a. Good luck; bad luck.
    b. Personal characteristics; environmental circumstances.
    c. Outside circumstances; bad luck.
    d. Personal characteristics; personal characteristics.

8. According to Hall and Nougaim (1968), the longer a need is satisfied: (p. 414)
    a. The more important it becomes.
    b. The more we want other things.
    c. The less important it becomes.
    d. The less we want other things.

9. What is one negative effect of being raised in an individualist culture? (p. 414)
    a. People in individualist cultures have lower needs for achievement than people in collectivist cultures.
    b. People in individualist cultures have greater needs for dominance than people in collectivist cultures.
    c. People in individualist cultures don't live as long as people in collectivist cultures.
    d. People in individualist cultures don't like themselves as much as people in collectivist cultures.

10. Learned helplessness may lower the levels of _____ in the brain. (pp. 415-416)
    a. Dopamine
    b. Serotonin
    c. GABA
    d. Endorphins

11. Blocking dopamine can disrupt: (p. 410)
    a. Classical conditioning.
    b. Positive reinforcement.
    c. Punishment.
    d. Cognitive learning.

12. Which of the following is NOT a criticism of Maslow's theory? (p. 414)
    a. There is not much evidence that needs are organized in a hierarchy.
    b. The importance of needs seems to differ across cultures.
    c. This theory can't explain why people do dangerous things to save others.
    d. It is impossible to meet all of these needs and become a self-actualized person.

13. Leanne likes to bungee jump and sky-dive. Leanne is probably highly motivated by a need: (p. 409)
    a. For cognition.
    b. For arousal.
    c. To be unique.
    d. For achievement.

14. When a person is not deprived, the pleasure of a nondeprived reward comes primarily from: (p. 411)
    a.   The brain stem.
    b.   Dopamine.
    c.   Serotonin.
    d.   The hypothalamus.

15. Seligman found that when dogs were put in a cage in which they received shocks and from which they could not escape, the dogs: (pp. 415-416)
    a.   Eventually gave up trying to escape, even when they could have escaped.
    b.   Eventually died.
    c.   Always associated cages with shocks.
    d.   Became aggressive.

PRACTICE TEST #3:
HUNGER AND EATING

True/False Questions

Circle TRUE or FALSE for each of the following statements.

1.   TRUE   FALSE   Obese people have weaker personalities than trim people. (p. 420)

2.   TRUE   FALSE   Obesity is defined as being 30% above ideal body weight. (p. 420)

3.   TRUE   FALSE   Insulin increases the level of food in the blood. (p. 418)

4.   TRUE   FALSE   People who fidget more may be less likely to be obese. (p. 421)

5.   TRUE   FALSE   When people cut their caloric intake dramatically, they are more able to focus their attention. (p. 422)

6.   TRUE   FALSE   When the ventromedial hypothalamus is damaged, animals begin overeating carbohydrates. (p. 417)

7.   TRUE   FALSE   Feeling full depends on the level of food molecules in the blood. (p. 417)

8.   TRUE   FALSE   The set point is relatively constant throughout life. (p. 419)

Multiple-Choice Questions

For each question, circle the best answer from the choices given.

1.   Two systems in the brain regulate hunger: one system leads us to_____ and another system leads us to: (p. 416)
   a.   Feel hungry; feel satiated.
   b.   Be choosy about foods; feel satiated.
   c.   Feel hungry; feel bored.
   d.   Feel satiated; seek food for comfort.

2. When you first begin eating food that tastes good, _____ is (are) released. (p. 418)
   a. Opioids
   b. Protein molecules
   c. Glucose
   d. Serotonin

3. After neurons in the lateral hypothalamus stop firing in response to a food you have eaten a lot of, they will: (p. 418)
   a. Require a great deal of time to "recharge."
   b. Respond again vigorously to the same food after 24 hours.
   c. Still be stimulated to respond by other foods.
   d. Send out signals to suppress your appetite.

4. Even the thought of food can cause the pancreas to secrete _____, which may lead to feelings of hunger. (p. 418)
   a. Serotonin
   b. Dopamine
   c. Insulin
   d. Opiods

5. The best method of adjusting your set point is to: (p. 420)
   a. Eat fewer fats.
   b. Exercise.
   c. Eat fewer carbohydrates.
   d. Sleep.

6. Almost _____ of Americans are obese. (p. 420)
   a. One-fourth
   b. One-half
   c. One-third
   d. Two-thirds

7. Which of the following is NOT one of Rozin's (1986, 1996) findings? (p. 419)
   a. Once a food came into contact with something unpleasant, most people kept away from the food.
   b. People believe that "you are what you eat."
   c. Long-lasting taste aversions are formed through classical conditioning.
   d. Many people incorrectly believe that fat and salt are harmful even at trace levels.

8. According to psychodynamic theorists, people are obese because: (p. 420)
   a. They are storing fat for leaner times.
   b. They have cognitive distortions making them believe that they are more attractive when heavy.
   c. They overeat when stressed, as a defense mechanism.
   d. They have learned to associate food and love.

9. Which of the following factors supports the idea that differences in weight may be partially attributed to temperamental differences? (p. 421)
    a. "The fidget factor"
    b. The ob gene
    c. The neurotransmitter serotonin
    d. The release of leptin

10. A hormone called leptin may affect eating by: (p. 421)
    a. Signaling the brain that the amounts of stored fat and food intake are adequate.
    b. Decreasing fidgeting.
    c. Turning off the stress hormone cortisol.
    d. Converting excess fat in food to body fat, instead of energy.

PRACTICE TEST #4:
SEX

True/False Questions
Circle TRUE or FALSE for each of the following statements.

1.   TRUE   FALSE   Researchers found that Hispanic women were more open about sex than African-American women. (p. 423)

2.   TRUE   FALSE   Men stay aroused longer than women during sex. (p. 424)

3.   TRUE   FALSE   Most men can have multiple orgasms. (p. 423)

4.   TRUE   FALSE   If a man is worried about it, penis size *does* matter. (p. 424)

5.   TRUE   FALSE   Bisexual men tend to become heterosexual over time. (p. 428)

6.   TRUE   FALSE   Programs to train homosexuals to be heterosexual have failed. (p. 428)

7.   TRUE   FALSE   A small part of the hypothalamus is larger in homosexual men than in heterosexual men. (p. 428)

8.   TRUE   FALSE   There may be different biological bases for male and female homosexuality. (pp. 428-429)

9.   TRUE   FALSE   Homosexuality may be inherited on the X chromosome. (p. 429)

10.   TRUE   FALSE   Homosexuality is a psychological disorder. (p. 428)

Multiple-Choice Questions
For each question, circle the best answer from the choices given.

1. The second stage of the sexual response cycle is: (p. 424)
   a. Orgasm.
   b. Plateau.
   c. Excitement.
   d. Resolution.

2. Which of the following was NOT a conclusion of Masters and Johnson? (p. 424)
   a. Men and women follow the same stages of the sexual response cycle.
   b. Women are aroused more slowly than men.
   c. Women can have multiple orgasms, but men cannot.
   d. Women are more likely to have homosexual encounters than men.

3. Hormones _____ affect our physical characteristics and _____ affect our thoughts and behaviors. (p. 424)
   a. Directly; directly
   b. Indirectly; indirectly
   c. Directly; indirectly
   d. Indirectly; directly

4. Homosexuality is probably the result of: (p. 428)
   a. Inadequate parenting.
   b. Childhood sexual abuse.
   c. Extreme fear of the opposite sex.
   d. A biological predisposition.

5. Men have: (p. 424)
   a. Androgens.
   b. Estrogens.
   c. Testosterone.
   d. Androgens and estrogens.

6. When injected with testosterone, men who had difficulty having erections: (p. 425)
   a. Experienced more rigidity of the penis during sex.
   b. Ejaculated more often.
   c. Became more aggressive.
   d. Were less satisfied with sex.

7. Oxytocin is produced: (pp. 425-426)
   a. By the hypothalamus.
   b. After orgasm.
   c. In men only.
   d. In women only.

8. Which of the following statements best summarizes the research on arousing stimuli? (p. 426)
   a. Men are more influenced by visual stimuli and women, by odor.
   b. Men are more influenced by odor and women, by visual stimuli.
   c. Men and women are equally influenced by both visual stimuli and odor.
   d. Neither visual stimuli nor odor impacts sexual arousal.

9. Matt has sexual intercourse frequently with casual partners. According to evolutionary theory, this is probably because: (p. 427)
   a. Matt is less particular than women about his mates, since he will invest less than women will in nurturing and raising children.
   b. Matt's friends are also having the same types of relationships.
   c. Like most men, Matt does not want to be in a long-term stable relationship.
   d. Matt is trying to prove his heterosexuality to himself.

10. People with androgen insensitivity syndrome: (pp. 432-433)
    a. Are gay.
    b. Like to dress as the opposite sex.
    c. Should have been males but, as fetuses, became female because of a genetic mutation.
    d. Look like men.

COMPREHENSIVE PRACTICE TEST

True/False Questions

Circle TRUE or FALSE for each of the following statements.

1.   (TRUE)   FALSE   Blind people exhibit facial expressions they have never observed. (p. 391)

2.   TRUE   FALSE   "Putting on a happy face" can make one feel happier. (p. 396)

3.   TRUE   FALSE   People who are married are happier than people who are not. (p. 400)

4.   TRUE   FALSE   Women can register nonverbal signs of anger better than men can. (p. 403)

5.   TRUE   FALSE   It is impossible to voluntarily dampen emotional responses. (p. 404)

6.   TRUE   FALSE   Chinese children are better able to detect basic emotions than Australian children. (p. 403)

7.   TRUE   FALSE   The best way to adjust your set point is to eat less. (p. 419)

8.   TRUE   FALSE   Sexual orientation is a choice. (p. 428)

9.   TRUE   FALSE   There are no environmental factors involved in sexual orientation. (p. 429)

10.   TRUE   FALSE   Fetishes are considered psychological disorders. (p. 431)

Multiple-Choice Questions

For each question, circle the best answer from the choices given.

1.   The Fore in the New Guinea tribe that were interviewed by Ekman and Friesen in 1971 had the most difficulty distinguishing: (p. 391)
     a.   Fear from surprise.
     b.   Anger from sadness.
     c.   Joy from happiness.
     d.   Disgust from shame.

2. In general, the _____ tends to be more active when people experience approach emotions such as love and happiness. (p. 393)
    a. Right frontal lobe
    b. Ventromedial hypothalamus
    (c) Left frontal lobe
    d. Lateral hypothalamus

3. Walter Cannon's criticism of the James-Lange theory of emotion was: (p. 395)
    (a.) That people with spinal cord injuries still report feeling emotions.
    b. That people can experience both withdrawal and approach emotions at the same time.
    c. Behavior clearly comes before the experience of emotion.
    (d.) That emotions are instantaneous, but it takes seconds for the body to become aroused.

4. At least 20 muscles in your face are used for: (p. 396)
    a. Chewing.
    (b.) Forming facial expressions.
    c. Talking.
    d. Breathing.

5. The failure to interpret signs of bodily arousal correctly, leading to the experience of inappropriate emotions, is called: (p. 398)
    (a.) Misattribution of arousal.
    b. Misinterpretation of signals.
    c. Misattribution of emotion.
    d. Misinterpretation of emotion.

6. People with damage to the amygdala: (p. 399)
    a. Cannot feel happiness.
    (b.) Cannot recognize fear or anger in others.
    c. Feel emotions more intensely than others do.
    d. Are emotionally "dead" to all feelings.

7. Researchers found that women who walked _____ were rated as more likely to be sexually assaulted than women who walked smoothly and confidently. (p. 404)
    (a.) With their heads down
    b. With short, mincing steps
    c. With long, exaggerated strides
    (d.) Either B or C

8. Much of Freud's theory relied on the assumption that man's urges are: (p. 407)
    (a.) Instinctual.
    b. Need-motivated.
    c. Homeostatic.
    d. Related to an aversion to pain.

9. Drives _____ and incentives: (p. 408)
   a. Pull; push.
   b. Approach; withdraw.
   c. Push; pull.
   d. Withdraw; approach.

10. A meta-analysis revealed that needs for achievement that are _____ are most predictive of actual success. (p. 413)
   a. Extrinsic
   b. Implicit
   c. Intrinsic
   d. Explicit

11. The *appetizer effect* arises when _____ are released. (p. 418)
   a. Opioids
   b. Insulin molecules
   c. Neurotransmitters
   d. Fatty acids

12. Overeating may cause one's set point to: (p. 419)
   a. Become higher.
   b. Fluctuate widely.
   c. Become lower.
   d. None of the above; set point is stable.

13. Which of the following does NOT describe participants who are willing to complete sex surveys? (p. 423)
   a. They have had more sexual experience that people not willing to participate.
   b. They are more inclined to seek out sensation and excitement than people not willing to participate.
   c. They are less socially conforming than people not willing to participate.
   d. They are more extroverted and outgoing than people not willing to participate.

14. Hormones produce their effects: (p. 424-425)
   a. Because they are released into the bloodstream.
   b. By triggering receptors on neurons and other types of cells.
   c. Because they lead people to want to act in certain ways.
   d. All of the above.

15. Studies of bisexual men have shown that many of them tend to become _____ over time. (p. 428)
   a. More heterosexually inclined
   b. Less interested in sex
   c. More homosexually inclined
   d. More interested in sex

16. Which of the following is an example of a deprived reward? (p. 411)
    a. Having a big bottle of water after exercising hard
    b. Eating a piece of chocolate cake for your birthday
    c. Working hard to win your parents' praise, which is rarely given
    d. Bungee-jumping because you have been working hard at a boring job for months

17. Sexual abnormality is influenced by: (p. 430-432)
    a. Culture.
    b. The person.
    c. The relationship in which it is expressed.
    d. All of the above.

18. Some of the difficulties associated with studying sexuality include: (p. 423-424)
    a. A lack of statistical measures to analyze such data.
    b. People may lie about sexual matters.
    c. The impossibility of using observational measures.
    d. A lack of potential research questions on the topic.

19. Which of the following would be most likely to be predicted by an evolutionary psychologist? (p. 427)
    a. Men are more interested in short-term sexual encounters than women.
    b. Women are more upset than men at the idea of their mate being sexually involved with someone else.
    c. Men and women are equally as interested in having a long-term stable relationship.
    d. Men and women value similar characteristics in potential mates.

20. Sexual disorders may arise because of: (p. 431)
    a. Preoccupation with personal problems.
    b. Fears about the consequences of sex.
    c. Anxiety about performance.
    d. All of the above.

Essay Questions

Answer the following questions in the space provided.

1. What evidence do we have that the James-Lange theory of emotion is incorrect? _____
   _____
   _____
   _____
   _____
   _____
   _____
   _____
   _____

2.   Why are some people generally happy and others aren't?_____
_____
_____
_____
_____
_____
_____
_____
_____

3.   What role may the Yerkes-Dodson law play in your performance on an exam? _____
_____
_____
_____
_____
_____
_____

4.   If putting on a happy face can make one have a rosier outlook on life, do you think that
putting on a sad face can make one have a negative view on life? Think of people you know
who are "happy-go-lucky" and others who are always "down-in-the-mouth." How much of
their attitude might be attributed to their facial features? _____
_____
_____
_____
_____
_____
_____
_____
_____
_____
_____
_____

5.   Why might people from cultures where the expression of emotions is downplayed be better
able to read others' emotional expressions? Do you think that emotionally expressive
individuals are less sensitive to others' emotional cues? Why or why not?
_____
_____
_____
_____
_____
_____
_____
_____
_____

6. What factors might lead each individual to have a different hierarchy of motives? Think of your own hierarchy of motives. Is it similar to your parents'? To your siblings'? Have your parents or peers encouraged or discouraged certain motives? What role has your culture played? Have your motives changed over time? Why? How do you suspect they will change in the future? _____

    _____
    _____
    _____
    _____
    _____
    _____
    _____
    _____
    _____
    _____
    _____

7. Consider a perplexing phenomenon observed in this country. On the one hand, we appear to be increasingly weight-oriented: there are diet pills on the market, dieting books, a plethora of health clubs, etc. On the other hand, we are a very overweight culture: we love to "super-size" everything! Why the inconsistency? Are there two types of people: those who diet and those who super-size? Do you think the motives of health-conscious people are different from the motives of less healthy individuals? Why?_____

    _____
    _____
    _____
    _____
    _____
    _____
    _____
    _____
    _____
    _____
    _____
    _____

8. According to your text, homosexuality was once classified as a psychological disorder, but was removed from the classification manual after a poll of the members of the American Psychological Association in 1973. What does this tell you about how mental disorders are defined? What factors do you think led to the removal of homosexuality from the classification manual?_____

    _____
    _____
    _____
    _____
    _____
    _____

9.   How does culture influence the emotions that people feel and how they display them?

_____

_____

_____

_____

_____

_____

_____

_____

10.   Develop your own, comprehensive theory of motivation. _____

_____

_____

_____

_____

_____

_____

_____

_____

_____

_____

_____

When You Are Finished . . . Puzzle It Out

Across

1. Maintaining a steady state
7. A draw toward a goal
9. Internal imbalance pushing toward a goal
12. Proposed hierarchy of motivation
17. Female hormones
18. Emotions that are generally positive
20. Motive that is unconscious

Puzzle created with Puzzlemaker at DiscoverySchool.com.

Down

2. Being 20% above ideal weight
3. Highest of Maslow's levels
4. Rules about showing emotions
5. Male hormones
6. Arises from lack of requirement
8. Proposed most accepted emotion theory
10. Discovered basic emotions
11. Hormone that stimulates fat storage
13. Person attracted to both sexes
14. Turns goals into incentives
15. Commonly known as a lie detector
16. Body weight easiest to maintain
19. Number of basic emotions

Chapter 11
Personality: Vive la Difference!

Before You Read...

Are you the same person with your parents as you are with your best friend? How are you the same or different? In this chapter, you will learn about personality, including how and why it changes. You will also learn more about how different types of personalities can be described, and how personality is measured.

In addition, you will apply the three levels of analysis to personality. As you will see, personality has its roots in genetics, but is also affected by a variety of personal characteristics. You will learn how psychodynamic theorists, humanistic psychologists, and cognitive psychologists propose that personal characteristics influence personality. Finally, you will review some of the environmental factors that may affect personality, including birth order, peer influences, and culture.

Chapter Objectives

After reading this chapter, you should be able to:

♦ Define personality, and describe the roles of traits and situations in personality.

♦ Describe the number of dimensions in different models of personality.

♦ Explain the different ways that personality can be measured, and the different pros and cons of each of these methods.

♦ Describe the role of genetics in personality.

♦ Explain and critique Freud's view of personality, including the three parts of personality, the stages of development, and defense mechanisms.

♦ Summarize the humanistic theory of personality.

♦ Discuss the cognitive view of personality.

♦ Discuss the role of family, peers, birth order, gender, and culture on personality.

As You Read. . .Term Identification

Make flashcards using the following terms as you go. Use the definitions in the margins of this chapter for help. If you write the definitions in your own words, though, you will remember them better!

Activity
Archetype
"Big Five"
Castration anxiety
Defense mechanism
Ego
Emotionality
Expectancies
Flow
Id
Impulsivity
Inferiority complex
Interactionism
Locus of control
Minnesota Multiphasic Personality Inventory-
    2 (MMPI-2)
Neurosis

Personality
Personality inventory
Projective test
Psychological determinism
Psychosexual stages
Reciprocal determinism
Repression
Rorschach test
Self-actualization
Self-efficacy
Situationism
Sociability
Social desirability
Superego
Temperament
Unconditional positive regard

As You Read. . .Questions and Exercises

What is Personality?

Personality is a _____ set of characteristics that people display _____ and _____ and that distinguish individuals from each other.

Personality traits are consistent characteristics exhibited in different situations. Name some of your personality characteristics that you think are consistent:

- ♦ _____
- ♦ _____
- ♦ _____
- ♦ _____
- ♦ _____

Other theorists say that personality is largely determined by **situations**. Think of a characteristic that you display in some situations, but not in others. Explain. What determines whether or not you display this characteristic? _____

_____

_____

_____

_____

_____

_____

_____

Interactionism is a synthesis of the traditional trait view and **situationism**. There are two major ways that personalities can affect their situations. Provide an example of each of these ways in your own life.

#1   People choose their situations.

_____

_____

_____

_____

#2   People find opportunities to create their environments.

_____

_____

_____

_____

GO SURFING...

...to learn more about your personality. Take a web version of the **NEO-PI-R**, which is used to measure the **Big Five** or the **Five-Factor Model**. It is online at:
- http://www.outofservice.com/bigfive/
- http://cac.psu.edu/~j5j/test/ipipneo1.htm

How did you score on each of the following five **superfactors**:

- **Extraversion:** _____
- **Neuroticism:** _____
- **Agreeableness:** _____
- **Conscientiousness:** _____
- **Openness:** _____

List some of the **traits** that contribute to each of these **superfactors**:

- ◆ **Extraversion:** _____

- ◆ **Neuroticism:** _____

- ◆ **Agreeableness:** _____

- ◆ **Conscientiousness:** _____

- ◆ **Openness:** _____

Now, read this list of traits to a friend and ask how he or she thinks you would score on each **superfactor**. Write his or her predictions below:

- ◆ **Extraversion:** _____
- ◆ **Neuroticism:** _____
- ◆ **Agreeableness:** _____
- ◆ **Conscientiousness:** _____
- ◆ **Openness:** _____

How did your friend's observations compare with your results? Why do you think he or she was so accurate (or inaccurate)? Discuss. _____
_____
_____
_____
_____

Below are lists of the five **superfactors** of the **Five-Factor Model** and **Eysenck**'s three superfactors. Draw lines between the factors that are similar to each other.

Five-Factor Model

Extraversion

Neuroticism

Agreeableness

Conscientiousness

Openness

Eysenck's Three Superfactors

Extraversion

Neuroticism

Psychoticism

Name two problems with the **superfactors** approach to personality:

◆ _____

◆ _____
_____

List the pros and cons of using **self-report measures** (like personality inventories) to measure personality.

Pros	Cons

Do you think that personality can be revealed through people's interpretations of inkblots, as in the **Rorschach test**? Why or why not?_____
_____
_____

Looking at Levels

Consider again the results of the personality test you took online. How do factors at the **three levels** affect your personality, as reflected by this test? What evidence do you have that genetic factors are at play in your personality? How might these genetic factors have affected personal characteristics (such as your thoughts) and group-level factors? List the evidence for factors at each level below. Draw arrows indicating how the factors may interact

The Brain	The Person	The Group

TRY PRACTICE TEST #1 NOW!
GOOD LUCK!

The Brain: The Personality Organ

In the table below, indicate whether the following behaviors would be indicative of arousal in the **extraversion**, **neuroticism**, or **psychoticism systems of the brain**:

Description	Extraversion	Neuroticism	Psychoticism
Many phobias			
Criminality			
Bungee-jumping			
Schizophrenia			
Easily saddened			
Likes loud parties			

CALL...

...a parent or someone who knew you when you were young. Ask him or her to describe what you were like at age 3. Write his or her comments below. Be sure to ask specifically about the following dimensions:

♦ **Your vigor** (intensity of activity):_____
_____

♦ **Your tempo** (speed of activity): _____
_____

♦ **Your sociability** (preference of being with others):_____
_____

♦ **Your emotionality** (inclination to be physiologically aroused in emotional situations):
_____
_____

♦ **Your impulsivity** (propensity to respond to stimuli immediately):_____
_____

♦ **Other observations:**_____
_____
_____
_____

How are these dimensions of temperament similar to the **Big Five factors** of personality?

_____

_____

_____

_____

_____

_____

Compare your parent's observations with the results from the online personality test you took earlier and from your friend's rating of your personality. How similar or dissimilar are they?_____

_____

_____

_____

What reasons can you think of for these similarities and/or dissimilarities?_____

_____

_____

_____

Longitudinal studies have found correlations between children's temperaments at age 3 and their personalities at age 18. Is this true of you? Why or why not? _____

_____

_____

_____

GO SURFING...

...to find out whether you are high or low in **sensation seeking**. Online tests can be found at:

♦   http://www.bbc.co.uk/science/humanbody/mind/sensation/
♦   http://home.hkstar.com/~ttyu/psytests/sen.htm
♦   http://www.dushkin.com/connectext/psy/ch09/survey9.mhtml

Are you high or low in **sensation seeking**?_____

Would these tests suggest that you like or don't like to take physical risks?_____

_____

_____

Do you or don't you like to take physical risks? _____

_____

There is evidence that **sensation seeking** is genetic. Do any of your biological relatives share your tendency to seek or avoid risks? Discuss._____

_____

_____

_____

What does **MISTRA** stand for? What is it? Explain. _____

_____

_____

_____

MISTRA has found substantial **heritability** for two of the Big Five Factors:

◆ _____

◆ _____

In general, MISTRA and other studies have found that families do not play a large role in personality. However, there are several critiques of **twin studies** that may compromise this finding. Describe two of them:

◆ _____

   _____

◆ _____

   _____

What is the difference between **shared** and **nonshared environmental influences**? Give an example of each from your own life. _____

_____

_____

_____

_____

_____

Looking at Levels

List the factors at each of the **three levels** that contribute to shyness. Draw arrows between the factors to show how they might interact.

The Brain	The Person	The Group

Imagine a shy person growing up in a country where reserved behavior is the **norm**. How would an extroverted person do in such a situation? Consider what parents might do to shape an extroverted child's behavior in a socially reserved culture.

_____

_____

_____

_____

_____

TRY PRACTICE TEST #2 NOW!
GOOD LUCK!

The Person: Beliefs and Behaviors

According to Freud, in what part of your **consciousness** would the following information be found?

Information	Part of Consciousness
Your favorite color	
Feelings of aggression toward your teacher	
What you did on your last birthday	
Sexual feelings for your parent	
The name of your roommate	
Your mother's maiden name	

According to Freud, which part of your **personality** would be responsible for the following behaviors?

Behavior	Part of Personality
Delaying gratification	
Making you feel guilty	
Balancing reality and needs	
Eating a gallon of ice cream	
Telling you something is morally wrong	
Screaming when you're angry	

Describe the **developmental tasks** and **consequences of fixation** (if any) for each of the following stages of development:

Stage	Developmental task	Consequence of fixation
Oral		
Anal		
Phallic		
Latency		
Genital		

Describe the **Oedipal** and **Electra complexes** as explained by psychodynamic theory. _____
_____
_____
_____
_____
_____
_____
_____
_____
_____
_____
_____
_____

Give an example from your own life of each of the **common defense mechanisms** listed below:

Defense Mechanism	Example
Denial	
Intellectualization	
Projection	
Rationalization	
Reaction formation	
Repression	
Sublimation	
Undoing	

For each of the following theorists, describe their unique contribution to the understanding of **personality development**:

Theorist	Contribution
Carl Jung	
Alfred Adler	
Karen Horney	

Name three criticisms of the **psychodynamic theory** of personality development.

♦ _____
  _____

♦ _____
  _____

♦ _____
  _____

Name three aspects of **psychodynamic theory** that have been supported.

- ♦ _____
  _____
- ♦ _____
  _____
- ♦ _____
  _____

As opposed to psychodynamic theorists, humanistic theorists focus on the positive aspects of the individual. They say people have a drive toward **self-actualization**, which is _____
_____
_____

Do you know anyone who you believe is **self-actualized**? Describe him or her. What characteristics does this person have that makes you think he or she is self-actualized? (If you don't know anyone who is self-actualized, just write the characteristics of self-actualized people.)_____
_____
_____
_____
_____
_____
_____
_____
_____

What are the criticisms of the **humanistic theory** of personality? _____
_____
_____
_____

Consider how you felt about your performance on your last exam. Using the following terms, describe how you interpreted your success (or failure!), and how your experience will affect how you study for your next exam.

Term	My interpretation
Locus of control	
Efficacy expectancy	
Self-reinforcement	

Looking at Levels

Suppose that your friend asks you to go on a blind date with her cousin, "A really *nice* person." Consider the levels of the brain, the person, and the group. How might events at **each of these levels** affect your behavior during the date? Draw arrows to indicate how these events might interact.

The Brain	The Person	The Group

TRY PRACTICE TEST #3 NOW!
GOOD LUCK!

The World: Social Influences on Personality

Think of a family you know with at least three children (e.g., your own, one of your parent's, a friend's, etc.). In the table below, describe the first-born, middle-born, and later-born children. Then, describe Sulloway's findings on the personalities of children with these different birth orders.

Birth Order	Your Example	Sulloway's Findings
First-born		
Middle-born(s)		
Last-born		

According to **Judith Harris**, what are the only two ways in which parents can influence a child's personality and social behavior?

- ♦ _____
- ♦ _____

Describe the flaws in **Harris'** assertion that peers, not parents, influence their children's personality and social behavior._____
_____
_____
_____
_____

For each of the following **personality traits**, indicate with a mark in the appropriate column, whether men or women have consistently displayed the trait *more*, or if there have been mixed or inconsistent findings (or if men and women don't differ on the trait):

Trait	More in Women	More in Men	Inconsistent/ No Difference
Social anxiety			
Locus of control			
Impulsiveness			
Reflectiveness			
Social connectedness			
Individuality and autonomy			
Empathy			
Nurturing			
Assessing emotion			
Spotting deception			
Neuroticism Anger			
Aggression			
Assertiveness			

Describe how each of the following theories explains the sex differences in personality:

Theory	Explanation
Biological	
Social role	
Expectancy effects	
Cultural	

List the traits that distinguish **individualist** from **collectivist** cultures:

Individualist cultures are more . . .	Collectivist cultures are more . . .

Looking at Levels

How might individuals respond to emotional films when in the presence of a same-sex or opposite-sex person? Analyze this at the **three levels** of the brain, person, and world. Draw arrows to indicate how events at the different levels might interact.

The Brain	The Person	The Group

TRY PRACTICE TEST #4 NOW!
GOOD LUCK!

407

After You Read . . . Thinking Back

1. This chapter did not specifically consider the behaviorist perspective on personality. Based on what you learned about behaviorism in Chapters 1 and 6, can you speculate as to how behaviorists might think about personality? _____
    _____
    _____
    _____

2. Can you think of any ways to overcome the difficulties associated with response biases that are present in self-report methodologies, such as the NEO-PI-R? _____
    _____
    _____
    _____

3. How have the validity and reliability of some of the personality measures (such as the NEO-PI-R) been established? Why is this important?_____
    _____
    _____
    _____

4. In Chapter 4, you learned about top-down and bottom-up processing. Which theory of personality best represents top-down processing? Explain. _____
    _____
    _____
    _____

5. Which theory best represents bottom-up processing? Explain._____
    _____
    _____
    _____

6. In previous chapters, you have examined evolutionary theories. What is the evolutionary theory of gender differences in personality? What are some of the criticisms of evolutionary theories?_____
    _____
    _____
    _____

7. Do you think there is any relationship between intelligence (in Chapter 9) and personality? Why or why not? _____
    _____
    _____
    _____

After You Read . . . Thinking Ahead

1. What types of early life experiences may shape temperament? How so?_____
    _____
    _____
    _____

2. What do you think might happen if a child of one temperament was born to parents with
    very different personalities? _____
    _____
    _____
    _____

3. What types of temperamental dimensions would be more difficult for parents to cope with?
    Why? _____
    _____
    _____
    _____

4. How might early parent-child interactions influence expectancies?_____
    _____
    _____
    _____

5. What role could these expectancies have in shaping later intimate relationships? _____
    _____
    _____
    _____

6. What personality variables would help a person cope with stress and/or improve his or her
    health? Explain._____
    _____
    _____
    _____

7. There are several "personality disorders." What distinguishes a normal personality from a
    disordered one? Explain._____
    _____
    _____
    _____

8. Do you think a personality disorder could be treated? Why or why not? If so, how?_____
    _____
    _____
    _____

After You Read . . . Practice Tests

PRACTICE TEST #1:
WHAT IS PERSONALITY?

Multiple-Choice Questions

For each question, circle the best answer from the choices given.

1. Greg is very conscientious about his job; however, he is frequently behind in his studying. Which of the following does Greg's behavior best exemplify? (p. 440)
   a. The personality trait of neuroticism
   b. Situationism
   c. Interactionism
   d. The personality trait of consciousness

2. The term "central traits" refers to: (p. 439)
   a. Eysenck's three superfactors.
   b. The Big Five superfactors.
   c. The personality traits that affect a wide variety of behavior.
   d. Extraversion and neuroticism, because these are found in most models of personality.

3. Personality dimensions and superfactors: (p. 443)
   a. Help people to understand what causes behavior.
   b. Predict behavior.
   c. Help us to understand personality better.
   d. Are very reliable.

4. Why do people who believe in situationism call personality factors "mere illusions"? (p. 441)
   a. Because we tend to see people in similar types of situations, so their behavior appears consistent.
   b. Because these illusions are created by the viewer to retain control over the situation.
   c. Because these factors do not reveal the deeper self which is only available to close friends.
   d. Because these factors are based on self-reports and are therefore necessarily biased.

5. What is the value of defining a trait narrowly? (p. 439)
   a. It can be applied to more situations.
   b. It is more accurate in predicting behavior.
   c. It provides more information about a person.
   d. All of the above.

6.   Which of the following is <u>not</u> one of the "Big Five" factors of personality? (p. 442)
     a.   Openness
     b.   Neuroticism
     c.   Intellect
     d.   Extraversion

7.   Both _____ and _____ are on almost all lists of personality traits, suggesting that they are fundamental dimensions of personality. (p. 443)
     a.   Neuroticism; agreeableness
     b.   Neuroticism; extraversion
     c.   Extraversion; agreeableness
     d.   Conscientiousness; extraversion

8.   People who score high on Eysenck's trait of psychoticism may be more likely than others to: (p. 443)
     a.   Be alcoholics.
     b.   Be extraverted.
     c.   Be neurotic.
     d.   All of the above.

9.   The most common method of personality assessment is: (p. 444)
     a.   Personality inventories.
     b.   Observations.
     c.   Interviews.
     d.   Projective tests.

10. Miguel is completing a self-report measure of personality. He checks "strongly agree" to an item that reads "I like to take risks." Then, fifty items later, he checks "strongly agree" to an item that reads "I am not a very risky person." This response pattern is called: (p. 445)
     a.   Acquiescence.
     b.   Social desirability.
     c.   Ambiguity.
     d.   Novelty seeking.

11. Which of the following is a criticism of most self-report measures? (p. 444)
     a.   Their value depends on the reporter's honesty and accuracy.
     b.   Their value depends on whether the reporter has been through psychoanalysis.
     c.   They are very time-consuming.
     d.   They are not standardized.

12. The MMPI-2 is a(n): (p. 446)
     a.   Observational method of assessing personality.
     b.   Structured interview for assessing psychopathology.
     c.   Projective test of personality.
     d.   Paper-and-pencil personality inventory to assess psychopathology.

13.   "Projective" tests of personality are so named because: (p. 446)
    a.   Stimuli are projected onto the ceiling.
    b.   The examinee "projects" his or her personality when imposing structure onto ambiguous stimuli.
    c.   The examiner "projects" his or her knowledge of the examinee onto the assessment answers.
    d.   Aggression is projected by the stimuli.

14.   According to Eysenck, extraverts are: (p. 443)
    a.   Inwardly introverted.
    b.   Biologically defective.
    c.   Less arousable.
    d.   More arousable.

15.   Which of the five superfactors is not represented in Eysenck's model? (p. 443)
    a.   Extraversion
    b.   Neuroticism
    c.   Conscientiousness
    d.   Openness

16.   You would expect someone with an acquiescent response style to: (p. 445)
    a.   Complete an entire survey, no matter how long it is.
    b.   Answer "yes" or "agree" to most questions on a survey.
    c.   Answer "no" or "disagree" to most questions on a survey.
    d.   Leave survey questions blank if he or she doesn't agree with them.

17.   How are personality inventories commonly used? (pp. 444-445)
    a.   To assess mental illness.
    b.   To assess how personality traits relate to other personal characteristics.
    c.   To assess how personality relates to job performance.
    d.   All of the above.

18.   The TAT and the Rorschach tests are similar in that they both: (p. 447)
    a.   Ask respondents to make sense of ambiguous stimuli.
    b.   Use inkblots.
    c.   Are based on the Five-Factor Model.
    d.   Are based on Jungian theory.

19.   Which statistical technique was used to reveal superfactors? (p. 442)
    a.   Correlations
    b.   Standard deviations
    c.   Factor analysis
    d.   Means

20.	People with a particular gene that produces a type of dopamine receptor tend to be: (p. 447)
	a.	More depressed.
	b.	More introverted.
	c.	More novelty-seeking.
	d.	More conforming.

PRACTICE TEST #2:
THE BRAIN: THE PERSONALITY ORGAN

Multiple-Choice Questions
For each question, circle the best answer from the choices given.

1. Which of the following personality factors is most likely to predict criminality, according to Eysenck? (p. 451)
    a.   Extraversion
    b.   Introversion
    c.   Neurotocism
    d.   Psychoticism

2. According to Eysenck, how are introverts and extraverts different? (p. 450)
    a.   Introverts enjoy people and social stimulation more.
    b.   Extraverts have difficulty learning to refrain from certain behaviors.
    c.   Extraverts are more arousable than introverts.
    d.   It takes more stimulation to arouse extraverts.

3. The high-psychoticism nervous system may result from: (p. 451)
    a.   Underarousal of the autonomic and central nervous systems.
    b.   An overproduction of cells that produce dopamine.
    c.   An overactive amygdala.
    d.   Drug use.

4. According to Eysenck, the foundation of personality (at the base of the personality hierarchy) consists of: (p. 449)
    a.   Personality traits.
    b.   Personality dimensions.
    c.   Superfactors.
    d.   Stimulus-response associations.

5. Which of the following statements supports Eysenck's idea that there are different nervous systems involved in personality? (p. 450)
    a.   Extraverts have different skin conductance and EEG recordings than introverts.
    b.   People high in psychoticism are more likely to be impulsive.
    c.   Habit responses are built from learned stimulus-response associations.
    d.   Extraversion is found in almost every theory of personality.

6. Monica was the bank teller when the bank was robbed. Although she was not physically injured at the time, she now finds that she cannot go into banks without shaking and sweating. Based on Eysenck's theory, which of the following is most true of Monica? (pp. 450-451)
    a.   She is an extravert.
    b.   She is an introvert.
    c.   She has a neurotic nervous system.
    d.   She is high is psychoticism.

7.   Which of the following nervous systems is most likely to involve increased sensitivity of the amygdala? (p. 450)
      a.   Extraverted
      b.   Introverted
      c.   Neurotic
      d.   High-Psychoticism

8.   Introverts are more likely than extraverts to: (p. 450)
      a.   Like parties.
      b.   Be less arousable and so, seek greater stimulation.
      c.   Take drugs.
      d.   Be more sensitive to punishment.

9.   Which of the following is *not* a temperament, according to Buss and Plomin? (p. 452)
      a.   Activity
      b.   Sociability
      c.   Emotionality
      d.   Neuroticism

10.   Which of the following is true of temperament? (p. 451)
      a.   It is completely inherited.
      b.   It is not related to adulthood personality.
      c.   It refers to innate inclinations to engage in a certain style of behavior.
      d.   It does not appear until age 3.

11.   At 18 months old, Alexa loves to play with her friends and her brother. She screams when she is left alone. Which of the following superfactors do these behaviors probably reflect? (p. 450)
      a.   Sensation-seeking
      b.   Extraversion
      c.   Neuroticism
      d.   Activity

12.   Angelo prefers to play outside on the monkey bars or go biking than doing more sedate activities, like reading. He would probably be characterized as high on which of the following temperament dimensions?
      a.   Activity
      b.   Sociability
      c.   Emotionality
      d.   Impulsivity

13.   The MISTRA study found that: (p. 453)
      a.   There is little heritability for any of the personality dimensions.
      b.   Almost all of the Big Five personality traits are inherited.
      c.   There is high heritability for extraversion and neuroticism.
      d.   There is high heritability for psychoticism and openness to experience.

14. The MISTRA group found that the family environment contributed to: (p. 456)
    a. Social closeness.
    b. Psychoticism.
    c. Extraversion.
    d. Negative emotionality.

15. Which of the following is not a criticism of twin studies? (pp. 454-455)
    a. Adoptive and natural homes are often very similar.
    b. Some twins who are reared apart spent their early months or years in the same household.
    c. Adoption studies do not find as high correlations as twin studies.
    d. Adoptive parents are very similar to their adoptive children.

16. As measured by heritability, temperament is thought to be: (p. 452)
    a. Completely inherited.
    b. Not at all inherited.
    c. About 50% inherited.
    d. About 66% inherited.

17. Which of the following is not generally a large contributor to personality traits? (p. 456)
    a. Family environment
    b. Genes
    c. Personal experience
    d. Nonshared environmental influences

18. Children who are shy: (p. 457)
    a. Have sympathetic nervous systems that are more easily aroused.
    b. Are so self-conscious that they analyze their behavior after every social interaction.
    c. Can be helped by supportive parents.
    d. All of the above.

19. Jim loves to skydive, bungee-jump and ski. He is probably high in: (p. 451)
    a. Sensation seeking.
    b. Psychoticism.
    c. Extraversion.
    d. Emotionality.

20. Many aspects of the family environment are not shared because: (p. 456)
    a. Children create microenvironments based on their temperaments.
    b. Children may be different in their susceptibility to environmental forces.
    c. Parents may interact differently with each of their children.
    d. All of the above.

PRACTICE TEST #3:
THE PERSON: BELIEFS AND BEHAVIORS

Multiple-Choice Questions

For each question, circle the best answer from the choices given

1. The view that all behavior has an underlying psychological cause is called: (p. 458)
    a.   Psychological determinism.
    b.   The pleasure principle.
    c.   The reality principle.
    d.   Psychodynamic theory.

2. Material that can be brought into awareness but that people are not conscious of is held in: (p. 458)
    a.   The id.
    b.   The ego.
    c.   The conscious.
    d.   The preconscious.

3. The ego ideal is: (p. 459)
    a.   The underlying principle of the ego.
    b.   The ultimate standard of what a person should be.
    c.   Held in the conscious.
    d.   The result of a fixation.

4. The superego is responsible for: (p. 459)
    a.   A sense of right and wrong.
    b.   Preventing sexual and aggressive impulses.
    c.   Seeking pleasure.
    d.   Protecting the self from anxiety.

5. Arrested development, caused by fixation at an earlier stage of development, could create
    _____, according to Freud. (p. 460)
    a.   Neurosis
    b.   Depression
    c.   Psychosis
    d.   Aggression

6. For both boys and girls in the phallic stage of development, an intense feeling of dislike is initially directed toward the: (p. 460)
    a.   Mother.
    b.   Same-sex parent.
    c.   Father.
    d.   Opposite-sex parent.

7. A person who smokes probably became fixated in: (p. 460)
    a. The anal stage.
    b. The latency stage.
    c. The oral stage.
    d. The genital stage.

8. One of the most important defense mechanisms is _____, a process that occurs when the unconscious prevents threatening thoughts, impulses, and memories from entering consciousness. (p. 462)
    a. Regression
    b. Denial
    c. Repression
    d. Sublimation

9. According to Jung, we share common ideas and memories with all other humans through our: (p. 463)
    a. Ego ideal.
    b. Subconscious.
    c. Preconscious.
    d. Collective unconscious.

10. Alfred Adler believed that _____ was/were important in forming one's personality. (p. 463)
    a. Sexual and aggressive feelings
    b. Feelings of inferiority
    c. The collective unconscious
    d. Relationships with others

11. Karen Horney emphasized the importance of _____ in forming personality. (p. 463)
    a. Sexual and aggressive feelings
    b. Feelings of inferiority
    c. The collective unconscious
    d. Early parent-child interactions

12. Karen Horney suggested that little girls experience: (p. 463)
    a. Penis envy.
    b. The Oedipus complex.
    c. The Electra complex.
    d. Privilege envy.

13. Which of the following statements is true of humanistic psychologists? (p. 464)
    a. They focus on the positive aspects of the individual.
    b. They try to solve cultural, rather than personal, problems.
    c. They believe that actions have underlying, unconscious meanings.
    d. They believe that the drive to self-actualization is learned.

14. Which of the following terms refers to the sense of being able to produce the behaviors that one would like to? (p. 467)
     a.   Locus of control
     b.   Self-efficacy
     c   Self-regulation
     d.   Expectancies

15. When Betsy fails her test, she blames herself and vows to try harder next time. Betsy probably has: (p. 466)
     a.   Low self-regulation.
     b.   An internal locus of control.
     c.   An external locus of control.
     d.   Low self-efficacy.

PRACTICE TEST #4:
THE WORLD: SOCIAL INFLUENCES ON PERSONALITY

True/False Questions
Circle TRUE or FALSE for each of the following statements.

1. TRUE   FALSE   Sulloway found that first-born children tend to be less open to new experiences. (p. 469)

2. TRUE   FALSE   Sulloway found that first-born children are less supportive of parental authority. (p. 469)

3. TRUE   FALSE   Salmon found that middle-born children were less close to their families. (p. 470)

4. TRUE   FALSE   Judith Harris says that one way that parents influence children is through their values. (p. 471)

5. TRUE   FALSE   Women are generally more socially anxious than men. (p. 472)

6. TRUE   FALSE   The five factors have not been found in non-American cultures. (p. 474)

7. TRUE   FALSE   The personality differences within each sex are greater than the personality differences between the sexes. (p. 473)

8. TRUE   FALSE   People in collectivist cultures tend to be more extraverted than those from individualistic cultures. (p. 475)

9. TRUE   FALSE   Men are generally more neurotic than women. (p. 472)

10. TRUE   FALSE   People's personalities are generally stable, even when switching from a collectivist to an individualistic culture. (p. 475)

Multiple-Choice Questions
For each question, circle the best answer from the choices given.

1. Sulloway found that first-born children tend to be less _____ than younger siblings. (p. 469)
    a. Sociable
    b. Open to new experiences
    c. Driven for success
    d. Neurotic

2.	In Sulloway's research, "only" children were found to be similar to _____ children in their personalities. (p. 469)
	a.	First-born
	b.	Both first and later-born
	c.	Later-born
	d.	Middle-born

3.	Salmon found that in comparison to first- and later-born children, middle-born children are: (p. 470)
	a.	More extroverted.
	b.	More achievement-motivated.
	c.	Less close to their families.
	d.	More depressed and anxious.

4.	According to Judith Harris, the most influential determinant of children's personality and social behavior is their: (p. 471)
	a.	Mothers.
	b.	Siblings.
	c.	Fathers.
	d.	Peers.

5.	According to Harris, parents can influence their children's personalities by: (p. 471)
	a.	Choosing where they live and go to school.
	b.	Modeling appropriate behaviors.
	c.	Monitoring the amount of television they watch.
	d.	Maintaining open lines of communication.

6.	In general, personality differences between females and males: (p. 472)
	a.	Are pretty significant.
	b.	Are evident only in early childhood.
	c.	Are not very great.
	d.	Are more evident as people mature.

7.	Women tend to score higher on _____ than men do. (p. 472)
	a.	Social anxiety
	b.	Impulsiveness
	c.	Locus of control
	d.	Social connectedness

8.	Men score lower on _____ than women do. (p. 472)
	a.	Neuroticism
	b.	Aggression
	c.	Anger
	d.	Assertiveness

9. It is difficult to compare personalities across cultures because: (p. 474)
   a. Some personality concepts don't translate very well.
   b. Personality measures are not available in other languages.
   c. Ethical considerations prevent us from making comparisons.
   d. People in other cultures do not like to be compared to people in our culture.

10. Which of the following statements about collectivist countries is FALSE? (pp. 474-475)
    a. Collectivist countries tend to value group needs more than individual needs.
    b. People from collectivist cultures tend to see the self in relation to specific situations and contexts.
    c. Collectivist countries value personal freedom, equality, and enjoyment.
    d. Collectivist cultures exert considerable social control over individuals.

COMPREHENSIVE PRACTICE TEST

True/False Questions

Circle TRUE or FALSE for each of the following statements.

1.   TRUE   FALSE   Traits are relatively good predictors of behavior. (pp. 438-439)

2.   TRUE   FALSE   Like McCrae and Costa, Eysenck also found five superfactors. (p. 443)

3.   TRUE   FALSE   Psychodynamic theorists believe that people have an innate drive to self-actualize. (p. 464)

4.   TRUE   FALSE   Extraverts are "less arousable" than introverts. (p. 450)

5.   TRUE   FALSE   Most twin research finds evidence of substantial heritability of some personality dimensions. (p. 453)

6.   TRUE   FALSE   The ego is the home of the conscience. (p. 459)

7.   TRUE   FALSE   Freud developed his theory by studying college students. (p. 464)

8.   TRUE   FALSE   First-born children are generally more rebellious than later-born children. (p. 469)

9.   TRUE   FALSE   People with low self-efficacy are more likely to give up early than those with high self-efficacy. (p. 467)

10.   TRUE   FALSE   People from collectivist cultures tend to be less compliant than those from individualistic cultures. (p. 475)

Multiple-Choice Questions

For each question, circle the best answer from the choices given.

1.   What conclusion has been drawn about the consistency of personality traits within people? (pp. 438-439)
   a.   Most people display consistent levels of all of the important personality traits.
   b.   Everyone is consistent on some traits, but the particular traits on which people differ vary across individuals.
   c.   People are mostly inconsistent in their display of major personality traits.
   d.   Personality traits have proven so difficult to measure that it is impossible to conclude anything about their consistency.

2.   Researchers have found that children who cheat on a test will: (p. 440)
        a.   Lie to their parents.
        b.   Hurt others.
        c.   Steal.
        d.   Not necessarily do any of the above.

3.   A view of personality in which both traits and situations are believed to affect behavior,
        thoughts, and feelings is called: (p. 441)
        a.   Reciprocal determinism.
        b.   Interactionism.
        c.   Biopsychosocialism.
        d.   Multiplicity.

4.   Many factor analytic studies have revealed that traits can be reduced to _____
        superfactor(s). (p. 442)
        a.   1
        b.   4
        c.   5
        d.   6

5.   The traits of anxiety, hostility, depression, self-consciousness, impulsiveness, and
        vulnerability are all best defined by the superfactor: (p. 442)
        a.   Neuroticism.
        b.   Extraversion.
        c.   Psychoticism.
        d.   Openness.

6.   Criminals are likely to score: (p. 443)
        a.   High on extraversion.
        b.   High on neuroticism.
        c.   Low on agreeableness.
        d.   High on psychoticism.

7.   The superfactor _____ has no direct counterpart in Eysenck's model.
        (p. 443)
        a.   Neuroticism
        b.   Psychoticism
        c.   Openness
        d.   Agreeableness

8.   Interviews to assess personality are usually: (p. 444)
        a.   Structured.
        b.   Projective.
        c.   Unstructured.
        d.   Nondirective.

9. A person who checks off "agree" on a personality inventory, regardless of the content of the statement, is said to have a(n) _____ response style. (p. 445)
    a. Socially desirable
    b. Acquiescent
    c. Defensive
    d. Accepting

10. The Thematic Personality Test is a(n): (p. 446)
    a. Objective personality measure.
    b. Unstructured interview.
    c. Projective personality measure.
    d. Personality inventory.

11. People who score high on _____ are easily and intensely emotionally aroused and are more likely to experience conditioned emotional responses. (p. 450)
    a. Extraversion
    b. Psychoticism
    c. Neuroticism
    d. Openness

12. The temperament *activity* has two components: (p. 452)
    a. Vigor and tempo.
    b. Impulsivity and tempo.
    c. Vigor and impulsivity.
    d. Impulsivity and sociability.

13. Twins are most likely to be similar in terms of: (p. 453)
    a. Impulsivity.
    b. Extraversion.
    c. Openness.
    d. Agreeableness.

14. One of the criticisms of Freud's theory is that: (p. 464)
    a. Later research indicates that the unconscious does not have a role in personality.
    b. Later research indicates that early experiences are unimportant in personality formation.
    c. Most of his patients were upper-middle-class or upper-class Victorian women.
    d. His theory is too optimistic for modern times, when evil is rampant in the world.

15. Which of the following would not be a characteristic of a self-actualizing person? (pp. 464-465)
    a. Denies all difficult problems in order to maintain an optimistic worldview.
    b. Forms deep relationships with a few people.
    c. Appreciates ordinary events.
    d. Accepts himself or herself, others, and nature.

16. Humanists believe that people have a tendency toward _____, an inborn motivation to achieve the highest emotional and intellectual potential. (p. 464)
    a. Collective unconscious
    b. Unconditional positive regard
    c. Superiority striving
    d. Self-actualization

17. Which of the following people is least likely to maintain close relationships with his or her family? (p. 470)
    a. Bart, the eldest of three children
    b. Lisa, the middle of three children
    c. Maggie, the last-born of three children
    d. None of them are likely to maintain close relationships

18. Which of the following is a FALSE statement of gender differences in personality? (p. 472)
    a. There are many gender differences, of large magnitude, in personality.
    b. There are more differences within each sex than between them.
    c. Women generally score higher on measures of social connectedness than do men.
    d. Men generally score higher on measures of aggression than do women.

19. Marge has an external locus of control. As a result, when she fails her psychology test, she is likely to: (p. 466)
    a. Give up and stop going to class.
    b. Realize that she needs to start studying harder.
    c. Realize that she needs a tutor.
    d. Have a nervous breakdown.

20. Collectivist cultures are more likely than individualist cultures to value: (p. 474)
    a. Social order and humility.
    b. Equality.
    c. Personal freedom.
    d. Enjoyment.

When You Are Finished . . Puzzle It Out

Across

4. Men score lower on this superfactor
6. Said there are 16 personality factors
11. Proposed inferiority complexes
13. Consistent personality characteristics
14. Measure of genetic influence
15. Lives by the "pleasure principle"
16. Freud's stage from three to six years
17. Pursuit of novelty
18. He proposed 3 nervous systems, corresponding to 3 superfactors

Puzzle created with Puzzlemaker at DiscoverySchool.com.

Down

1. Number of superfactors, per Costa & McCrae
2. She said family influence on personality was small
3. Source of control in life
5. Proposed hierarchy of needs
6. Cultures emphasizing group needs
7. Grouping of 5 personality traits
8. Measures the Five Factor model
9. Personality test using inkblots
10. Most conscientious of children
11. "Yes" or "Agree" response style
12. Developed client-centered therapy

Chapter 12
Psychology Over The Lifespan:
Growing Up, Growing Older, Growing Wiser

Before You Read . . .

Did your mother enjoy being pregnant with you? When did you start walking and talking? Are you the same person now as you were as a child? Will you be the same person in your 60s? How will you change?

This chapter presents an overview of human development, from conception to death. In the first section, you will learn about prenatal development, from the gametes that start it to the infant that is born. You will learn about both positive and negative events (teratogens) that can affect the developing fetus. You will also learn about the newborn, its perceptual abilities, reflexes, and even personality (temperament).

In childhood, children grow rapidly and undergo remarkable physical changes. You will learn about these, as well as the qualitative and quantitative changes they experience in language and cognition. You will learn about Piaget's classical framework for understanding child development, as well as the new areas of understanding developed by more modern researchers.

You will also learn about adolescence and adulthood, including changes that you can expect in your sense of self, morality, and gender identity and changes that will occur as you develop new, mature relationships that wax and wane over time. Finally, you will learn about the natural processes of death and dying.

Chapter Objectives

After reading this chapter, you should be able to:

♦   Describe how development progresses in the womb.

♦   Describe the capabilities of a newborn.

♦   Explain how the ability to control the body develops with age.

♦   Explain physical, cognitive, social and emotional development during childhood and adolescence.

♦   Discuss whether or not adolescence is a time of emotional upheaval.

♦   Explain how aging affects physical abilities, perception, memory, and intelligence.

♦   Describe the course of social and emotional development during adulthood.

♦   Explain the ways in which people cope with death—both their own and that of others.

As You Read...Term Identification

Make flashcards using the following terms as you go. Use the definitions in the margins of this chapter for help. If you write the definitions in your own words, though, you will remember them better!

Accommodation	Grief
Adolescence	Longitudinal study
Assimilation	Maturation
Attachment	Moral dilemmas
Bereavement	Object permanence
Cohort	Private speech
Concrete operation	Psychosocial development
Conservation	Puberty
Cross-sectional study	Self-concept
Egocentrism	Separation Anxiety
Embryo	Schema
Fetus	Teratogen
Formal operation	Theory of mind
Gender identity	Zygote
Gender roles	

As You Read . . . Questions and Exercises

In the Beginning: From Conception to Birth

Prenatal Development: Nature and Nurture from the Start

How do **nature** and **nurture** interact, even in terms of conception? Explain._____

_____

_____

_____

_____

Why do siblings turn out so differently? Discuss the different factors that ensure **human variety**:

♦   _____
     _____
     _____
     _____
     _____

♦   _____
     _____
     _____
     _____
     _____
     _____

GO SURFING...

...to see photographs of the developing **embryo**.
♦   http://www.visembryo.com/
♦   http://www.w-cpc.org/fetal.html
♦   http://anatomy.med.unsw.edu.au/CBL/Embryo/embryo.htm

Name the important developments that happen at each of the following **prenatal stages**:

♦   **3 days:**_____
     _____

♦   **2 weeks:** _____
     _____

♦   **8 weeks:** _____
     _____

♦   **20 - 25 weeks:**_____
     _____

♦   **28 weeks:** _____
     _____

♦   **25 - 34 weeks:**_____
     _____

Describe what effect the following can have on developing babies:

Teratogen	Effect
Rubella in the embryonic period	
HIV	
Heroin/cocaine	
Environmental pollutants	
Excessive caffeine	
Tobacco smoke	
Poor maternal diet	
Maternal stress	

The Newborn: A Work in Progress

Describe a newborn's sensory **capabilities**.

♦   **Sight:** _____
_____
_____

♦   **Hearing:** _____
_____
_____
_____

♦   **Smell:** _____
_____
_____
_____

Complete the following table of **reflexes**:

Reflex	Description
Rooting	
	The startle reflex
	Looks like a fencing position
Babinski	
	Toes curl under when pressing the ball of the foot

What is **temperament**? _____
_____
_____
_____
_____
_____

What is meant by an **"approach" temperament**? What is meant by a **"withdrawal"
temperament**? _____
_____
_____
_____
_____
_____

CALL…

…your parents. Describe the different **temperament** types. What type of **temperament** do they
think you had? Why?_____
_____
_____

How is this similar to your personality now? _____
_____
_____

What is the evidence that there are **biological factors** in infant **temperament**?

- ◆ _____
  _____
  _____
- ◆ _____
  _____
  _____
- ◆ _____
  _____
  _____
- ◆ _____
  _____
  _____
- ◆ _____
  _____
  _____

How **stable** is temperament?_____
_____
_____
_____

How might the **environment** influence the **stability** of **temperament**?_____
_____
_____
_____

Looking at Levels

How does a baby learn emotional reactions through interactions with his or her mother? Discuss this at the **levels of the brain, person, and group**. Draw arrows to indicate how events at the different levels may interact.

The Brain	The Person	The Group

TRY PRACTICE TEST #1 NOW!
GOOD LUCK!

Infancy and Childhood: Taking Off

Physical and Motor Development: Getting Control

What type of **motor control** is gained first? After this?_____
_____
_____
_____

Does the **environment** play any role at all in the development of **motor control**?_____
_____
_____
_____
_____
_____

Perceptual, Linguistic, and Cognitive Development: Extended Horizons

Describe the **visual abilities** of infants._____
_____
_____
_____
_____
_____
_____
_____
_____
_____
_____

Describe the **auditory abilities** of infants._____
_____
_____
_____
_____
_____
_____
_____
_____
_____

Explain the **habituation technique**. What does this technique tell us about infants?_____
_____
_____
_____
_____
_____
_____
_____
_____
_____

Several studies have shown that **infants** can store information both **implicitly** and **explicitly**.
Discuss this evidence.

Type of Memory	Age	Evidence
Implicit		
Explicit		

How does **memory** change through **childhood**?_____
_____
_____
_____
_____
_____

Complete the table below, indicating the **approximate age** of each stage and the **accomplishments** by the end of each period. Use the information Piaget hypothesized, not more contemporary researchers.

Cognitive Stage	Approximate Age	Accomplishments
Sensorimotor		
Preoperational		
Concrete Operational		
Formal Operational		

What are **schemas**, according to **Piaget**?_____

_____

_____

_____

_____

_____

What two processes does the child use to change his or her **schemas**?

◆ _____

_____

_____

◆ _____

_____

_____

How do **schemas** change as the child develops?

♦ _____
   _____
   _____
♦ _____
   _____
   _____
   _____

More contemporary researchers, using different research methodology, have suggested that **Piaget underestimated** the age at which children achieve certain cognitive goals. In the table below, indicate the age at which *contemporary* researchers believe children attain each goal.

Goal	Age of Attainment & Evidence
Imitation	
Object permanence	
Conservation of amount/mass	
Theory of mind	

How does **culture** influence the development of **theory of mind**?_____
_____
_____
_____
_____
_____
_____

Modern theories have looked at changes in **information processing**. What changes are found in the following memory systems?

♦ **Sensory Memory:**_____
   _____

♦ **Working Memory:** _____
   _____

♦ **Long-term Memory:** _____
   _____

437

How might **brain changes** affect these information-processing abilities?_____

_____

_____

_____

_____

_____

_____

Briefly summarize the following ideas of **Lev Vygotsky**, in your own words.

♦   **The role of adults in cognitive development.** _____

_____

_____

_____

♦   **The role of language in cognitive development.**_____

_____

_____

_____

Social and Emotional Development: The Child in the World

Why does **separation anxiety** occur between the ages of six months and two years? _____

_____

_____

_____

Provide the name of the **type of attachment** described by the following reactions of babies to the **Strange Situation**.

Reaction	Type of Attachment
Babies will leave mother, but are upset when mother leaves and are not comforted by a stranger. Babies calm down when mother returns.	
Babies stay close to mother and become angry when she leaves. When mother returns, babies are still angry and won't calm down easily.	
Babies don't care if mother is present or absent, and are easily comforted by a stranger.	
Babies become depressed and unresponsive, with sudden spurts of emotion at the end of the *Strange Situation*.	

What **type of attachment** do you think you had as a child? Support your answer._____

_____

_____

_____

_____

GO SURFING...

...to http://p034.psch.uic.edu/cgi-bin/crq.pl to see what **type of attachment** you currently have.

Describe here:_____

_____

_____

_____

_____

Is this consistent with your **attachment type** as a child?_____

_____

_____

_____

_____

Would you send your child to **daycare**? Why or why not? _____

_____

_____

_____

_____

What is **self-concept**?_____

_____

_____

_____

_____

At what age do children first exhibit a **self-concept**?_____

_____

_____

_____

_____

How would a child define himself or herself at the following ages:

♦   **3 years old:**_____

♦   **8 years old:**_____

♦   **11 years old:**_____

How does **culture** influence **self-concept**?_____
_____
_____
_____
_____

What factor(s) most strongly influence **gender identity** in childhood?_____
_____
_____
_____
_____

Bobby just received too much money from the teller at the bank. At what level of **moral development** is Bobby if he says to himself:

Bobby's Thought	Stage of Moral Development
"I could use this money to buy a bike, as long as I don't get caught!"	
"If I kept this money, my dad would think I'm a bad person."	
"It would be in the best interest of everyone who has an account at this bank if I give the money back."	
"Taking this money is the same thing as stealing, and stealing is wrong."	

Explain **Gilligan**'s criticisms of **Kohlberg**'s theory of **moral development**. _____
_____
_____
_____
_____

What has later work concluded about **Gilligan**'s criticisms. _____
_____
_____
_____
_____

Some researchers emphasize the difference between **moral reasoning** and **moral behavior**. What factors influence whether a child acts morally?

- ◆ _____
  _____

- ◆ _____
  _____

- ◆ _____
  _____

- ◆ _____
  _____

- ◆ _____
  _____

Looking at Levels

Describe the biological, psychological, and social factors that influence **gender role development**. Use arrows to indicate how these factors may interact.

The Brain	The Person	The Group

TRY PRACTICE TEST #2 NOW!
GOOD LUCK!

Adolescence: Between Two Worlds

Physical Development: In Puberty's Wake

Describe the **physical changes** that happen to boys and girls during **puberty**.

Changes to Boys	Changes to Girls

What is the **secular trend**? What has caused it?_____

_____

_____

_____

_____

Cognitive Development: Getting It All Together

How does thinking change during **adolescence**?

- _____
- _____
- _____
- _____
- _____
- _____

Think back to adolescence. What were you interested in doing and reading? Were these changes from earlier in your life? How do they reflect changes in **thinking** during **adolescence**?

_____

_____

_____

_____

What are the possible reasons for these cognitive changes?

♦ _____
_____

♦ _____
_____
_____

Think back to adolescence. Do you remember using any **cognitive distortions**? How could this be dangerous for teens? _____
_____
_____
_____
_____
_____

What is an **imaginary audience**? Give a personal example of a time when you experienced this.
_____
_____
_____
_____

What is a **personal fable**? Give a personal example of a time when you experienced this. _____
_____
_____
_____
_____

Social and Emotional Development: New Rules, New Roles

What are the three **problems** that have been identified as "normal" during **adolescence**?

♦ _____

♦ _____

♦ _____

Did you experience any or all of these **problems** during **adolescence**? Discuss. _____
_____
_____
_____

How do **biology** and **culture** interact to affect adolescence?_____
_____
_____
_____
_____
_____

Did you experience **"storm and stress"** during adolescence? Why or why not, do you think?
_____
_____
_____
_____
_____

What types of **life experiences** will positively impact later **intimate relationships**?

♦   _____
♦   _____

What types of negative **peer relationships** sometimes occur during adolescence?_____
_____
_____
_____

Did you experience **positive** or **negative peer relationships** during adolescence? Describe.
_____
_____
_____
_____

Looking at Levels

Consider the fact that only about half of pregnant teens choose to keep their babies. What factors do you think play a role in their decision, at the **levels of the brain, person, and group**? Draw arrows to indicate how events at the different levels may interact.

The Brain	The Person	The Group

TRY PRACTICE TEST #3 NOW!
GOOD LUCK!

Adulthood and Aging: The Continuously Changing Self

The Changing Body: What's Inevitable, What's Not

When do noticeable changes in the **body** begin to occur?_____

What are some of the inevitable **age-related changes** that are programmed into our **genes**?
_____
_____
_____
_____
_____

What was **Hayflick's** important finding about how human cells divide in the lab? _____
_____
_____
_____

What are two ways that this finding can be interpreted?

♦ _____
_____
_____

♦ _____
_____
_____

How can people minimize **age-related changes**? _____
_____
_____
_____
_____

Perception and Cognition in Adulthood: Taking the Good with the Bad

Describe the **age-related changes** in each of the following areas:

Area	Age-related changes
Vision	
Hearing	
Semantic memory	
Storage of new episodic memories	
Recall of specific episodic memories	
Working memory	
Crystallized intelligence	
Fluid intelligence	

Think of any elderly people you know. Do they appear to have **age-related changes** in any of the above areas? If so, which ones? How do you know? _____

_____

_____

_____

_____

_____

_____

_____

Why is it important to note what type of **research design** was used when examining **intelligence** during adulthood? _____

_____

_____

_____

_____

_____

_____

What is the **Flynn effect**? What are some possible explanations for it?_____

_____

_____

_____

_____

What is the **cerebral reserve hypothesis**? How can you use this to your advantage as you age?

_____

_____

_____

_____

Social and Emotional Development During Adulthood

What are the three **psychosocial stages** of adulthood (**Erikson**), and the goal at each stage?

Stage	Goal

Is there a **midlife crisis** for men? Explain. _____

_____

_____

_____

_____

Does **personality** remain relatively stable, or does it change, over the lifespan? Does it differ for men and women? _____

_____

_____

_____

_____

_____

Do people generally feel **happier** or **sadder** as they get older? Explain emotional changes associated with aging._____

_____

_____

_____

_____

Do **interpersonal relationships** improve or weaken over time? Explain. _____

_____

_____

_____

_____

Death and Dying

What are the three stages through which one passes when **grieving** for a loved one who has died?

- ◆ _____
- ◆ _____
- ◆ _____

What factors influence how much people **grieve** for their loved ones?

- ◆ _____
- ◆ _____
- ◆ _____
- ◆ _____
- ◆ _____
- ◆ _____

Have you ever lost a loved one? What **coping methods** were most effective for you? Which ones were least so? In the future, given the research evidence, what methods might you try? _____

_____

_____

_____

_____

_____

_____

How does **culture** influence the way that people think about death? _____

_____

_____

_____

_____

_____

Looking at Levels

Should elderly people be encouraged to engage in **mental workouts** to keep their minds sharp? What of the elderly person who does not wish to do so? What factors, at the **levels of the brain, person, and group**, may lead to diminished motivation for such tasks? Use arrows to indicate how these factors may interact.

The Brain	The Person	The Group

TRY PRACTICE TEST #4 NOW!
GOOD LUCK!

After You Read . . . Thinking Back

1. This chapter underscores a point made earlier: that memory is not a single entity, but is instead comprised of multiple systems that develop at different rates._____
    _____
    _____
    _____
    _____
    _____
    _____

2. This chapter revisits an issue initially raised in Chapter 3: the nature-nurture debate. What are some of the ways that theorists have thought about nature and nurture interacting?
    _____
    _____
    _____
    _____
    _____
    _____
    _____

3. Given that even young infants have been shown to learn, what does this say about the biological basis of learning?_____
    _____
    _____
    _____
    _____
    _____
    _____

4. Can you think of confounds that may influence what appear to be age-related changes in intelligence? Explain._____
    _____
    _____
    _____
    _____
    _____

5. Think back to Chapter 2, where you learned about research in psychology. Why is it particularly difficult to make causal statements in developmental studies? For example, why can't you say, "Age causes memory decline?"_____
    _____
    _____
    _____
    _____
    _____
    _____

After You Read . . . Thinking Ahead

1. What environmental factors may influence whether or not people behavior morally? For example, what types of situations existed in WWII that contributed to the immoral acts of the Nazis?_____

    _____

    _____

    _____

    _____

    _____

    _____

2. Why do you think that peer interactions are positive for some adolescents and negative for others? Are there any environmental changes that can be made to facilitate more positive interactions?_____

    _____

    _____

    _____

    _____

    _____

    _____

3. How might stress affect a person's development, at all 3 levels of analysis?_____

    _____

    _____

    _____

    _____

    _____

    _____

4. What can a parent do for a child to facilitate his or her later social interactions, both in groups and in intimate relationships?_____

    _____

    _____

    _____

    _____

    _____

5. Can you think of any environmental factors in childhood that might contribute to later psychological disorders?_____

    _____

    _____

    _____

    _____

    _____

After You Read . . . Practice Tests

PRACTICE TEST #1:
IN THE BEGINNING

Fill-in-the-Blank Questions
Fill in the following blanks with words from the following word bank.

WORD BANK	
Egg	Male
Embryo	Sperm
Female	Trimesters
Fetus	Zygote
Gametes	

Life begins when the _____ from the woman meets the _____ from the man. These specialized sex cells are called _____, and when they join together, they form a zygote, a combination of cells with 23 pairs chromosomes. If the sperm contributes an X chromosome, the offspring will be _____; if the sperm contributes a Y chromosome, the offspring will be _____. Development in the womb is divided into __ _____, three equal periods of time. The first period of time is divided into three stages: _____, _____, and _____. (p. 482-484)

True/False Questions
Circle TRUE or FALSE for each of the following statements.

1.   TRUE   FALSE   Male fetuses are more active than female fetuses. (p. 485)

2.   TRUE   FALSE   A fetus is sensitive to sound and light. (p. 485)

3.   TRUE   FALSE   By 10 weeks, a fetus can detect human speech. (p. 485)

4.   TRUE   FALSE   There is evidence that fetuses can learn. (p. 485)

5.   TRUE   FALSE   Drugs taken by the father cannot affect the developing fetus. (p. 486)

Multiple-Choice Questions

For each question, circle the best answer from the choices given.

1. The fertilization of the egg by the sperm creates a cell called a(n): (p. 483)
    a. Zygote.
    b. Germinal cell.
    c. Blastocyst.
    d. Embryo.

2. Which of the following depicts the order of prenatal development? (p. 484)
    a. zygote → fetus → embryo → blastocyst
    b. blastocyst → zygote → fetus → embryo
    c. zygote → blastocyst → embryo → fetus
    d. blastocyst → zygote → embryo → fetus

3. Drugs taken and illnesses incurred by the mother during her pregnancy are called: (p. 485)
    a. Teratogens.
    b. Alleles.
    c. Toxins.
    d. Gametes.

4. Differences in temperament are apparent as early as: (p. 489)
    a. Birth.
    b. 1 month.
    c. 1 week.
    d. 2 months.

5. Babies with greater activation in the right frontal lobes tend to be _____ later. (p. 490)
    a. More difficult
    b. Happier
    c. More depressed
    d. More relaxed

6. What are the effects of teratogens? (p. 486)
    a. It depends on what organs are developing at a given time.
    b. They all affect the intellectual functioning of the developing child.
    c. They all affect behavior.
    d. They all cause emotional difficulties.

7. All cells in the human body contain 23 pairs of chromosomes, except the _____, which contain(s) _____ chromosomes. (p. 483)
    a. Zygote; 11
    b. Zygote; 23
    c. Gametes; 23
    d. Games; 11

8.   What may happen to a fetus when a pregnant woman is stressed? (p. 487)
       a.   The operation of genes guiding brain growth may slow down.
       b.   The infant may have attentional difficulties later.
       c.   The child may have unusual social behaviors later.
       d.   All of the above.

9.   Genomic imprinting refers to the process by which: (p. 484)
       a.   The zygote divides and recombines.
       b.   The child inherits a unique combination of genes.
       c.   The same genetic material can produce different results, depending on which parent
             it comes from.
       d.   A and B.

10.   By the time that it is 34 weeks of gestation, a fetus: (p. 484)
       a.   Is sensitive to light and sound.
       b.   Can respond to external stimulation.
       c.   Can detect human speech.
       d.   All of the above.

PRACTICE TEST #2:
INFANCY AND CHILDHOOD

True/False Questions
Circle TRUE or FALSE for each of the following statements.

1. TRUE   FALSE   The working memory of young children is comparable to that of adults. (p. 503)

2. TRUE   FALSE   Improvements in working memory over time probably have a biological basis. (p. 503)

3. TRUE   FALSE   Vygotsky emphasized the role of biological maturation in the cognitive development of children. (p. 504)

4. TRUE   FALSE   Vygotsky found that children use private speech during difficult tasks. (p. 504)

5. TRUE   FALSE   According to Kohlberg, it was not the answer to his moral dilemmas that was so important, but rather how each person arrived at the solution. (p. 509)

6. TRUE   FALSE   Gilligan critiqued Kohlberg's work on the basis that it makes women appear to be immoral. (p. 509)

Fill-in-the-Blank Questions
Fill in the following blanks with words from the following word bank.

WORD BANK	
Accommodation	Differentiated
Articulated	Schemas
Assimilation	

Piaget believed that babies begin with simple, innate _____, mental

structures that organize perceptual input and connect it to the appropriate responses.

Through the process of _____, infants use existing schemas to take

in new stimuli, and by the process of _____, infants adjust their

schemas to cope with novel situations that the original schemas can't satisfy. Schemas

develop in two ways. First they become _____, or more precise, and then

_____, giving rise to two or more separate schemas. (p. 497-498)

Fill-in-the-Blank Questions

Fill in the following blanks with words from the following word bank.

WORD BANK	
Cognitive	Self concept
Collectivist	Social relations
Culture	Three
Formal operational period	Two
Individualist	

The term _____ refers to the beliefs, desires, values, and attributes

that define a person to him or herself. The development of self-concept in childhood

closely follows _____ development. By the age of _____,

virtually all children will recognize themselves in a mirror, although other researchers

argue that self-concept is present even earlier. By the age of _____, children begin to

appreciate that they have distinct psychological characteristics, but it is not until between 8 and 11

that children describe themselves in terms of _____, such as the relationships they

have with their siblings and friends. This ability to self-label depends on reasoning abilities that

develop during the _____. Self-concept is clearly influenced by

_____. In _____ cultures, self-concepts revolve about group relations,

whereas in _____ cultures, self-concepts revolve around defining themselves as

distinct entities. (p. 507)

Multiple-Choice Questions

For each question, circle the best answer from the choices given.

1.   The development of physical control in an infant progresses from: (p. 492)
       a.   Legs → arms → trunk → head.
       b.   Head → trunk → arms → legs.
       c.   Trunk → head → arms → legs.
       d.   Head → trunk → legs → arms.

2.   When Mariah says that she is artistic and creative, she is reflecting on her: (p. 506-507)
       a.   Self-concept.
       b.   Gender identity.
       c.   Attachment style.
       d.   Self-esteem.

3.   Mariah says, "I am artistic and creative." Mariah is probably: (p. 507)
      a.   3 years old.
      b.   5 years old.
      c.   6 years old
      d.   10 years old.

4.   A baby who puts everything in her mouth, even if it doesn't belong there, is _____, according to Piaget. (p. 497)
      a.   Assimilating
      b.   Scheming
      c.   Accommodating
      d.   Adjusting

5.   The two key achievements of the sensorimotor period are: (pp. 498-499)
      a.   Conservation and logic.
      b.   Objective permanence and imitation.
      c.   Imitation and humor.
      d.   Hypothetical thinking and loss of egocentricity.

6.   To understand other people's mental states (intentions, goals, beliefs), a child must have: (p. 502)
      a.   Developed a theory of mind.
      b.   The ability to conserve.
      c.   Overcome egocentrism.
      d.   Abstract reasoning abilities.

7.   Charlie said that it was wrong for his brother, Patrick, to take a cookie from the cookie jar because he would get spanked for it. Charlie is reasoning at a _____ level. (p. 509)
      a.   Formal operational
      b.   Preconventional
      c.   Conventional
      d.   Postconventional

8.   More recent studies on moral development indicate that: (p. 509)
      a.   There are no fundamental differences in how men and women reason morally.
      b.   Both men and women use justice and caring perspectives.
      c.   The type of reasoning people use depends on the dilemma they are given.
      d.   All of the above.

9.   Eighteen-month-old Alicia screams whenever her mother leaves, but is easily soothed when her mother returns. What type of attachment does Alicia probably have to her mother? (p. 505)
      a.   Secure
      b.   Avoidant
      c.   Resistant
      d.   Disorganized/disoriented

10. Harry Harlow's findings indicate that: (p. 505)
    a. Parents' ability to feed their children is the primary reason for children to attach to them.
    b. The desire to be comforted is an innate characteristic of mammals.
    c. Securely attached children usually don't go to daycare.
    d. Attachment is dependent on the amount of time that children spend with their parents.

PRACTICE TEST #3:
ADOLESCENCE

Multiple-Choice Questions

For each question, circle the best answer from the choices given.

1. Puberty begins around the age of _____ for girls and _____ for boys. (p. 512)
    a.   8-14; 9-15
    b.   12-14; 13-15
    c.   10-12; 12-16
    d.   7-10; 12-14

2. American girls typically stop growing at around age _____, while American boys typically grow until they are _____. (p. 513)
    a.   12; 13
    b.   16; 13
    c.   13; 16
    d.   14; 18

3. The major cognitive development of adolescence is: (p. 513)
    a.   The attainment of concrete operations.
    b.   The development of a working memory.
    c.   The ability to reason abstractly.
    d.   The sense of personal responsibility.

4. The frequency of parent-child conflict is greatest in _____-adolescence, and the intensity of conflict is greatest in _____-adolescence. (p. 515)
    a.   Early; mid
    b.   Early; late
    c.   Mid; early
    d.   Late; early

5. Approximately _____ of teens are seriously depressed by mid-adolescence. (p. 515)
    a.   One-tenth
    b.   One-third
    c.   One-fourth
    d.   One-half

6. The emotional mood swings occurring in adolescence can be attributed to: (p. 516)
    a.   Cultural stressors.
    b.   School pressures.
    c.   Family stressors.
    d.   Hormonal changes.

7. Which of the following is evidence of adolescent egocentrism? (p. 514)
   a. The inability to take another person's perspective
   b. The inability to believe the world exists outside of one's interaction with it
   c. The belief that they are the actors and everyone else is the audience
   d. The belief that everyone in their community knows them

8. Adolescents may engage in risky behavior because of: (p. 514)
   a. Fluctuating hormones.
   b. A desire to "cheat death."
   c. Decreased parental monitoring.
   d. A perception of invulnerability.

9. The secular trend refers to the fact that: (p. 512-513)
   a. Puberty now occurs earlier than in the past.
   b. The body grows from the limbs inward during adolescence.
   c. Girls' growth spurts start earlier than do boys' growth spurts.
   d. There are cognitive changes that accompany adolescence.

10. The greatest risk factors for teen pregnancy are: (p. 517)
    a. Being poor and without a clear career plan.
    b. Being African-American and from a lower socioeconomic group.
    c. Lacking a clear sense of self and having low self-esteem.
    d. Being from a broken family and having negative opinions of the opposite sex.

PRACTICE TEST #4:
ADULTHOOD AND AGING

True/False Questions

Circle TRUE or FALSE for each of the following statements.

1.   TRUE   FALSE   Fear of death increases with age. (p. 527)

2.   TRUE   FALSE   Women report fearing death more than men do. (p. 527)

3.   TRUE   FALSE   Menopause is always a negative life event for women. (p. 518)

Multiple-Choice Questions

For each question, circle the best answer from the choices given.

1.   Significant age-related cognitive changes occur after the age of: (p. 519)
   a.   20.
   b.   30.
   c.   40.
   d.   50.

2.   Aging most severely affects: (p. 519)
   a.   The occipital lobe.
   b.   Communication among neurons in the brain.
   c.   Lower brain functioning, for example, in the limbic system.
   d.   The parietal and temporal lobes of the brain.

3.   A clouding of the lens of the eye that occurs after the age of 65 is called: (p. 519)
   a.   Cataracts.
   b.   Myopia.
   c.   Glaucoma.
   d.   Hyperopia.

4.   Which of the following types of memory is most impaired in elderly people? (p. 520)
   a.   Visual memory
   b.   Storage of new episodic memories
   c.   Semantic memory
   d.   Recall of specific episodic memories

5.   Which of the following types of intelligence declines after the age of 20? (p. 521)
   a.   Crystallized
   b.   Both A & B
   c.   Fluid
   d.   Neither A nor B

6.   Cohorts are: (p. 522)
      a.   Groups of friends.
      b.   People born at about the same time.
      c.   People who are experiencing the same cognitive changes during adulthood.
      d.   People who have the same job.

7.   According to Erikson, the second stage of psychosocial development in adulthood is: (p. 522)
      a.   Generativity vs. self-absorption.
      b.   Integrity vs. despair.
      c.   Intimacy vs. isolation.
      d.   Identity vs. diffusion.

8.   Costa and McCrae (1988) found age-related changes in personality in: (p. 524)
      a.   Men, but not women.
      b.   Both men and women.
      c.   Women, but not men.
      d.   Neither men nor women

9.   Which of the following is an accurate statement about perceptions of death and dying? (p. 527)
      a.   Men become more worried about death as they age.
      b.   Women report fearing death more than men do.
      c.   Men tend to witness more death in their lifetime.
      d.   All people pass through five stages, from denial to acceptance, when faced with their own impending death.

10.   To keep the brain functioning at a peak level, an elderly person would be best advised to: (p. 528)
      a.   Take a multivitamin every day.
      b.   Avoid drinking alcohol and taking drugs.
      c.   Engage in mentally stimulating tasks.
      d.   None of the above—age-related changes are inevitable.

COMPREHENSIVE PRACTICE TEST

True/False Questions
Circle TRUE or FALSE for each of the following statements.

1.   TRUE   FALSE   The ovum is the largest cell in the human body. (p. 483)

2.   TRUE   FALSE   Half of all fertilized eggs contain some kind of abnormality. (p. 485)

3.   TRUE   FALSE   If females are exposed to male hormones in utero, they tend to engage in more rough-and-tumble play later. (p. 508)

4.   TRUE   FALSE   In general, Piaget seems to have *underestimated* the abilities of infants. (p. 501)

5.   TRUE   FALSE   All adolescents learn to reason abstractly. (p. 513)

6.   TRUE   FALSE   One-third of adolescents are seriously depressed. (p. 515)

7.   TRUE   FALSE   Everyone follows predictable stages of death acceptance. (p. 526)

8.   TRUE   FALSE   Crystallized intelligence declines during adulthood, while fluid intelligence increases. (p. 521)

9.   TRUE   FALSE   People tend to expand their circle of friends throughout adulthood. (p. 525)

10. TRUE   FALSE   Even 3-month-olds can form memories. (p. 496)

Multiple-Choice Questions
For each question, circle the best answer from the choices given.

1.   The male gender is determined by the contribution of a(n) _____ sex chromosome by the: (p. 483)
     a.   X; father.
     b.   X; mother.
     c.   Y; father.
     d.   Y; mother.

2.   The first stage of the third trimester of prenatal development is called the: (p. 484)
     a.   Zygote.
     b.   Embryo.
     c.   Ovum.
     d.   Fetus.

3. Insufficient folic acid during pregnancy can lead to: (p. 486)
    a.   Disruptions in the development of the nervous system.
    b.   Sudden infant death syndrome.
    c.   Miscarriage.
    d.   Lower birth weight.

4. The reflex in which a newborn infant curls his toes under when the ball of his foot is pressed is called: (p. 489)
    a.   Moro.
    b.   Babinski.
    c.   Plantar.
    d.   Tonic.

5. Which of the following senses is *least* well-developed at birth? (p. 493)
    a.   Hearing
    b.   Touch
    c.   Smell
    d.   Vision

6. In 2003, Dr. McKinley tests a group of 20-year-olds, a group of 40-year-olds, and a group of 60-year-olds on memory skills. This type of study is a(n): (p. 521)
    a.   Experiment.
    b.   Cross-sectional study.
    c.   Longitudinal study.
    d.   Time-lag design.

7. According to Piaget, when does a child begin fantasy play? (p. 499)
    a.   During the sensorimotor period
    b.   During the preoperational period
    c.   During the concrete operational period
    d.   At various times throughout development

8. Vygotsky's theory emphasizes the role of _____ in the development of children's cognitive abilities. (p. 504)
    a.   Theory of mind
    b.   Culture
    c.   Working memory
    d.   Biological changes

9. The least common type of attachment among American babies is: (p. 506)
    a.   Avoidant.
    b.   Resistant.
    c.   Secure.
    d.   Disorganized.

10. Children in the _____ level of moral development behave in ways that focus on the rules that maintain social order. (p. 509)
    a. Preconventional
    b. Postconventional
    c. Conventional
    d. Formal operational

11. In Maccoby's view, _____ are the key to learning gender roles. (p. 511)
    a. Peer group interactions
    b. Interactions with parents
    c. Interactions with siblings
    d. Hormonal influences

12. Adolescents are mostly influenced by their peers in domains of: (p. 511)
    a. Basic values.
    b. Religion.
    c. Life goals.
    d. Social behavior.

13. Menopause typically occurs between: (p. 518)
    a. 35 and 45.
    b. 55 and 65.
    c. 45 and 55.
    d. 65 and 75.

14. After the age of 50 or so, people have increased difficulty hearing: (p. 519)
    a. Low frequency sounds.
    b. Background noise.
    c. High frequency sounds.
    d. Voices.

15. As people age, _____ influences on general intelligence increase. (p. 521)
    a. Environmental
    b. Peer
    c. Genetic
    d. Academic

Essay Questions

Answer the following questions in the space provided.

1. How does physical development in infancy differ from physical development in adolescence? _____

    _____

    _____

    _____

    _____

    _____

    _____

2. Was Piaget accurate in his description of cognitive development? _____

    _____

    _____

    _____

    _____

    _____

    _____

3. Is adolescence a period of "storm and stress"? _____

    _____

    _____

    _____

    _____

    _____

4. Are there age-related declines in memory? _____

    _____

    _____

    _____

    _____

    _____

5. Was Kubler-Ross accurate in her description of the stages of death acceptance? _____

    _____

    _____

    _____

    _____

    _____

6.   Researchers have recently uncovered almost all of the genetic sequence. Armed with such knowledge, what benefits do you foresee? What dangers may lie ahead?_____

_____

_____

_____

_____

_____

_____

7.   After the age of two, separation anxiety begins to diminish in young toddlers. Why do you think this happens? Why do you think that some children then later develop a psychological disorder in which they fear separation from their parent(s), even though they have clearly developed object permanence?_____

_____

_____

_____

_____

_____

_____

8.   What are your thoughts on the effects of day care on child development? Do you think mothers return to work too early? If you were raising a child, how would you balance your emphasis on academic achievement with messages about the importance of family? Do you expect to put your children in day care? If not, how do you plan to balance your career with your family life?_____

_____

_____

_____

_____

_____

_____

9.   What was your adolescence like? Was there strife in your family? Did you experience more conflict with your mother or with your father? What was the source of your conflict? How is your relationship with both parents now?_____

_____

_____

_____

_____

_____

_____

10.   The successful resolution of the integrity versus despair stage of psychosocial development may be related to an elderly person's fear of death, with those who resolve it successfully (looking back and having no regrets) having less fear than those who do not. Why do you think this is? Could this explain why women report more fear of death than men do? Is it possible that women are not as likely to successfully resolve this stage? Why? Or do you think there are other more plausible reasons for the gender differences?_____

_____

_____

_____

_____

_____

_____

When You Are Finished. . . Puzzle It Out

Across
4. Developed theory of moral thinking
8. A fertilized ovum
10. Has been reduced by sleeping on backs
13. Group of people born at same time
14. Chemical that can damage the fetus
15. Developed the theory of attachment
16. Mental structure organizing events
18. Looking-time technique
19. Emotional bond between parent and child
20. Tests infant's depth perception

Down
1. Automatic response to an event
2. Distress following loss of loved one
3. AKA the startle reflex
5. They mature faster than boys
6. He emphasized culture in development
7. Number of stages in Piaget's theory
9. Piaget's period from 2-7 years
11. Puberty to end of teen years
12. Contained on the chromosomes in a series of "rungs"
17. Developing baby from eight weeks to birth

Puzzle created with Puzzlemaker at DiscoverySchool.com.

Chapter 13
Stress, Health, and Coping

Before You Read . . .

Do you feel *stressed*? If so, what does this feel like physically and emotionally? In this chapter, you will learn exactly what stress is, from the physiology of it, to the sources of stress. You will learn that stress is a subjective experience, and that there are certain qualities of situations (perceived controllability and predictability) that make them more or less difficult to handle. You will also read about the different areas in your life which might lead you to feel stressed including internal conflicts, hassles, and feelings of anger.

Be careful—too much stress can take a toll on your health, as you'll read about in the second section. Immune dysfunction, cancer, heart disease, and sleep disturbances are all linked to stress. But at least there's something you can do about it. You *can* change your health-impairing behaviors and develop more effective coping strategies. You will learn about these strategies in the last section of this chapter, where you'll also read about the link between coping and social support. Mind-body interventions, gender, and culture are covered as well.

Chapter Objectives

After reading this chapter, you should be able to:

♦　　Define stress.

♦　　Describe the physiology of stress.

♦　　Name common sources of stress.

♦　　Explain how stress affects health.

♦　　Name and describe the different types of coping strategies.

♦　　Describe how relationships affect stress and health.

♦　　Explain mind-body interventions.

♦　　Describe the role of gender and culture in coping.

As You Read. . . Term Identification

Make flashcards using the following terms as you go. Use the definitions in the margins of this chapter for help. If you write the definitions in your own words, though, you will remember them better!

Acute stressor
Aggression
Alarm phase
Approach-approach conflict
Approach-avoidance conflict
Atherosclerosis
Avoidance-avoidance conflict
B cell
Burnout
Chronic stressor
Coping
Emotion-focused coping
Enacted social support
Exhaustion phase
General adaptation syndrome (GAS)
Glucocorticoids

Hardy personality
Health psychology
Hostile attribution bias
Hostility
Internal conflict
Natural killer (NK) cell
Nocebo effect
Perceived social support
Problem-focused coping
Resistance phase
Social support
Stress
Stressor
Stress response
T cell
Thought suppression

As You Read . . . Questions and Exercises

What is Stress?

Stress: The Big Picture

Distinguish between **stress** and **stressor**._____
_____
_____
_____
_____
_____
_____
_____

Provide an example from your life of each of the following types of **stressors**:

	Acute Stressor	Chronic Stressor
Physical Stressor		
Psychological Stressor		
Social Stressor		

The Biology of Stress

Describe what happens during each phase of the **General Adaptation Syndrome**:

Phase	Body's Response
Alarm	
Resistance	
Exhaustion	

How can **glucocorticoids** be both good and bad for our bodies? _____
_____
_____
_____
_____
_____

The Sources of Stress

Provide a personal example of a **stressor** in your life that might not be a **stressor** to someone else.
_____
_____
_____
_____

Distinguish between **primary appraisal** and **secondary appraisal**. _____
_____
_____
_____
_____
_____

Fill in the table below with examples of **stressors** that are either **controllable** or **uncontrollable**, and **predictable** or **unpredictable**. Which would be more stressful to you? Why?

Controll-ability / Predictability	Controllable	Uncontrollable
Predictable		
Unpredictable		

Under what circumstances is **predictability** unlikely to be helpful in dealing with an upcoming stressor?_____

_____

_____

_____

_____

_____

_____

What is the importance of the **form** and **timing** of warnings in helping to reduce stress?_____

_____

_____

_____

_____

_____

Identify the following situations as being **approach-approach conflicts, approach-avoidance conflicts,** or **avoidance-avoidance conflicts:**

Situation	Type of Conflict
Two people you really like ask you out on a date!	
You have to take biology or chemistry, and you can't stand either one!	
You <u>love</u> the new Miata, but you can't really afford it.	
Only one graduate school accepted you, and you have nowhere else to go.	
Your mom offers you two tickets to the movies, but you have to take your sister.	
You can't decide between chocolate or vanilla ice cream.	

GO SURFING...

...to find out how you would score on a **Life Events Stress Test**. You can find these tests at the following sites:

♦   http://www.stresstips.com/lifeevents.htm
♦   http://www.eap.com.au/stress_test.htm
♦   http://www.stress-help.co.uk/SRRS.htm
♦   http://www.success.net.au/stress_test.html

This type of test is no longer thought to be a good measure of **stress**. Why not? _____
_____
_____
_____
_____
_____

What is meant by "**daily hassles**," and what are the negative effects of such hassles on a person's functioning? _____
_____
_____
_____
_____
_____
_____

What are some of the **daily hassles** in your life that create **stress**? _____
_____
_____
_____
_____
_____

If you were the manager of a company, how would you design your office space so as to reduce your employees' **stress**? _____
_____
_____
_____
_____
_____
_____

As the manager of a company, what other policies could you institute to reduce **stress**? _____

_____

_____

_____

_____

_____

What is **burnout**? What are the symptoms? _____

_____

_____

_____

_____

_____

Do you think that you will be likely to experience **burnout**? Why or why not? _____

_____

_____

_____

_____

_____

What other personal and environmental characteristics contribute to **stress**?_____

_____

_____

_____

_____

_____

GO SURFING...

...to find out if you have a **Type A personality**. Short inventories are available at the following sites:

- ♦ http://itech.fgcu.edu/cgi-bin/lchallenges/survey/typea.html
- ♦ http://www.prenhall.com/whetten_dms/chap2_3.html
- ♦ http://attila.stevens-tech.edu/~rreilly/TYPE_A/TYPE_A.HTM

What did these surveys indicate? _____

Do you agree or disagree with the results? _____

_____

Looking at Levels

How can **hostility** lead to illness, at the levels of the **brain, the person, and the group**? Use arrows to indicate how factors at the different levels may interact.

The Brain	The Person	The Group

TRY PRACTICE TEST #1 NOW!
GOOD LUCK!

Stress, Disease, and Health

The Immune System: Catching Cold

What types of stressors are most likely to alter **immune functioning**? _____
_____
_____
_____
_____
_____
_____

How does stress harm the **immune system**? _____
_____
_____
_____
_____
_____
_____

Cancer

What are the two ways in which stress can affect the growth of cancerous cells?

♦ _____

♦ _____

What role does **perception of control** play in the progression of cancer? _____

_____

_____

_____

_____

_____

_____

Heart Disease

Describe the link between **stress** and **heart disease**._____

_____

_____

_____

_____

_____

Health-Impairing Behaviors

Why do people engage in **health-impairing behaviors**?_____

_____

_____

_____

_____

_____

In your own words, describe each of the 5 stages of **Prochaska's** model of change.

♦ _____

_____

_____

♦ _____

_____

_____

_____

◆ _____
_____
_____

◆ _____
_____
_____
_____

◆ _____
_____
_____
_____

Is there any **health-impairing behavior** that you are trying to change?_____
If so, what **stage** of Prochaska's model do you think you are in? Why?_____
_____
_____

If you had a friend and were trying to get them to stop smoking, what could you do to move them along in the different **stages**?

◆ _____

◆ _____

◆ _____

◆ _____

◆ _____

◆ _____

◆ _____

Looking at Levels

Should **support groups** be a necessary component of treatment for cancer? Why or why not?
What negative effects might forcing someone to go to a support group have on the progression of the cancer?_____
_____
_____
_____

TRY PRACTICE TEST #2 NOW!
GOOD LUCK!

Strategies for Coping

Coping Strategies: Approaches and Tactics

Identify the following coping responses below as problem-focused or emotion-focused:

Coping response	Emotion-focused	Problem-focused
"I refuse to feel bad about this grade – everyone else got a bad grade too!"		
"This is a bad grade. I better buckle down and study harder for the next exam."		
"This is a bad grade. I think I'll go and talk to the teacher about how I can do better."		
Joan calls her mother and talks for hours on end about her boss, her husband, and her kids – they're driving her crazy!		

Name a situation in which you have tried each of the following **coping strategies**.

Coping Strategy	Definition	Example
Active coping		
Planning		
Instrumental social support		
Suppression of competing activities		
Restraint coping		
Emotional social support		
Venting emotions		

Coping Strategy	Definition	Example
Positive reinterpretation/growth		
Behavioral disengagement		
Mental disengagement		
Thought suppression		
Humor		

Did you notice if you have a preference for certain **coping strategies** over others? If so, which ones? Why? Are these known to be effective coping strategies?_____

_____

_____

_____

_____

_____

Explain the opposite effects that **stimulants** and **depressants** have on the individual, both physiologically and psychologically.

Drug	Physiological Effects	Psychological Effects
Alcohol		
Cocaine		

Explain how **cocaine**, a drug that initially produces pleasure, can ultimately lead to the loss of pleasure from other sources (e.g., food and sex). _____

_____

_____

_____

_____

_____

_____

Name the factors at each of the following levels that may lead to **aggression**.

Personal Factors	Environmental Factors

Personality and Coping

GO SURFING...

...to find out if you have an **optimistic personality**. Short inventories are available at the following sites:

- http://www.myprimetime.com/health/optimism/optimism_quiz.jsp
- http://www.discord.org/~lippard/optimism.html
- http://www.healthyexpectations.gmu.edu/7lhp/Optimism.htm
- http://www.bilk.ac.uk/college/research/allpd/Optimism.htm

What did these surveys indicate? _____

Do you agree or disagree with the results? _____

_____

What are the **personality variables** that make people better able to cope with **stress**?

- _____
- _____
- _____
- _____
- _____
- _____
- _____
- _____

Think of someone you know who seems about to cope with stress well. (This could be you, if appropriate.) Which of these **personality variables** does this person have?_____

_____

_____

Coping and Social Support

Describe five noted benefits of a good **social support system**.

- ♦ _____
- ♦ _____
- ♦ _____
- ♦ _____
- ♦ _____

Distinguish between **perceived social support** and **enacted social support**. Which is more important in buffering against stress? _____

_____

_____

_____

_____

_____

Evaluate your **social support network**. Do you feel like you have adequate social support? Why or why not?_____

_____

_____

_____

_____

_____

Mind-Body Interventions

List four **mind-body interventions**:

- ♦ _____
- ♦ _____
- ♦ _____
- ♦ _____

How do **mind-body interventions** appear to work? _____
_____
_____
_____
_____
_____

What is a **placebo**? How can it be effective?_____
_____
_____
_____
_____
_____
_____

Gender, Culture, and Coping

Describe the **positive** and **negative effects** of **multiple roles** for women:

Negative Effects	Positive Effects

Looking at Levels

How might the **nocebo effect** work on a psychological level, for example when you expect to do poorly on a test?_____
_____
_____
_____
_____
_____
_____

TRY PRACTICE TEST #3 NOW!
GOOD LUCK!

After You Read . . . Thinking Back

1. Why might some people **perceive** stress differently than others? Relate this to top-down and bottom-up processing that you learned about in Chapter 4._____

    _____
    _____
    _____
    _____
    _____
    _____
    _____

2. How might **sleep** and **stress** interact? Discuss._____

    _____
    _____
    _____
    _____
    _____
    _____
    _____

3. Use your knowledge of sensation and perception to discuss how **placebos** work?

    _____
    _____
    _____
    _____
    _____
    _____
    _____

4. Given what you know about personality and its origins, how successful do you think it will be to try to develop programs to help individuals become **hardy** and **optimistic**?_____

    _____
    _____
    _____
    _____
    _____
    _____

5. How can principles of learning be used to help individual end **health-impairing behaviors**?

    _____
    _____
    _____
    _____
    _____
    _____

After You Read . . . Thinking Ahead

1. Why does **stress** lead to psychological disorders (such as posttraumatic stress disorder) in some cases but not others?_____
    _____
    _____
    _____
    _____
    _____
    _____

2. What other psychological disorders do you think might be influenced by **stress**? Why?
    _____
    _____
    _____
    _____
    _____
    _____

3. How could public health officials use **Prochaska's model** to develop campaigns to help individuals end health-impairing behaviors?_____
    _____
    _____
    _____
    _____
    _____
    _____

4. How do you think **stress** affects relationships with others, including relationships with intimate partners? How do women's multiple roles influence this **stress**?_____
    _____
    _____
    _____
    _____
    _____
    _____
    _____
    _____

5. How might group norms, such as in an office place, affect individuals' **stress**? Explain.
    _____
    _____
    _____
    _____
    _____

After You Read . . . Practice Tests

PRACTICE TEST #1:
WHAT IS STRESS?

Multiple-Choice Questions

For each question, circle the best answer from the choices given.

1.   The body's naturally-produced anti-inflammatory agent is/are called: (p. 536)
    a.   Endorphins and enkephalins.
    b.   Dopamine and serotonin.
    c.   Glucocorticoids.
    d.   Epinephrine and norepinephrine.

2.   Stage two of Selye's three-stage stress response is called: (p. 536)
    a.   Alarm.
    b.   Exhaustion.
    c.   Resistance.
    d.   Coping.

3.   When the stress response is triggered, the hypothalamas secretes a substance that causes the release of: (p. 536)
    a.   Epinephrine.
    b.   Dopamine.
    c.   Norepinephrine.
    d.   Glucocorticoids.

4.   During the primary appraisal of a situation: (p. 538)
    a.   Cortisol is released.
    b.   The GAS is activated.
    c.   It is as if the person asks "What can I do about this?"
    d.   It is as if the person asks, "What's going on here?"

5.   After the secondary appraisal comes: (p. 538)
    a.   Tertiary appraisal.
    b.   Coping.
    c.   Fight or flight.
    d.   General adaptation.

6.   A perceived lack of control in the face of a stressor may lead to: (p. 538)
    a.   Chronic ulcers.
    b.   Learned helplessness.
    c.   Heart disease.
    d.   An anxiety disorder.

7.   In general, perceived control is helpful: (p. 539)
      a.   When you can see how much worse things *could* have been.
      b.   In most situations.
      c.   In situations that are unpredictable.
      d.   When you are depleted of coping resources.

8.   When you can't decide between the double-chocolate cake and strawberry mousse pie, because you like them both, you are experiencing an _____ conflict. (p. 539)
      a.   Approach-approach
      b.   Avoidance-approach
      c.   Approach-avoidance
      d.   Avoidance-avoidance

9.   A significant number of daily hassles has been linked to: (p. 540)
      a.   Psychological symptoms.
      b.   Suppressed immune functioning.
      c.   Physical symptoms.
      d.   All of the above.

10.   Which of the following is likely to cause the most work-related stress? (pp. 541-542)
      a.   An open-plan office
      b.   A closed-plan office
      c.   A quiet office
      d.   A well-lit office

PRACTICE TEST #2:
STRESS, DISEASE AND HEALTH

Fill-in-the-Blank Questions

Fill in the following blanks with words from the following word bank.

WORD BANK	
B cells	Immune
Glucocorticoids	Natural killer (NK) cells
Sympathetic nervous system	T cells

The _____ system functions to defend the body against infection. There are two classes

of white blood cells: _____, which mature in the bone marrow, and _____

_____, which mature in the thymus. One type of T-cell is the _____

_____, which detects and destroys damaged or altered cells before they become cancerous. _____

_____, which are released when the stress response is triggered, hinder the

formation of or kill NK cells, making the body more vulnerable to infection and tumor growth.

People whose _____ responds significantly to

stress show the most change in immune system functioning. (p. 545)

Multiple-Choice Questions

For each question, circle the best answer from the choices given.

1. Stress can cause: (pp. 545-546)
    a. An increased risk of infection following injury.
    b. Increased healing time.
    c. Post-traumatic stress disorder.
    d. All of the above.

2. Glucocorticoids affect the immune system by: (p. 545)
    a. Enhancing the production of some white blood cells.
    b. Hindering or killing some white blood cells.
    c. Enhancing the production of some red blood cells.
    d. Hindering or killing some red blood cells.

3. In general, trauma survivors who have _____ immediately after the trauma
   are more likely to develop post-traumatic stress disorder. (p. 546)
    a. Higher heart rates
    b. Perceived loss of control
    c. Lower heart rates
    d. Perceptions of overcontrol

4. A stressor that increases the likelihood of heart disease is: (p. 548)
    a. Marriage.
    b. Major disasters.
    c. Graduate school.
    d. Depression.

5. People who intend to take action *in the next month* to change their health behaviors are in the
    _____ stage. (p. 549)
    a. Contemplation
    b. Preparation
    c. Precontemplation
    d. Maintenance

6. Rewarding oneself with a trip to the movies for not smoking for a week is an example of:
    (p. 551)
    a. Consciousness raising.
    b. Social liberation.
    c. Countering.
    d. Self re-evaluation.

7. Women with breast cancer who attended support groups: (p. 552)
    a. Were cured of the cancer.
    b. Suffered fewer relapses.
    c. Tolerated chemotherapy better.
    d. Were just as likely to be depressed.

8. Studies that investigate the relationship between stress and the immune system typically
    measure _____ as an index of immune system activity. (p. 545)
    a. The number of circulating white blood cells
    b. The number of circulating red blood cells
    c. The amount of damage to white cells
    d. A and B

9. The stress response increases capillary growth in order to carry more white blood cells to the
    site of an injury; however, this also: (p. 547)
    a. Stimulates tumor growth.
    b. Causes tumor growth.
    c. Lowers NK activity.
    d. All of the above.

10. After his grandfather died from lung cancer, Ramon realized the dangers of his own
    smoking and quit immediately. In terms of Prochaska's (1994) stages for changing an
    unhealthy behavior, Ramon is in the _____ stage and using the process of
    _____. (p. 551)
    a. Preparation; emotional arousal
    b. Preparation; self re-evaluation
    c. Action; emotional arousal
    d. Action; self-re-evaluation

PRACTICE TEST #3:
STRATEGIES FOR COPING

True/False Questions
Circle TRUE or FALSE for each of the following statements.

1.   TRUE   FALSE   Venting relieves internal "pressure." (p. 555)

2.   TRUE   FALSE   Thought suppression is an effective way to diminish stress. (p. 556)

3.   TRUE   FALSE   Adult males are more physically aggressive than females and children. (p. 558)

4.   TRUE   FALSE   Males are more likely to be aggressive in response to criticisms of their intellectual ability than are females. (p. 559)

5.   TRUE   FALSE   In general, people with low self-esteem are particularly likely to be aggressive. (p. 559)

6.   TRUE   FALSE   The perception of social support is unrelated to actual social support. (p. 564)

7.   TRUE   FALSE   Crowding is an example of a culturally defined stressor. (p. 567)

8.   TRUE   FALSE   Westerners seem to need less personal space than Asians. (p. 567)

9.   TRUE   FALSE   In Western cultures, women are more stressed than men. (p. 566)

10. TRUE   FALSE   For men, bad marriages are linked to suppressed immune function. (p. 564)

Multiple-Choice Questions
For each question, circle the best answer from the choices given.

1.   Problem-focused coping tends to be used by people who score high on the personality factor of: (p. 553)
   a.   Openness to experience.
   b.   Extraversion.
   c.   Conscientiousness
   d.   Neuroticism.

2. Writing about traumatic experiences in detail resulted in all of the following EXCEPT: (p. 555)
    a.   Improved social support systems.
    b.   Positive moods in the long run.
    c.   Enhanced immune functioning.
    d.   Decreased absenteeism from work.

3. The tendency to interpret the intentions of others negatively is called: (p. 558)
    a.   Avoidant attribution bias.
    b.   Anger bias.
    c.   Hostile attribution bias.
    d.   Misinterpretation bias.

4. Hostile people are more likely to use aggression as a coping mechanism if they: (p. 559)
    a.   Have unstable high self-esteem.
    b.   Have unstable low self-esteem.
    c.   Are female.
    d.   Are easily frightened.

5. Narcissists are likely to respond to a negative evaluation of their performance on a task with: (p. 560)
    a.   Disbelief.
    b.   Humor.
    c.   Annoyance.
    d.   Aggression.

6. If people believe that their actions can influence a stressor, they are likely to use _____; if they believe that a stressor cannot be influenced by their actions, they are more likely to use _____. (p. 553)
    a.   Avoidant coping strategies; nonavoidant coping strategies
    b.   Nonavoidant coping strategies; avoidant coping strategies
    c.   Problem-focused coping; emotion-focused coping
    d.   Emotion-focused coping; problem-focused coping.

7. Carla had been under tremendous stress recently and had gained a lot of weight. After several ineffective attempts to lose weight, she stopped dealing with it entirely and ate whatever she wanted. After that, Carla got involved in a wide variety of new activities, so that she was too busy to think. Carla was first using _____ and later was using _____. (p. 554)
    a.   Mental disengagement; instrumental social support
    b.   Behavioral disengagement; mental disengagement
    c.   Venting; thought suppression
    d.   Thought suppression; venting

8.   Humor can aid in stress reduction by allowing people to: (p. 556)
        a.   Vent their emotions.
        b.   Mentally disengage.
        c.   Make a positive reinterpretation of the stressor.
        d.   All of the above.

9.   Mind-body interventions: (p. 565)
        a.   Work by helping a person change a stressor.
        b.   Work by helping a person adapt to a stressor.
        c.   Don't work.
        d.   Both a & b.

10.   Which of the following is an example of a mind-body intervention? (p. 565)
        a.   Hypnosis
        b.   Social support
        c.   Relaxation techniques
        d.   All of the above

COMPREHENSIVE PRACTICE TEST

True/False Questions

Circle TRUE or FALSE for each of the following statements.

1.   TRUE   FALSE   Everyone copes better with a situation they
                           feel they can control. (p. 538)

2.   TRUE   FALSE   Using avoidant coping strategies has possible negative effects
                           on health. (p. 562)

3.   TRUE   FALSE   Trying to suppress a thought can make you think of it more.
                           (p. 556)

4.   TRUE   FALSE   For certain problems, placebos can be an effective treatment,
                           particularly if presented enthusiastically. (p. 566)

5.   TRUE   FALSE   Women report more stress with multiple roles than do men.
                           (p. 566)

Multiple-Choice Questions

For each question, circle the best answer from the choices given.

1.   The more extreme a stressor is, the more your body produces _____ in an
      attempt to restore equilibrium. (p. 536)
      a.   Glucocorticoids
      b.   Acetylcholine
      c.   Serotonin
      d.   Epinephrine

2.   Walking alone in a dark alley one night, Carrie hears footsteps behind her. Her primary
      appraisal of the situation will lead her to: (p. 538)
      a.   Run.
      b.   Ask herself if she should be concerned.
      c.   Hide.
      d.   Ask herself what she can do about the situation.

3.   We are less likely to be stressed about uncontrollable situations if the situations are at
      least: (p. 538)
      a.   Positive.
      b.   Predictable.
      c.   Unexpected.
      d.   Quick.

494

4. Maria is feeling very burnt out at her job. She may well: (p. 542)
   a. Be tired all the time.
   b. Not sense any social support.
   c. Have an inconsiderate supervisor.
   d. All of the above.

5. In what way(s) can stress affect the growth of cancerous tumor cells? (p.546)
   a. It can suppress the production of NK cells, which prevent the spread of tumors.
   b. It can "feed" the tumors by supplying blood through capillaries.
   c. Both A and B
   d. None of the above—stress has little affect on tumor growth.

6. Patti has four children and a job as a chemistry professor, yet she does not feel stressed. This is probably because: (p. 566)
   a. Patti's husband is extremely supportive.
   b. Patti feels a sense of control in her job.
   c. Patti's family has sufficient financial resources.
   d. All of the above.

7. Mary Jane has failed several of the past statistics exams. As a result, she is certain that she will fail the next exam. Mary Jane's attitude is typical of: (p. 562)
   a. Realism.
   b. Defensive pessimism.
   c. True pessimism.
   d. Optimism.

8. Shirley just failed her psychology midterm and called her mother for advice. Her mother listened and reinterpreted Shirley's failure as an opportunity to pursue other majors. Shirley used a(n) _____-focused coping strategy, and her mother used a(n) _____ -focused coping strategy. (p. 553-554)
   a. Problem; problem
   b. Problem; emotion
   c. Emotion; emotion
   d. Emotion; problem

9. Bob is worried that his wife is cheating on him. He attempts to cope with it by trying to suppress the thought, both at home and at work. What is likely to happen to Bob? (p. 556)
   a. He will be able to suppress the thought at work, but not at home.
   b. He will be able to suppress the thought at home, but not at work.
   c. He will be able to suppress the thought at both work and home.
   d. He will actually think about his wife's possible infidelity even more.

10. Which of the following people is most likely to have an aggressive response to a bad grade? (p. 560)
    a. Zachary, who is extremely narcissistic
    b. Yolanda, who has negative self-esteem
    c. Xavier, who has positive self-esteem
    d. William, who is low in narcissism

11. Two personality traits that play a significant role in coping style are: (pp. 561-562)
    a. Neuroticism and humor.
    b. Optimism/pessimism and sensitizer/repressor.
    c. Conscientiousness and humor.
    d. Hardiness and realism.

12. A person with a hardy personality: (p. 561)
    a. Views life's challenges as opportunities to learn.
    b. Are less committed to their jobs than others.
    c. Experience fewer life challenges.
    d. Are less likely to have physical deformities.

13. People with high levels of social support are likely to: (p. 563)
    a. Live longer.
    b. Get sick less often.
    c. Experience less depression.
    d. All of the above.

14. The most important factor in protecting against getting a cold is: (p. 563)
    a. The number of friends you have.
    b. The variety of support you have.
    c. Having more friends than family members.
    d. Having more family members than friends.

15. Women with multiple roles (e.g., mother, employee, wife) experience all of the following EXCEPT: (p. 566)
    a. Increased social support outside of the home.
    b. Decreased feelings of self-esteem and control.
    c. Increased workload.
    d. Decreased psychological stress.

Essay Questions

Answer the following questions in the space provided.

1. Is controllability always a good thing when it comes to dealing with stressors?

    _____
    _____
    _____
    _____
    _____
    _____
    _____
    _____

2. Is aggression simply a way for people with low self-esteem to feel better about themselves?_____

    _____
    _____
    _____
    _____
    _____
    _____
    _____
    _____

3. What aspects of social support are most important for protecting against stress?

    _____
    _____
    _____
    _____
    _____
    _____
    _____
    _____

4. Given that some people cope better when they perceive control over a situation, while others cope better when they do <u>not</u> perceive control, what are the implications for working with children who have to have repeated painful procedures (e.g., needle sticks). How could we assess for the need (or lack thereof) for control? And once we know what type of control the child wants, how could we give it to him or her? _____

    _____
    _____
    _____
    _____
    _____
    _____
    _____

5. Links between stress and cancer have permeated the media. However, the majority of people do not understand the specific links and the indirect ways in which stress and cancer are related. How might misperceptions of the links between stress and cancer lead an individual down the "wrong" path to health? _____

_____

_____

_____

_____

_____

_____

_____

6. Despite the serious negative consequences of alcohol and other drugs, significant numbers of people use and abuse them. Why? What is the allure? What is the solution?

_____

_____

_____

_____

_____

_____

_____

7. Why do you think that it is the variety of social support that is so important in protecting against getting a cold? Does it follow, then, that it is best to have a large of number of diverse friendships rather than a single best friend? What has been your pattern of relationships in the past, and how have they helped you cope in times of stress? _____

_____

_____

_____

_____

_____

_____

8. What are the personality characteristics associated with a better response to stress? Are there ways that you can develop these characteristics? Discuss._____

_____

_____

_____

_____

_____

_____

_____

9.   How stressed have you felt this year? What factors have contributed to your stress levels?
        How have you dealt with your stress?_____
        _____
        _____
        _____
        _____
        _____
        _____

10.   What are the different ways that culture may mediate the effect of stress? _____
        _____
        _____
        _____
        _____
        _____
        _____
        _____

When You Are Finished . . . Puzzle It Out

Across
1. Type of white blood cell in bone marrow
3. Also called "repressors"
7. First phase of the GAS
10. One component of Type-A personality
12. Stimulus that disrupts equilibrium
13. Behavior intended to harm another
15. Person's reaction to stress
16. Developed the 3-stage stress response
17. Caused by chronic job stressors
18. Developed 5-stage model of change
19. One employee concern in open plan

Down
2. Hormone facilitating "fight or flee"
4. Opposite of pessimism
5. Last phase of the GAS
6. Expressing distressing feelings
7. Short-term stress
8. Plaque build-up in arteries
9. Health-associated personality traits
11. First cognitive appraisal of stressor
14. Destroys damaged or altered cells

Puzzle created with Puzzlemaker at DiscoverySchool.com.

Chapter 14
Psychological Disorders

Before You Read . . .

Have you ever known anyone with a psychological disorder? How did you know that he or she had a disorder? In this chapter, you will learn about some of the symptoms of psychological disorders. It begins with a definition of abnormality, including the various explanations of the causes of abnormality (the brain, the person, and the group) and how abnormal behaviors are categorized into the major psychological disorders and personality disorders using the Diagnostic and Statistical Manual of Mental Disorders.

The major disorders covered in this chapter include some of the more common – depression, anxiety, and eating disorders – and some of the more unusual and less common – schizophrenia and dissociative disorders. For each disorder, a description and discussion of causes is provided.

Chapter Objectives

After reading this chapter, you will be able to:

♦ Define abnormality.

♦ Explain what psychological disorders are and how they are classified and diagnosed.

♦ Define mood disorders and explain what causes them.

♦ Describe the main types of anxiety disorders, including their symptoms and causes.

♦ Describe the symptoms and causes of the different types of schizophrenia.

♦ Define dissociative disorders and explain what causes them.

♦ Describe the symptoms and causes of eating disorders.

♦ Explain what personality disorders are.

As You Read. . . Term Identification

Make flashcards using the following terms as you go. Use the definitions in the margins of this chapter for help. If you write the definitions in your own words, though, you will remember them better!

Agoraphobia

Anorexia nervosa

Antisocial personality disorder (ASPD)

Anxiety disorder

Attributional style

Bipolar disorder

Bulimia nervosa

Compulsion

Delusions

Diathesis-stress model

Dissociative amnesia

Dissociative disorder

Dissociative fugue

Dissociative identity disorder (DID)

Dysthymia

Eating disorder

Generalized anxiety disorder

Hallucinations

High expressed emotion

Hypomania

Manic episode

Major depressive disorder (MDD)

Mood disorder

Negative symptom

Obsession

Obsessive-compulsive disorder (OCD)

Panic attack

Panic disorder

Personality disorder

Phobia

Positive symptom

Posttraumatic stress disorder (PTSD)

Psychological disorder

Psychosis

Schizophrenia

Social causation

Social phobia

Social selection

Specific phobia

As You Read . . . Questions and Exercises

Identifying Disorders: What's Abnormal?

Defining Abnormality

Provide a definition of **abnormality**. Be sure to use the words *distress*, *disability*, and *danger*._____
_____
_____
_____
_____
_____

How can the line between **normal** and **abnormal** be drawn? What is the role of culture in drawing this line?_____

_____

_____

_____

_____

_____

Explaining Abnormality

How was abnormal behavior explained . . .

In ancient Greece:
In the 17th century:
In the middle of the 20th century:

What is the **biopsychosocial model?** _____

_____

_____

_____

_____

What is the **diathesis-stress model?**_____

_____

_____

_____

_____

Explain some of the things that can "go wrong" at each of the following **levels**, which may eventually lead to a psychological disorder.

Level	What Can Go Wrong?
Brain	
Person	
Group	

Describe **David Rosenhan's study** and findings. _____
_____
_____
_____
_____
_____

Categorizing Disorders: Is a Rose Still a Rose by Any Other Name?

The guide used to diagnose mental disorders in the United States is the _____
_____. It is published by the _____
_____, and is in the _____ edition.

Describe what is noted on each of the five **axes** of the **DSM-IV**:

Axis	Description
I	
II	
III	
IV	
V	

Name four criticisms of the **DSM-IV**:

♦ _____

♦ _____

♦ _____

♦ _____

Looking at Levels

Do all acts of violence constitute evidence of a **psychological disorder**? Look back at your definition of a psychological disorder and consider each of the **levels of analysis** (brain, person, and group). Use arrows to indicate how events at the different levels may interact.

The Brain	The Person	The Group

TRY PRACTICE TEST #1 NOW!
GOOD LUCK!

Mood Disorders

Major Depressive Disorder

GO SURFING...

...to find out if you might have depression. Short depression inventories are available at the following sites:

♦   http://www.mentalhelp.net/poc/view_doc.php?id=973&type=doc&cn=Depression%20%28Unipolar%29
♦   http://psychcentral.com/depquiz.htm
♦   http://www.allina.com/ahs/bhs.nsf/page/t_depression
♦   http://discoveryhealth.queendom.com/access_depression_abr.html
♦   http://www.thewayup.com/newsletters/zung.htm

What did these surveys indicate? _____
Do you agree or disagree with the results? _____
_____

What are the "**ABC**s" that are affected by **depression**?
A: _____
B: _____
C: _____

How does **depression** affect the workplace?_____
_____
_____
_____

GO SURFING...

...to find some of the warning signs of **suicide**. (There are lots of good sites out there.) List the signs here:

- ◆ _____
- ◆ _____
- ◆ _____
- ◆ _____
- ◆ _____
- ◆ _____
- ◆ _____
- ◆ _____
- ◆ _____
- ◆ _____

What is **dysthmia**? _____
_____
_____

Bipolar Disorder: Going to Extremes

What is the difference between **mania** and **hypomania**? _____
_____
_____
_____
_____

Explaining Mood Disorders

Summarize the causes of depression at the **levels of the brain, person, and group:**

The Brain	The Person	The Group

How do events at the **different levels interact** with each other?_____

_____

_____

_____

_____

Looking at Levels

Have you ever been around someone who is depressed? What behaviors did the person engage in that either drew you in or pushed you away? How did it make you feel?_____

_____

_____

_____

_____

_____

_____

TRY PRACTICE TEST #2 NOW!
GOOD LUCK!

Anxiety Disorders

Identify the following **psychological disorders**.

Description	Disorder
Avoidance of places where escape may be difficult if a panic attack occurs	
Fear of public embarrassment or humiliation	
Re-experiencing of a traumatic event, avoidance of stimuli, and hypervigilance	
Frequent attacks of inexplicable autonomic arousal, accompanied by fear	
Persistent and intrusive thoughts accompanied by irrational behaviors	
A persistent and excessive fear focused on a specific object or situation	

Describe what is happening at the **level of the brain** for each of the following **disorders**:

Disorder	Level of the Brain
Panic disorder	
Phobias	
Posttraumatic stress disorder	
Obsessive-compulsive disorder	

Operant conditioning is implicated in the maintenance of several **anxiety disorders**. Describe how, for each of the following:

Disorder	Operant Conditioning Process
Phobias	
Obsessive-compulsive disorder	
Posttraumatic stress disorder	

Cognitive factors have also been implicated in a number of disorders. Describe the cognitive distortions that may precipitate or maintain the following disorders:

Disorder	Cognitive Processes
Panic Disorder	
Agoraphobia	
Social phobia	
Obsessive-compulsive disorder	

Panic Disorder

GO SURFING...

...to find out if you might have panic disorder (or another anxiety disorder). Short self-surveys are available at the following sites:

- ◆ http://www.psychcanada.com/en/panic/self_test.html
- ◆ http://www.livingwithanxiety.com/anxiety-quiz.htm
- ◆ http://www.conqueranxiety.com/anxiety_self_quiz.asp

What did these surveys indicate? _____

Do you agree or disagree with the results? _____

_____

Have you or a friend ever had a **panic attack**? If so, how would you or your friend describe it?

_____

_____

_____

_____

Summarize the causes of **panic disorder** at the **levels of the brain, person, and group:**

The Brain	The Person	The Group

How do events at the **different levels interact** with each other?_____
_____
_____
_____
_____

Phobias: Social and Specific

What is **social phobia** (or **Social Anxiety Disorder**)? What are the symptoms? How prevalent is it?_____
_____
_____
_____

Do you have any **phobias**? If so…

GO SURFING…

…to find out the names of these phobias. See complete lists of phobias at the following sites:
♦	http://www.phobialist.com/reverse.html
♦	http://www.geocities.com/beckygretz19/weird_facts_phobias.html
♦	http://www.designedthinking.com/Fear/Phobias/Topics/topics.html

What do you have **phobias** of? What are the names of the **phobias**?_____
_____
_____
_____
_____

A common misconception is that **agoraphobia** is a fear of leaving the house. What is a more accurate definition? _____
_____
_____
_____
_____

Summarize the causes of **phobias** at the **levels of the brain, person, and group:**

The Brain	The Person	The Group

How do events at the **different levels interact** with each other?_____
_____
_____
_____

Obsessive-Compulsive Disorder

GO SURFING...

...to find out if you might have OCD. Short self-surveys are available at the following sites:

♦   http://www.ocfoundation.org/ocf1070a.htm
♦   http://epigee.org/ocd/ybocs.html#test
♦   http://www.nimh.nih.gov/publicat/ocdtrt1.htm

What did these surveys indicate? _____
Do you agree or disagree with the results? _____
_____

Summarize the causes of **OCD** at the **levels of the brain, person, and group:**

The Brain	The Person	The Group

How do events at the **different levels interact** with each other?_____
_____
_____
_____
_____

Posttraumatic Stress Disorder

The diagnosis of **PTSD** is made when three conditions are met:

♦ _____

♦ _____

♦ _____

Three sets of **symptoms** are persistently experienced by the person with **PTSD**:

♦ _____

♦ _____

♦ _____

Summarize the causes of **PTSD** at the **levels of the brain, person, and group**:

The Brain	The Person	The Group

How do events at the **different levels interact** with each other?_____
_____
_____
_____
_____

TRY PRACTICE TEST #3 NOW!
GOOD LUCK!

Schizophrenia

Symptoms: What Schizophrenia Looks Like

Is **schizophrenia** another name for multiple personality disorder? Explain._____

_____

_____

_____

List the **positive** and **negative symptoms** of **schizophrenia**:

Positive Symptoms	Negative Symptoms

Identify the following types of **schizophrenia**, based on the descriptions below:

_____ Bizarre movements, may not speak

_____ Outside of delusions, may seem normal; best prognosis

_____ Inappropriate affect and social behaviors

_____ Doesn't meet criteria for any of other subtypes

Summarize the causes of **schizophrenia**, at **the levels of the brain, person, and group**:

The Brain	The Person	The Group

How do events at the **different levels interact** with each other?_____

_____

_____

_____

_____

Looking at Levels

If the Genain quadruplets had grown up in a less impoverished and punishing environment, do you
think they would have turned out differently? All of them? Which ones and why?_____

_____

_____

_____

_____

_____

_____

_____

_____

_____

TRY PRACTICE TEST #4 NOW!
GOOD LUCK!

Other Axis I Disorders: Dissociative and Eating Disorders

Dissociative Disorders

Identify the following dissociative disorders:

_____	Once called multiple personality disorder
_____	Amnesia and sudden departure from home or work
_____	An inability to remember important personal information

What two characteristics are shared by most individuals with **dissociative identity disorder**?

♦ - _____

♦ _____

How can these two characteristics interact to lead to **dissociative identity disorder**?_____

_____

_____

_____

How is **dissociative identity disorder** similar to **post-traumatic stress disorder**? How is it different? _____

_____

_____

_____

_____

_____

_____

Eating Disorders: You Are How You Eat?

GO SURFING...

...to find out if you might have an eating disorder:
- http://psychcentral.com/eatingquiz.htm
- http://www.sfsu.edu/~shs/dpm/eating.htm
- http://www.eating-disorders.com/doyouqz.htm
- http://www.joannapoppink.com/quiz/bottom.html

What did these surveys indicate? _____

Do you agree or disagree with the results? _____

_____

What characteristic distinguishes between **anorexia** and **bulimia**? _____

_____

_____

_____

_____

Summarize the causes of **anorexia** and **bulimia**, at the **levels of the brain, person, and group**:

Level of Brain		Level of Person		Level of Group	
Anorexia	Bulimia	Anorexia	Bulimia	Anorexia	Bulimia

Looking at Levels

What is meant by the **abstinence violation effect**? How might you help a friend, at the level of the group, whom you suspect has bulimia?_____

_____
_____
_____
_____
_____
_____
_____
_____

TRY PRACTICE TEST #5 NOW!
GOOD LUCK!

Personality Disorders

How are **Axis II disorders** different from **Axis I disorders**? _____

_____
_____
_____
_____
_____

Name 3 criticisms of including **personality disorders** under Axis II (or at all) in the DSM-IV?

◆ _____
_____
_____

◆ _____
_____
_____
_____

◆ _____
_____
_____
_____

Look at the list of **Axis II personality disorders** found in the textbook. Do you know anyone who has a personality disorder, do you think? Who? Which disorder? What leads you to believe this?

◆ _____
_____

◆ _____
_____
_____

◆ _____
_____
_____

List the characteristics of **antisocial personality disorder**. _____
_____
_____
_____

Explain **antisocial personality disorder** at the **levels of the brain, person, and group**. Use arrows to indicate how events at the different levels may interact.

The Brain	The Person	The Group

TRY PRACTICE TEST #6 NOW!
GOOD LUCK!

After You Read . . . Thinking Back

1. In Chapter 6, you learned about biological preparedness. Based on this, are there some phobias that you think are more common? Some that are less? Why? _____
    _____
    _____
    _____
    _____
    _____

2. Sleep and Circadian rhythms appear to play a role in several different psychological disorders. How? _____
    _____
    _____
    _____
    _____
    _____
    _____

3. How would you explain the amnesia associated with the dissociative disorders, given what you learned about memory in Chapter 7?_____
    _____
    _____
    _____
    _____
    _____
    _____

4. In Chapter 10, you learned about different theories of emotions. How might these theories be important in studying psychological disorders? _____
    _____
    _____
    _____
    _____
    _____
    _____

5. How can the idea of critical or sensitive periods, which you learned of in Chapter 12, be applied to the development of psychological disorders?_____
    _____
    _____
    _____
    _____
    _____
    _____

After You Read . . . Thinking Ahead

1.   Different types of therapies will work differently for different disorders. Which disorders do you think could probably best be treated by trying to change someone's thoughts? By trying to change someone's behaviors?

_____
_____
_____
_____
_____

2.   Are there any disorders in which you think the best that can be hoped for is that the symptoms are controlled? In other words, are there some disorders in which the underlying causes cannot be treated? If so, which ones? Why these disorders? _____

_____
_____
_____
_____
_____

3.   What might the consequences be of labeling a person as disordered, both at the individual and group levels?_____

_____
_____
_____
_____
_____

4.   Assume that a person moves to this culture. In their previous culture, the person's behavior was not considered disordered. Here, it is. In such a case, should the person's behavior be considered a psychological disorder or not? What about if it is questionably illegal (e.g., questionable child-rearing practices)?_____

_____
_____
_____
_____
_____

5.   Some psychological disorders may pose problems in forming intimate relationships and friendships. Which disorders? What types of problems?_____

_____
_____
_____
_____
_____

After You Read . . . Practice Tests

PRACTICE TEST #1:
IDENTIFYING PSYCHOLOGICAL DISORDERS

True/False Questions
Circle TRUE or FALSE for each of the following statements.

1. TRUE   FALSE   20% of Americans have a diagnosable mental illness in any given year. (p. 573)

2. TRUE   FALSE   Delusions are mental images so vivid that they appear real. (p. 574)

3. TRUE   FALSE   In 17th century New England, abnormality was thought to be the work of the devil. (p. 575)

4. TRUE   FALSE   The first edition of the DSM was published in the 1950s. (p. 577)

5. TRUE   FALSE   There are four axes in the DSM. (p. 577)

6. TRUE   FALSE   White patients are more likely than African-Americans to be evaluated negatively. (p. 577)

7. TRUE   FALSE   One criticism of the DSM is that it creates psychiatric diagnoses for medical problems. (p. 578)

8. TRUE   FALSE   There are 17 categories of disorders included in the DSM. (p. 578)

9. TRUE   FALSE   Whether hearing voices should be considered abnormal depends on the cultural context. (p. 574)

10. TRUE   FALSE   Either a diathesis or stress alone can explain a psychological disorder. (p. 575)

Multiple-Choice Questions

For each question, circle the best answer from the choices given.

1.   The inability to accurately perceive and comprehend reality, combined with a gross disorganization of behavior, is called: (p. 574)
    a.   Insanity.
    b.   Neurosis.
    c.   Incompetency.
    d.   Psychosis.

2.   Mental images so vivid that they seem real, but lacking in objective reality, are called: (p. 574)
    a.   Hallucinations.
    b.   Psychoses.
    c.   Delusions.
    d.   Neuroses.

3.   The definition of a psychological disorder includes all of the following elements except: (p. 573)
    a.   Distress.
    b.   Disability.
    c.   Disease.
    d.   Danger.

4.   According to some estimates, up to _____ percent of Americans have experienced at least one common psychological disorder in their lives. (p. 573)
    a.   36
    b.   48
    c.   57
    d.   64

5.   The biopsychosocial model focuses on factors at the level of the _____ as causing psychological illness. (p. 575)
    a.   Brain
    b.   Group
    c.   Person
    d.   All of the above

6.   Which of the following would be an example of a *diathesis*? (p. 575)
    a.   An imbalance of neurotransmitter levels
    b.   A natural catastrophe
    c.   Relationship loss
    d.   Culture

7. David Rosenhan's experiment demonstrated the power of: (p. 576)
    a. The diathesis
    b. Labeling
    c. The catharsis
    d. Healing

8. The DSM is the: (p. 577)
    a. Diagnostic and Statistical Manual of Mental Disorders.
    b. Dictionary of Symptoms of Mental Disorders.
    c. Definitive Symptomotology of Mental Illness.
    d. Diary of Symptoms of Mental Illness.

9. Joel is clinically depressed. He has just been diagnosed with cancer and is having difficulty coping with his medical regimen. Joel's cancer would be noted on Axis _____ of the DSM-IV. (p. 577)
    a. I
    b. II
    c. III
    d. IV

10. Which of the following is NOT a criticism of the DSM-IV-TR? (p. 578)
    a. There are too many diagnoses.
    b. Some of the diagnoses are about medical problems.
    c. There is no such thing as mental illness.
    d. Some of the diagnoses are not distinct from each other.

PRACTICE TEST #2:
MOOD DISORDERS

True/False Questions

Circle TRUE or FALSE to each of the following statements.

1.   TRUE   FALSE   People who talk about suicide don't actually attempt suicide. (p. 584)

2.   TRUE   FALSE   People who attempt suicide are "crazy." (p. 584)

3.   TRUE   FALSE   Most suicidal people really want to die. (p. 584)

4.   TRUE   FALSE   People who think about suicide don't want to be helped. (p. 584)

5.   TRUE   FALSE   Discussing suicide with a person who is suicidal can be helpful. (p. 584)

Multiple-Choice Questions

For each question, circle the best answer from the choices given.

1.   The most common psychological disorder is: (p. 583)
   a.   Depression.
   b.   Obsessive-compulsive disorder.
   c.   Panic disorder.
   d.   Schizophrenia.

2.   Most suicide attempts are motivated by the sense of _____ that is part of depression. (p. 583)
   a.   Hopelessness
   b.   Guilt
   c.   Helplessness
   d.   Sadness

3.   In people with bipolar disorder, the _____ is sometimes enlarged. (p. 586)
   a.   Amygdala
   b.   Locus coeruleus
   c.   Hypothalamus
   d.   Occipital lobe

4. Marita has experienced a depressed mood for most of the day for at least two years, as well as problems sleeping and feeling tired during the day. The most appropriate diagnosis for Marita would probably be: (p. 583)
   a. Major depressive disorder.
   b. Dysthymia.
   c. Bipolar disorder.
   d. Mania.

5. Which of the following is NOT one of the diagnostic criteria for major depressive disorder? (p. 581)
   a. Significant weight gain
   b. Daily fatigue
   c. Daily insomnia or hypersomnia
   d. Depressed mood most of the day, almost daily

6. The early phase of a manic attack is called: (p. 585)
   a. Hypomania.
   b. Dysthymia.
   c. The prodromal phase.
   d. Agitation.

7. For people with depression, unsupportive and critical relatives can increase the: (p. 587)
   a. Risk of onset.
   b. Risk of relapse.
   c. Length of first episode.
   d. Response time to medication.

8. Which of the following is likely to be true of a person with bipolar disorder? (p. 586)
   a. She may have a larger amygdala than most people.
   b. She may have a larger hippocampus than most people.
   c. She may show an abnormal pattern of activation in the brainstem.
   d. She may have smaller occipital lobes than most people.

9. Which of the following neurotransmitters has been implicated in depression? (p. 586)
   a. Substance P
   b. Serotonin
   c. Norepinephrine
   d. All of the above

10. Recent increases in bipolar disorder may be attributable to: (p. 588)
    a. Fewer available treatment programs.
    b. The development of electric lights, which has unnaturally lengthened the day.
    d. The lengthening of the life span.
    d. More stress in childhood.

PRACTICE TEST #3:
ANXIETY DISORDERS

Fill-in-the-Blank Questions

Complete the following paragraph by filling in the blanks with the following words:

WORD BANK	
Crime	Negative reinforcement
Limbic system	Social support
Locus coerulus	Type of trauma
Natural disasters	

The majority of people who experience trauma do not go on to experience PTSD. The

_____ makes a difference in whether PTSD will be experienced. For example,

women are more likely to develop PTSD when their traumas resulted from _____

_____ than from _____. A genetic predisposition to develop PTSD may be a

hypersensitivity of the _____. In addition, the _____ may be more

easily activated by mental imagery of traumatic events. At the level of the person,

_____ helps to explain why people with PTSD develop substance abuse

because when the substances are taken, the symptoms subside. Group factors can both increase or

decrease the likelihood that PTSD will develop because group factors usually play an integral role in

creating the trauma; on the other hand, _____ can also mitigate the effects

of the trauma. (p. 596-598)

Multiple-Choice Questions

For each question, circle the best answer from the choices given.

1. A person who suffers attacks of intense fear or discomfort, accompanied by heightened sympathetic nervous system activity, would be diagnosed with: (p. 590)
   a. Generalized anxiety.
   b. Depression.
   c. Panic disorder.
   d. Agoraphobia.

2. People with *anxiety sensitivity*: (p. 591)
   a. Have an abnormally sensitive locus coeruleus.
   b. Have an abnormally sensitive withdrawal system in the right frontal lobe.
   c. Believe that everything in the world is dangerous.
   d. Believe that the physiological symptoms of autonomic arousal can be harmful.

3. Phobias are typically *maintained* through: (p. 594)
   a. Classical conditioning.
   b. Counterconditioning.
   c. Operant conditioning.
   d. Cognitive reinterpretation.

4. Which of the following traumas would be most likely to result in post-traumatic stress disorder in women? (p. 597)
   a. A mugging
   b. A plane crash
   c. A hurricane
   d. Being fired from work

5. Recurrent, persistent, intrusive, and uncontrollable thoughts, impulses or images that cause anxiety are called: (p. 594)
   a. Daily hassles.
   b. Phobias.
   c. Compulsions.
   d. Obsessions.

6. The neurotransmitter _____ probably plays a role in obsessive-compulsive disorder. (p. 595)
   a. Dopamine
   b. GABA
   c. Acetylcholine
   d. Serotonin

7. People with panic disorder tend to: (p. 592)
   a. Have recently experienced trauma.
   b. Have experienced more stressful life events in childhood and adolescence.
   c. Also have a personality disorder.
   d. Have had depressed mothers.

8. Which of the following ways of coping would best *protect* someone from developing PTSD following a traumatic event? (p. 598)
   a. Social support
   b. Ruminating about the event
   c. Using relaxation techniques after the event
   d. Using thought suppression about the event

9. Phobias involve hypersensitivity of the: (p. 593)
   a. Hippocampus.
   b. Hypothalamus.
   c. Amygdala.
   d. Caudate nucleus.

10.   Not everyone who experiences an extremely traumatic event develops PTSD, suggesting that: (pp. 596-598)
   a.   Certain traumatic events are more likely triggers for the disorder.
   b.   It probably involves a genetic predisposition.
   c.   It is more likely to occur only in people with certain personality types.
   d.   All of the above.

PRACTICE TEST #4:
SCHIZOPHRENIA

True/False Questions
Circle TRUE or FALSE for each of the following statements.

1. TRUE   FALSE   Most people with a parent or sibling with schizophrenia do not develop the illness themselves. (p. 602)

2. TRUE   FALSE   Children who are at-risk for schizophrenia are more reactive to stress than their peers. (p. 603)

3. TRUE   FALSE   There is a higher incidence of prenatal and birth complications in the mothers of babies who later develop schizophrenia. (p. 603)

4. TRUE   FALSE   Early signs of schizophrenia typically emerge during adolescence. (p. 603)

5. TRUE   FALSE   Home movies of children who later develop schizophrenia reveal that they show more expressions of joy as children than their unaffected counterparts. (p. 603)

Multiple-Choice Questions
For each question, circle the best answer from the choices given.

1. Positive symptoms of schizophrenia are those that: (p. 599)
    a. Must be present for a diagnosis to be made.
    b. Are healthy and desirable, but not very common.
    c. Are present during the first half of the disorder.
    d. Mark the presence or excess of certain functions.

2. Alogia and flat affect are _____ symptoms of schizophrenia. (p. 599)
    a. Positive
    b. Necessary
    c. Negative
    d. Crucial

3. The type of schizophrenia with the best prognosis for recovery is: (p. 601)
    a. Paranoid.
    b. Catatonic.
    c. Disorganized.
    d. Undifferentiated

4. People with schizophrenia have enlarged: (p. 602)
   a. Occipital lobes.
   b. Ventricles.
   c. Temporal lobes.
   d. Sulci and gyri.

5. As children, people who later develop schizophrenia often have: (p. 603)
   a. Hallucinations and delusions.
   b. Obsessions and compulsions.
   c. Positive and negative symptoms.
   d. Involuntary movements.

6. High expressed emotion families are those that are: (p. 603)
   a. Critical, hostile, and overinvolved.
   b. Loving but underinvolved.
   c. Angry and withdrawn from one another.
   d. Overly expressive in both positive and negative emotions.

7. Fiona often twists her body into contorted positions and stands like that for hours. Fiona is probably suffering from which subtype of schizophrenia? (p. 603)
   a. Catatonic
   b. Paranoid
   c. Undifferentiated
   d. Disorganized

8. If someone has relatives with schizophrenia, they have _____ probability of developing the disorder and the probability _____ with the degree of closeness of the relative. (p. 601)
   a. No higher; does not increase
   b. A higher; does not increase
   c. A higher; increases
   d. It varies with the subtype of schizophrenia.

9. Research indicates that people with schizophrenia: (p. 602)
   a. Have lower levels of cortisol.
   b. Are more reactive to stress.
   c. Have smaller ventricles.
   d. Do not produce enough dopamine.

10. Which of the following is NOT one possible explanation for schizophrenia? (p. 602)
    a. There is excessive pruning of neural connections during adolescence.
    b. Mothers of people with schizophrenia were malnourished during pregnancy.
    c. There is a genetic predisposition to schizophrenia.
    d. People with schizophrenia are particularly affected by seasonal changes in light.

PRACTICE TEST #5:
OTHER AXIS I DISORDERS

True/False Questions

Circle TRUE or FALSE for each of the following statements.

1.   TRUE   FALSE   Dissociative disorders may be overdiagnosed. (p. 607)

2.   TRUE   FALSE   All alter personalities know the other alter personalities. (p. 608)

3.   TRUE   FALSE   In a dissociative fugue, people may abruptly disappear from home or work. (p. 607)

4.   TRUE   FALSE   People with bulimia nervosa may be overweight. (p. 611)

5.   TRUE   FALSE   Lower levels of serotonin might predispose people to bulimia nervosa. (p. 612)

Multiple-Choice Questions

For each question, circle the best answer from the choices given.

1.   An abrupt, unexpected departure from home or work, combined with an inability to remember some or all of the past, is called: (p. 607)
    a.   Psychogenic amnesia.
    b.   Dissociative identity disorder.
    c.   Dissociative fugue.
    d.   Depersonalization.

2.   Some researchers believe that dissociative identity disorder is a subtype of: (p. 609)
    a.   Dissociative amnesia.
    b.   Post-traumatic stress disorder.
    c.   Dissociative fugue.
    d.   Schizophrenia

3.   In what way are people with bulimia <u>always</u> different from people with anorexia? (p. 610)
    a.   Anorexics are underweight; bulimics are not.
    b.   Bulimics binge and purge; anorexics do not.
    c.   Anorexics restrict their eating; bulimics do not.
    d.   Bulimics take laxatives; anorexics do not.

4. Kinsey is always dieting and never ever eats chocolate brownies. One day, she can't resist the brownies that her mother has baked and she eats a corner of one. If Kinsey experiences the abstinence violation effect when she eats the brownie, then: (p. 613)
   a. She will feel extremely guilty for eating the brownie.
   b. She will immediately stop eating the brownie and purge it from her system.
   c. She will continue eating and gorge herself on brownies.
   d. She will finish the one brownie and then exercise it off tomorrow.

5. According to a major theory of the development of dissociative identity disorder, abused children learn to dissociate because: (p. 608)
   a. They have a genetic predisposition in this direction.
   b. It protects them from experiencing the psychological effects of the abuse.
   c. They have an overly rich fantasy life.
   d. A and C are true.

6. The experience of feeling as if you are observing yourself from the outside is called: (p. 607)
   a. Identity confusion.
   b. Amnesia.
   c. Derealization.
   d. Depersonalization.

7. Which of the following is NOT exhibited by people with eating disorders? (p. 612)
   a. Irrational beliefs
   b. Inappropriate expectations about themselves
   c. Black-and-white thinking
   d. Higher levels of serotonin

8. Which of the following individuals would be LEAST likely to have an eating disorder? (p. 613)
   a. Beth, whose mother was a model
   b. John, who lives in South Africa
   c. Troy, who is a high-school wrestler
   d. Susan, whose family just immigrated from China

9. The dissociative disorders are: (p. 607)
   a. Less frequently diagnosed now than in the past.
   b. More frequently diagnosed now than in the past.
   c. Equally diagnosed now than in the past.
   d. Probably underdiagnosed.

10. Dissociative fugues may increase during: (p. 607)
    a. Large-scale natural disasters.
    b. Winter months.
    c. Economic downturns.
    d. People's adolescent years.

PRACTICE TEST #6:
PERSONALITY DISORDERS

True/False Questions
Circle TRUE or FALSE for each of the following statements.

1. TRUE   FALSE   People with antisocial personality disorder are egocentric and lack charm. (p. 616)

2. TRUE   FALSE   People with antisocial personality disorder lack conscience, empathy, and remorse. (p. 616)

3. TRUE   FALSE   People with antisocial personality disorder have the capacity to care for others. (p. 616)

4. TRUE   FALSE   Antisocial personality disorder occurs in approximately 20 percent of people. (p. 616)

5. TRUE   FALSE   Antisocial personality disorder is not found in non-Western cultures. (p. 616)

Multiple-Choice Questions
For each question, circle the best answer from the choices given.

1. Someone with no guilt, conscience, or empathy for others most likely has a(n) _____ personality disorder. (p. 616)
    a. Avoidant
    b. Narcissistic
    c. Borderline
    d. Antisocial

2. Research suggests that criminality: (p. 617)
    a. Depends on how many criminal acts someone has witnessed.
    b. Is not heritable.
    c. Involves heritable personality traits.
    d. Involves gene Apo27.

3. Personality disorders: (p. 614)
    a. Are usually very obvious.
    b. May be observed only after knowing someone for a long time.
    c. Are inflexible and maladaptive personality traits.
    d. B and C

4. As compared to someone with OCD, a person with obsessive-compulsive personality disorder would have: (p. 615)
   a. Only obsessions.
   b. Only compulsions.
   c. Either obsessions or compulsions, but not both.
   d. Neither obsessions nor compulsions.

5. Some researchers argue that personality disorders should not be included in the DSM as disorders because: (p. 616)
   a. Too few people have them.
   b. They are too difficult to diagnose.
   c. They are really no different than the corresponding Axis I diagnosis.
   d. They are so prevalent.

6. Cathy always seems to need attention to be directed toward her. Further, she is frequently very dramatic. Cathy probably has: (p. 615)
   a. Narcissistic personality disorder.
   b. Histrionic personality disorder.
   c. Avoidant personality disorder.
   d. Paranoid personality disorder.

7. Nick is uncomfortable in group settings. Whenever he sees people talking, he assumes that it must be about him. Nick probably has: (p. 615)
   a. Borderline personality disorder.
   b. Paranoid personality disorder.
   c. Schizoid personality disorder.
   d. Schizotypal personality disorder.

8. Carol rarely asks about other people and often talks about herself and her accomplishments. Carol probably has: (p. 615)
   a. Narcissistic personality disorder.
   b. Histrionic personality disorder.
   c. Antisocial personality disorder.
   d. Obsessive-compulsive personality disorder.

9. People with antisocial personality disorder: (p. 617)
   a. Often had a poor attachment to their caregiver during childhood.
   b. May have witnessed a lack of concern for the welfare of others by peers or parents.
   c. May have an underreponsive central nervous system.
   d. All of the above.

10. Which of the following is NOT true of antisocial personality disorder? (p. 616)
    a. It occurs more in men than women.
    b. It affects about 10% of the population.
    c. It is found in both Western and non-Western cultures.
    d. It is frequently found in male prisoners.

COMPREHENSIVE PRACTICE TEST

True/False Questions
Circle TRUE or FALSE for each of the following statements.

1. TRUE   FALSE   Only about 10 percent of Americans suffer from a psychological disorder in their lifetime. (p. 573)

2. TRUE   FALSE   African Americans are prescribed higher doses of psychotropic medication than are white Americans. (p. 577)

3. TRUE   FALSE   More men than women have antisocial personality disorder. (p. 616)

4. TRUE   FALSE   The most common psychological disorder is schizophrenia. (p. 581)

5. TRUE   FALSE   Obsessive-compulsive disorder is a psychotic disorder. (p. 574)

6. TRUE   FALSE   Paranoid schizophrenia has the best prognosis of all of the subtypes. (p. 604)

7. TRUE   FALSE   Schizophrenia is another name for multiple personality disorder. (p. 599)

8. TRUE   FALSE   Some people with anorexia binge eat. (p. 611)

Multiple-Choice Questions
For each question, circle the best answer from the choices given.

1. Donte is convinced the CIA is out to get him, although in fact they are not. In this case, Donte's false belief is a(n): (p. 600)
    a.   Hallucination.
    b.   Diathesis.
    c.   Delusion.
    d.   Neurosis.

2. The diathesis-stress model proposes that mental illnesses arise from: (p. 575)
    a.   Genetic vulnerabilities.
    b.   Biochemical imbalances.
    c.   Environmental stressors.
    d.   Some combination of the above.

3.	For the past 2 weeks, Regina has felt very fatigued. She has slept almost all the time and lost a considerable amount of weight. Not even her favorite activities, such as horseback riding, can rouse her interest. Which of the following disorders does Regina probably have? (p. 581)
	a.	Major depressive disorder
	b.	Chronic fatigue syndrome
	c.	Anorexia
	d.	Dysthymia

4.	Which of the following is NOT a criticism of the DSM-IV-TR? (p. 578)
	a.	It includes medical problems as psychological disorders.
	b.	It does not provide a discrete boundary separating abnormality from normality.
	c.	It has too few disorders to adequately describe the range of mental illness.
	d.	The disorders are presented as clearly distinct from one another, even though they're not.

5.	The most studied personality disorder is: (p. 616)
	a.	Depressive personality disorder.
	b.	Dependent personality disorder.
	c.	Antisocial personality disorder.
	d.	Paranoid personality disorder.

6.	Panic attacks may arise from hypersensitivity involving cells in the: (p. 591)
	a.	Occipital lobe.
	b.	Locus coeruleus.
	c.	Hypothalamus.
	d.	Heart.

7.	Frank was been asked to present his company's proposal to a funding board in a few days. However, Frank was *terrified* to speak in public, and consequently quit his job to avoid what he perceived would be great embarrassment. Most likely, Frank would be diagnosed with: (p. 594)
	a.	Social phobia.
	b.	Generalized anxiety disorder.
	c.	Specific phobia.
	d.	Panic disorder.

8.	People who experience a depressed mood for most of the day for at least two years, and two other symptoms of depression as outlined in the DSM-IV, would be diagnosed with: (p. 583)
	a.	Bipolar disorder.
	b.	Mild depression.
	c.	Depression.
	d.	Dysthymia.

9.   As children, people who later developed schizophrenia: (p. 602-603)
     a.   Were happier than others.
     b.   Were more "emotionally dampened" than their peers.
     c.   Slept more.
     d.   Had more irregular schedules.

10. For people with depression, unsupportive and critical relatives can increase the: (p. 587)
     a.   Risk of onset.
     b.   Length of the first episode.
     c.   Risk of relapse.
     d.   Response time to medication.

11. If a person has OCD, other members of the family are more likely to: (p. 595)
     a.   Have an anxiety disorder.
     b.   Have OCD.
     c.   Have some psychological disorder.
     d.   Have schizophrenia.

12. The belief that others are out to "get" you is an example of a(n) _____ symptom of schizophrenia. (p. 600)
     a.   Positive
     b.   Disorganized
     c.   Negative
     d.   Undifferentiated

13. If you have a parent with schizophrenia, the odds are you: (p. 601)
     a.   Will develop schizophrenia in your early 20's.
     b.   Will develop schizophrenia later in life.
     c.   Will develop schizophrenia—if you are female.
     d.   Won't develop schizophrenia.

14. Research has shown that _____ is linked to the later diagnosis of dissociative identity disorder. (p. 608)
     a.   Abnormal levels of serotonin in the amygdala
     b.   Having a parent with schizophrenia
     c.   Severe abuse during childhood
     d.   Surviving a catastrophe while others die

15. An increased risk of developing anorexia occurs among women who are: (p. 612)
     a.   Depressed.
     b.   Anxious.
     c.   Perfectionistic.
     d.   Conscientious.

Essay Questions

Answer the following questions in the space provided.

1. What *is* abnormality? _____
    _____
    _____
    _____
    _____
    _____
    _____

2. Why doesn't everyone who suffers a trauma develop post-traumatic stress disorder (PTSD)?
    _____
    _____
    _____
    _____
    _____
    _____

3. Why do women in the United States have higher rates of depression than men? _____
    _____
    _____
    _____
    _____
    _____
    _____

4. Why is a higher rate of schizophrenia found among lower socioeconomic classes and in urban areas? _____
    _____
    _____
    _____
    _____
    _____
    _____

5. What are the criticisms of including personality disorders under Axis II (or at all) in the DSM-IV? _____
    _____
    _____
    _____
    _____
    _____
    _____
    _____

6. Do you or one of your friends have any characteristics that might be considered "abnormal"? Do you consider yourself or your friend abnormal? What is the distinction between abnormal traits and abnormality as a whole? _____

_____

_____

_____

_____

_____

7. Do you have a phobia? Most people do, and yet very few people seek help for their fears. Why? What would motivate you to seek help? If a problem doesn't bother someone, is it a problem at all? Can you think of disorders that don't cause personal distress?_____

_____

_____

_____

_____

_____

_____

8. Are thoughts of suicide "abnormal"? Look back at the text's definition of abnormality. Does it matter whether the person wants to die because he/she is depressed or because he/she is terminally ill? _____

_____

_____

_____

_____

_____

_____

9. Do you know anyone with an eating disorder? How well does the text's description of abnormality fit your friend? Have you ever tried to help your friend? Why or why not? What did you do? How was your help received?_____

_____

_____

_____

_____

_____

10. Most of what we know about antisocial personality disorder is from studying criminals in the prison system. What is faulty about this methodology? Is it possible that criminals represent one type of antisocial personality disorder, and that there is another type that has eluded our study?_____

_____

_____

_____

_____

_____

When You Are Finished . . . Puzzle It Out

Across

1. Less intense mania
3. Experienced by some victims of rape
4. Bizarre false beliefs
7. Fear of object interfering with life
8. Clinicians' guide for classifying disorders
9. Type of symptom involving loss of functioning
10. DSM axis for personality disorders
12. Number of axes in DSM
14. Less intense MDD
15. 8th leading cause of death in U.S.
17. Previously called manic-depressive disorder

Down

2. Recurrent thought, hard to ignore
5. Mental images that seem real
6. "Fear of the marketplace"
7. Episode of intense fear
8. Predisposition to a disorder
11. Disorder of compulsive handwasher
13. Loss of memory
16. Cause of dissociative identity disorder
18. Five types of information described in DSM

Puzzle created with Puzzlemaker at DiscoverySchool.com.

Chapter 15
Treatment

Before You Read . . .

Have you ever been in therapy? Was it helpful? Do you know anyone who takes Prozac or another medication to treat a psychological disorder? This chapter presents an overview of the treatment of mental disorders. The first two sections cover the principles of the most common and most studied types of therapy: behavior, cognitive, and insight-oriented therapies (including psychodynamic and humanistic therapies). The origins of these theories, the theories behind their use, and the specific techniques are described.

In the next section, a detailed look at psychopharmacology is presented, with a description of the major classes of medications and their indications. You will also read about electroconvulsive therapy and transcranial magnetic stimulation in this section. Finally, this chapter explores the effectiveness of therapy and presents good information on how to pick a therapist, should you ever need one.

Chapter Objectives

After reading this chapter, you should be able to:

♦   Describe the goals and methods of behavior and cognitive therapies.

♦   Describe the focus of treatment and techniques used in psychodynamic therapy.

♦   Explain how client-centered therapists approach treatment.

♦   Explain how medications are used to treat psychological disorders.

♦   Describe electroconvulsive therapy, as it is used today.

♦   Explain what transcranial magnetic stimulation is, and how it is used in treatment.

♦   Explain what other forms, or modalities, of treatment are used besides individual therapy.

♦   Discuss recent trends in psychotherapy that might affect the future of mental health care.

♦   List the key issues you should keep in mind when reading research studies of psychotherapy.

♦   Describe some good ways to find a therapist.

As You Read. . . Term Identification

Make flashcards using the following terms as you go. Use the definitions in the margins of this chapter for help. If you write the definitions in your own words, though, you will remember them better!

Antipsychotic medication
Behavior modification
Behavior therapy
Benzodiazephine
Bibliotherapy
Client-centered therapy
Cognitive distortion
Cognitive restructuring
Cognitive therapy
Common factor
Curative factor
Cybertherapy
Dream analysis
Electroconvulsive therapy (ECT)
Exposure
Family therapy
Free association
Group therapy
Incongruence
Individual therapy
Insight-oriented therapy
Interpretation
Modality
Monoamine Oxidase Inhibitor (MAOI)
Outcome research

Paradoxical intention
Progressive muscle relaxation
Psychoanalysis
Psychodynamic therapy
Psychoeducation
Psychopharmacology
Psychotherapy integration
Reframing
Resistance
Selective serotonin reuptake inhibitor (SSRI)
Self-help group
Self-monitoring techniques
Serotonin/norepinephrine reuptake inhibitor (SNRI)
Specific factor
Stimulus control
St. John's wort
Systematic desensitization
Systems therapy
Tardive dyskinesia
Technical eclecticism
Token economy
Transference
Tricyclic antidepressant (TCA)
Validation

As You Read . . . Questions and Exercises

Behavior and Cognitive Therapy

Behavior Therapy

What are the **ABC**'s of **behavior therapy**?
A = _____
B = _____
C = _____

Ask a friend to read the instructions for **progressive muscle relaxation** aloud to you. Practice this several times over the next week. Did you notice that this made you more relaxed? _____

_____

Explain how **exposure with response prevention** could be used to treat a client's checking compulsions (e.g., checking that the oven is turned off multiple times before leaving the house).

_____
_____
_____
_____
_____
_____

Name a **behavior** that you would like to **modify**: _____

_____

How could you use **operant conditioning techniques** to **modify** this **behavior**? _____

_____
_____
_____

Do you have any problematic behavior that may benefit from **self-monitoring techniques**? If so, what are they? What information could **self-monitoring techniques** provide you? _____

_____
_____
_____

Identify the following **behavioral techniques**:

Description	Technique
Relaxation in the presence of a feared object or situation	
Making a binge eater eat, but not letting her purge	
Relaxing from head to toe	
A person with anorexia exercises only when alone; don't leave her alone!	
Rewarding a child for staying on task by giving her stickers that can later be traded for pencils, etc.	

On what grounds did **cognitive psychologists** criticize **behavior therapy**? Discuss. _____

_____
_____
_____

GO SURFING...

...to find out how **behavior therapy** is used with children who have Attention Deficit Hyperactivity Disorder . (There are lots of good sites out there!)

Explain. _____

_____

_____

_____

_____

_____

_____

_____

_____

_____

Cognitive Therapy: It's the Thought That Counts

According to cognitive therapists, psychological disorders arise from _____

_____

According to **Albert Ellis**, there are 3 processes that interfere with healthy functioning. Define each and provide an example of this process in your life.

Process	Definition	Personal Example
Self-downing		
Hostility and rage		
Low frustration tolerance		

Compare and contrast **Albert Ellis'** and **Aaron Beck's** theories of **cognitive therapy**.

Similarities	Differences

Below are five common **cognitive distortions**. For each, give a definition and a personal example (*not* from your textbook).

Distortion	Definition	Personal Example
Dichotomous Thinking		
Mental filter		
Mind reading		
Catastophic exaggeration		
Control beliefs		

Using the alphabetic sequence, **ABCDEF**, fill in the following blanks to describe how **RET** works:

Distressing feelings arise because an **A**_____, along with a person's
B_____ lead to **C**_____. The therapist
must help the client to **D**_____ the beliefs, which will lead to an
E_____ and **F**_____ by the client.

What is **cognitive restructuring**? Can you think of a thought that you would like to restructure?
_____
_____
_____
_____

Why is **psychoeducation** an important part of **cognitive therapy**? _____
_____
_____
_____
_____

Cognitive-Behavior Therapy: An Assertiveness Training Example

In the **Assertiveness Training** example discussed in the text, identify the **cognitive** and
behavioral components:

♦   **Cognitive:** _____
_____
_____
_____
_____
_____
_____
_____

♦   **Behavioral:**_____
_____
_____
_____
_____
_____
_____
_____

How do the **cognitive** and **behavioral** components of this treatment type interact?

_____
_____
_____
_____
_____
_____

Suppose that you wanted to develop a training program to help aggressive children develop better social skills. How could you use **cognitive-behavioral therapy** to do this? Name the **cognitive** and the **behavioral** components that you might include in your treatment.

♦　　**Cognitive:** _____
_____
_____
_____
_____
_____
_____
_____

♦　　**Behavioral:**_____
_____
_____
_____
_____
_____
_____
_____
_____

Looking at Levels

Parents often use **token economies** to modify the **behavior** of their children. Explain how such programs may work to decrease aggression in a child, at the levels of the brain, person, and group. Draw arrows to indicate how events at the different levels might interact.

The Brain	The Person	The Group

Are there moral and ethical issues to using this type of program? Discuss. _____

_____

_____

_____

_____

TRY PRACTICE TEST #1 NOW!
GOOD LUCK!

Insight-Oriented Therapies

What do **insight therapies** have in common?_____

_____

_____

_____

_____

Psychodynamic Therapy: Origins in Psychoanalysis

Freud said that there are 3 parts to personality: the **id, ego**, and **superego**. How can this structure of personality create psychological disorders?_____

_____

_____

_____

_____

How did Freud say that traditional **psychoanalysis** can resolve these disorders?_____

_____

_____

_____

_____

What techniques did Freud use during **psychoanalysis**?

◆ _____

◆ _____

◆ _____

How is **psychoanalysis** different from contemporary **psychodynamic therapy**?_____

_____

_____

_____

_____

What factors led to these changes?

◆ _____
_____
◆ _____
_____

In addition to **free association** and **dream analysis,** what other technique do psychodynamic theorists use? Explain. _____
_____
_____
_____
_____

How is **transference** helpful? How is it harmful? _____
_____
_____
_____
_____
_____
_____

Humanistic Therapy: The Self in a Mirror

How does humanistic therapy differ from psychodynamic therapy? _____
_____
_____
_____
_____

How would **client-centered** and other **humanistic therapists** approach treatment? What techniques would they use? _____
_____
_____
_____
_____

Which type of **therapist** would you prefer to see: a psychodynamic therapist or a humanistic therapist? Why? _____
_____
_____
_____
_____

GO SURFING...

...and make up a problem to ask "Eliza," an artificial intelligence program that was initially designed to simulate a client-centered therapist. There are various Eliza programs on the Web, including at:

- http://www-ai.ijs.si/eliza/eliza.html
- http://www.manifestation.com/neurotoys/eliza.php3
- http://www.wilprint.com/eliza.html
- http://www.uwp.edu/academic/psychology/demos/elizaj/eliza.htm

In what ways, if any, is Eliza like a **client-centered therapist**? In what ways is she dissimilar?

_____
_____
_____
_____
_____
_____
_____

Looking at Levels

If expressive writing has the same long-term effect as psychotherapy, in terms of improving mood, should people be encouraged to write rather than to seek counseling? Why or why not? Consider all **levels of analysis** (brain, person, group). Draw arrows to illustrate how events at the different levels might interact.

The Brain	The Person	The Group

TRY PRACTICE TEST #2 NOW!
GOOD LUCK!

Biomedical Therapies

Psychopharmacology

Complete the following table, including the names of specific **drugs** under each classification, the type(s) of disorders typically treated by each classification, and the side effects.

Classification	Specific Drugs	Disorders Treated	Side Effects
Antipsychotics (Atypical)			
Antipsychotics (Traditional)			
Benzodiazepines			
Depakote or Tegretol			
Lithium			
Monoamine Oxidase Inhibitors (MAOIs)			
St. John's Wort			
Selective Serotonin Reuptake Inhibitors (SSRIs)			
Serotonin/Norepinephrine Reuptake Inhibitors (SNRIs)			
Tricyclics			

Electroconvulsive Therapy

What is **ECT**? Why was it developed?_____

_____

_____

_____

_____

From whom is **ECT** now appropriate? How is it administered? What are the potential side effects?

_____
_____
_____
_____
_____

Would you ever have **ECT** performed on you? Why or why not?_____

_____
_____
_____
_____
_____

Transcranial Magnetic Stimulation

What is **transcranial magnetic stimulation**?_____

_____
_____
_____
_____

For whom is **transcranial magnetic stimulation** appropriate? _____

_____
_____
_____
_____

How is **transcranial magnetic stimulation** different from **ECT**?_____

_____
_____
_____

Does **transcranial magnetic stimulation** have any advantages over **ECT**? Discuss. _____

_____
_____
_____
_____

Looking at Levels

How might a placebo work at the **levels of the brain, person, and group** to effect changes that resemble those of an antidepressant? Draw arrows to indicate how events at the different levels might interact.

The Brain	The Person	The Group

TRY PRACTICE TEST #3 NOW!
GOOD LUCK!

Other Forms of Treatment

Modalities: When Two or More Isn't a Crowd

What can **group therapy** offer that individual therapy cannot? _____
_____
_____
_____
_____

What is the fundamental assumption of **systems therapy**? _____
_____
_____
_____
_____

What would your family's graph of **family interaction** look like? Graph below.

Define the following techniques that are typically used in **family therapy**:

♦ **Paradoxical intention:** _____
_____

♦ **Reframing:** _____
_____

♦ **Validation:** _____
_____
_____

Have you ever been involved in any **group therapy**? If so, what type? What techniques were used? Did you feel it was helpful? If so, how?_____
_____
_____
_____
_____

Innovations in Psychotherapy

What is **psychotherapy integration**? _____
_____
_____
_____
_____

What is **technical eclecticism**?_____
_____
_____
_____
_____

What is the difference between **psychotherapy integration** and **technical eclecticism**?_____
_____
_____
_____

What are the benefits of using either of these **integrative approaches**? _____
_____
_____
_____

What are the factors common to all **theoretical orientations**? _____

_____

_____

_____

_____

How have each of the following recent trends affect the practice of **psychotherapy**?

Managed Care	Therapy Protocols	Cybertherapy

How might these or other trends affect the future of **mental health care**? _____

_____

_____

_____

_____

Prevention: Sometimes Worth More Than a Pound of Cure

Describe the following types of **preventive interventions** and give an example of each.

Intervention	Description	Example
Universal preventive interventions		
Selective preventive interventions		
Indicated preventive interventions		

Looking at Levels

Explain what the three **levels of analysis** tell us about OCD. Draw arrows to indicate how events at the different levels may interact.

The Brain	The Person	The Group

TRY PRACTICE TEST #4 NOW!
GOOD LUCK!

Which Therapy Works Best?

Issues in Psychotherapy Research

What is **outcome research**? _____
_____
_____
_____

What are the questions that should be asked when designing and **evaluating** studies of **psychotherapy**? Why is each of these questions important?

♦ _____
_____
_____

♦ _____
_____
_____

♦ _____
_____
_____

♦ _____
_____
_____
_____
♦ _____
_____
_____
_____
♦ _____
_____
_____
_____
♦ _____
_____
_____
_____

Summarize the results of the **Treatment of Depression Collaborative Research Program (TDCRP)**, sponsored by the National Institute of Mental Health._____
_____
_____
_____
_____

What are the disadvantages of taking **medication** over **therapy**?

♦ _____
♦ _____
♦ _____
♦ _____
♦ _____

For what two disorders is **medication** clearly the preferred form of treatment? Why?

♦ _____
_____
♦ _____
_____

What type of therapy would be the most **effective** at treating:

- ♦ Depression? _____
- ♦ Obsessive-compulsive disorder? _____
- ♦ Panic disorder? _____
- ♦ Agoraphobia? _____
- ♦ Specific phobias? _____
- ♦ Social phobia? _____
- ♦ Posttraumatic stress disorder? _____

Is it important to match **personality** to **treatment modality**?_____

_____

_____

_____

_____

_____

_____

Why is it important to understand a client's **ethnic background** when determining the diagnosis, process of therapy, and its goals?_____

_____

_____

_____

_____

How to Pick a Psychotherapist

What steps should you take to find a psychotherapist?

- ♦ _____
- ♦ _____
- ♦ _____
- ♦ _____
- ♦ _____

Looking at Levels

How might the effectiveness of therapy be measured at the levels of the brain, person, and group? Draw arrows to indicate how events at the different levels might interact.

The Brain	The Person	The Group

TRY PRACTICE TEST #5 NOW!
GOOD LUCK!

After You Read . . . Thinking Back

1. In Chapter 2, you learned how psychological topics are studied. The effectiveness of psychological treatment is especially difficult to study. Why is this?_____
    _____
    _____
    _____
    _____
    _____

2. In Chapter 3, you learned about neural functioning. How does Prozac (or any of the other SSRIs) work, at the neural level?_____
    _____
    _____
    _____
    _____
    _____

3. In Chapter 5, you learned about dreaming. Does Sigmund Freud's technique of dream analysis make sense, given current knowledge about dreaming? Why or why not?_____
    _____
    _____
    _____
    _____
    _____

4. What are the principles of cognitive psychology (as discussed in Chapter 1)? How do you see these in cognitive therapy?_____
    _____
    _____
    _____
    _____

5. Given what you learned about repressed memories in Chapter 7, how successful do you think psychoanalytic techniques are likely to be? Explain. _____
    _____
    _____
    _____
    _____

After You Read . . . Thinking Ahead

1. How might the culture affect people's views of themselves? What are the implications of this for treatment purposes? Discuss._____

   _____
   _____
   _____
   _____
   _____

2. In this chapter, you learned how therapists help clients change irrational attitudes about themselves. In the next chapter, you will learn how advertisers and others help clients try to change attitudes about products and other people. Can you imagine some of the ways that the techniques you learned in this chapter could be applied to changing stereotypes, for example? Explain._____

   _____
   _____
   _____
   _____
   _____

3. How might Beck's common cognitive distortions lead you to think about others? How would this affect interpersonal relationships? Explain. _____

   _____
   _____
   _____
   _____
   _____
   _____
   _____
   _____

4. Can you think of situations in which family or group therapy might have negative consequences? Why might this happen? Explain._____

   _____
   _____
   _____
   _____

5. How might culture influence a person's choice of treatment? For example, consider the frequent use of Ritalin in treating Attention Deficit Hyperactivity Disorder. How does media attention and the popularity of this drug affect others' choices? Is this good or bad? Discuss. _____

   _____
   _____
   _____
   _____

After You Read . . . Practice Tests

PRACTICE TEST #1:
BEHAVIOR AND COGNITIVE THERAPY

True/False Questions
Circle TRUE or FALSE for each of the following statements.

1.   TRUE   FALSE   RET was developed by Aaron Beck. (p. 630)

2.   TRUE   FALSE   Self-monitoring techniques are important because they help to identify the triggers of problematic behaviors. (p. 629)

3.   TRUE   FALSE   RET says that people develop illogical thoughts because of what happened to them during their childhoods. (p. 629)

4.   TRUE   FALSE   Beck viewed cognitive distortions as hypotheses to be tested. (p. 630)

5.   TRUE   FALSE   RET is successful with psychotic disorders. (p. 632)

6.   TRUE   FALSE   Cognitive therapy is helpful for anger management. (p. 633)

7.   TRUE   FALSE   Cognitive and behavioral techniques are often integrated in practice. (p. 633)

8.   TRUE   FALSE   Exposure with response prevention is a common cognitive distortion. (p. 631)

9.   TRUE   FALSE   The only effective treatment for OCD is medication. (p. 628)

10.   TRUE   FALSE   The "D" in the RET alphabetical sequence ABCDEF stands for "dispute." (p. 631)

Multiple-Choice Questions
For each question, circle the best answer from the choices given.

1.   Which of the following techniques is NOT based on classical conditioning principles? (p. 625)
    a.   Systematic desensitization
    b.   Progressive muscle relaxation
    c.   Behavior modification
    d.   Exposure

2. Stimulus control is a technique used by: (p. 628)
   a. Psychoanalysts.
   b. Gestalt therapists.
   c. Client-centered therapists.
   d. Behavior therapists.

3. Albert Ellis developed a treatment called: (p. 630)
   a. Client-centered therapy.
   b. Insight-oriented therapy.
   c. Rational-emotive therapy.
   d. Free association.

4. Donita is afraid that she will not be admitted to nursing school and that she will end up on welfare, like her mother. In fact, Donita's GPA is 3.4, making admittance very likely. Donita is using which cognitive distortion? (p. 631)
   a. Mind reading
   b. Control beliefs
   c. Mental filter
   d. Catastrophic exaggeration

5. Daphne is seeing a psychologist to address her depression. Her psychologist asks her to keep a written record of her automatic negative thoughts. In this case, Daphne's psychologist is most likely to follow _____'s theory and is using the technique of _____. (p. 632)
   a. Ellis; systematic desensitization
   b. Freud; psychoanalysis
   c. Beck; cognitive restructuring
   d. Ellis; psychoeducation

6. Cognitive therapy also makes extensive use of: (p. 633)
   a. Family therapy.
   b. Psychoanalysis.
   c. Insight therapy.
   d. Psychoeducation.

7. In the case of OCD, the goal of exposure with response prevention would be to: (p. 628)
   a. Get the client to habituate (or get used to) whatever provokes the anxiety.
   b. Reduce the client's cognitive distortions.
   c. Change the client's obsessive thoughts.
   d. Educate the client about the cause of her anxiety.

8. Which of the following is NOT one of the processes that Ellis says interferes with healthy functioning? (p. 630)
   a. Thinking that you know what others are thinking of you
   b. Being critical of oneself for performing poorly or being rejected
   c. Being unkind to or critical of others for performing poorly
   d. Blaming everyone and everything for undesireable conditions

9. In behavior therapy, ABC stands for: (p. 631)
   a. Affect, behavior, cognition.
   b. Antecedents, behavior, consequences.
   c. Antecedents, belief, control.
   d. Attitude, behavior, consequences.

10. Which of the following treatments is not based on classical conditioning? (p. 629)
    a. Systematic desensitization
    b. Exposure with response prevention
    c. Stimulus control
    d. Behavior modification

PRACTICE TEST #2:
INSIGHT-ORIENTED THERAPIES

True/False Questions
Circle TRUE or FALSE for each of the following statements.

1.   TRUE   FALSE   Humanistic therapists use the term "client" in place of "patient." (p. 638)

2.   TRUE   FALSE   Rogers viewed people's distressing symptoms as caused by unconscious conflicts. (p. 638)

3.   TRUE   FALSE   Client-centered therapists are sometimes confrontational with clients. (p. 639)

4.   TRUE   FALSE   Client-centered therapists help clients to see that only bad people do bad things. (p. 639)

5.   TRUE   FALSE   Humanistic therapies are especially effective in treating schizophrenia. (p. 640)

Fill-in-the-Blank Questions
Complete the following paragraph by filling in the blanks with the following words:

WORD BANK	
Defense mechanisms	Interpretation
Dreams	Resistance
Free association	Transference
Hypnosis	

Freud started out using _____, but eventually developed

_____ as his method of getting patients to talk about whatever

was on their minds. He particularly wanted them to talk about their _____,

as he considered these to be the "royal road to the unconscious." Psychodynamic

therapists also use _____ to understand the unconscious meanings of

the patients' words and behaviors. Through this process, patients become aware of their

_____, which are designed to minimize the anxiety that arises

from unconscious but negative thoughts and feelings. At some point during the therapy

process, patients may experience _____ (for example,

by coming in late to sessions) and _____ (which allows them

to "correct" earlier relationships by interacting with the therapist as if he/she were a person from the past). (p. 635-640)

Multiple-Choice Questions

For each question, circle the best answer from the choices given.

1.   The original insight-oriented therapy is: (p. 635)
        a.   Gestalt therapy.
        b.   Psychoanalysis.
        c.   Client-centered therapy.
        d.   Integrative psychotherapy.

2.   The goal of psychoanalysis is: (p. 635)
        a.   Changing one's reward structure in life.
        b.   Understanding one's unconscious motivations.
        c.   Developing healthier interpersonal relationships.
        d.   Changing the way one thinks about life's stressors.

3.   People rarely use psychoanalysis today because it: (p. 636)
        a.   Doesn't provide enough understanding about the cause of their problems.
        b.   Can lead to painful realizations.
        c.   Can negatively transform personality.
        d.   Is costly and time-consuming.

4.   Which of the following is a FALSE statement about how current psychodynamic therapies are different from traditional psychoanalysis? (p. 636)
        a.   Past relationships are seen as less important in current therapies.
        b.   The relationship with the therapist is less important in current therapies.
        c.   The emphasis on sexual and aggressive drives is downplayed in current therapies
        d.   Current psychodynamic therapy takes longer and is more costly than psychoanalysis.

5.   When patients come to relate to their therapist as they did to someone who was important in their lives, _____ is said to have taken place. (p. 638)
        a.   Transference
        b.   Insight
        c.   Countertransference
        d.   Interpretation

6.   Carl Rogers developed _____ therapy. (p. 638)
        a.   Short-term psychodynamic
        b.   Patient-centered
        c.   Gestalt
        d.   Client-centered

7.   Carl Rogers defined incongruence as a mismatch between: (p. 639)
      a.   What others think you should be and what you are.
      b.   What you used to be and what you are now.
      c.   What you are and what you want to be.
      d.   How you behave and how you think.

8.   Viktor begins to cancel his appointments with his therapist, citing work conflicts. Viktor is most likely experiencing: (p. 637)
      a.   Transference.
      b.   Hostility.
      c.   Resistance.
      d.   Interpretation.

9.   The goal of the client-centered therapist is to: (p. 639)
      a.   Help the client uncover unconscious motivations.
      b.   Provide unconditional positive regard.
      c.   Help to change irrational thought patterns.
      d.   Reward the client for progress toward his or her goals.

10.   The clients most likely to benefit from insight therapies: (p. 640)
      a.   Have affective disorders.
      b.   Are older.
      c.   Have the time and money to spend on extensive therapy.
      d.   Are relatively healthy, articulate people.

PRACTICE TEST #3:
BIOMEDICAL THERAPIES

True/False Questions
Circle TRUE or FALSE for each of the following statements.

1.   TRUE   FALSE   Electroconvulsive therapy (ECT) is an effective treatment for schizophrenia. (p. 643)

2.   TRUE   FALSE   ECT is the treatment of choice for nonpsychotic depression. (p. 643)

3.   TRUE   FALSE   We don't know why ECT works. (p. 644)

4.   TRUE   FALSE   ECT is administered under anesthesia. (p. 644)

5.   TRUE   FALSE   ECT causes memory loss for general life events occurring in early childhood. (p. 644)

6.   TRUE   FALSE   Usually, only one session of ECT is necessary to treat depression. (p. 644)

7.   TRUE   FALSE   Since the 1980s, the use of ECT has decreased. (p. 644)

8.   TRUE   FALSE   ECT is particularly likely to be offered to poor patients who can't afford insurance. (p. 645)

Multiple-Choice Questions
For each question, circle the best answer from the choices given.

1.   The atypical antipsychotic medications are effective at decreasing: (p. 641)
     a.   Hallucinations.
     b.   Negative symptoms.
     c.   Delusions.
     d.   All of the above.

2.   Selective serotonergic reuptake inhibitors are used to treat: (p. 642)
     a.   The positive symptoms of schizophrenia.
     b.   The negative symptoms of schizophrenia.
     c.   Mood disorders.
     d.   Antisocial personality disorder.

3. Prozac is a(n): (p. 642)
   a. MAOI.
   b. Benzodiazepine.
   c. SSRI.
   d. Atypical neuroleptic.

4. Lithium is often the treatment of choice for: (pp. 643-644)
   a. Schizophrenia.
   b. Bipolar disorder.
   c. Depression.
   d. Anxiety.

5. Which of the following medications would be most likely to be used to treat someone with obsessive-compulsive disorder? (p. 643)
   a. Benzodiazepines
   b. Lithium
   c. Antipsychotic medications
   d. SSRIs

6. Which of the following statements about electroconvulsive therapy (ECT) is FALSE? (p. 643)
   a. It is once again being used to treat mental illness.
   b. It is only used in state-run hospitals.
   c. It is sometimes used to treat severe depression.
   d. It is the first treatment of choice for schizophrenia if medication does not work.

7. A side effect of ECT is: (p. 644)
   a. Memory loss.
   b. High blood pressure.
   c. Dry mouth.
   d. Tardive dyskinesia.

8. Although it is now an experimental treatment, transcranial magnetic stimulation (TMS) shows early signs of being an effective treatment for: (p. 645)
   a. Psychotic depression.
   b. Generalized anxiety disorder.
   c. Nonpsychotic depression.
   d. Obsessive-compulsive disorder.

9. An advantage of TMS over ECT is that TMS: (p. 645)
   a. Results in fewer side effects.
   b. Can be administered without anesthesia.
   c. Does not require hospitalization.
   d. All of the above.

10.   Long-term use of antipsychotic medications can cause tardive dyskinesia, which is: (p. 641)
    a.   An irreversible movement disorder of the facial muscles.
    b.   Uncontrollable drooling and shouting.
    c.   Shuffling movements of feet.
    d.   Blunted affect and unresponsiveness.

PRACTICE TEST #4:
OTHER FORMS OF TREATMENT

True/False Questions
Circle TRUE or FALSE for each of the following statements.

1. TRUE FALSE Studies have revealed that time-limited therapy helps clients get better faster. (p. 650)

2. TRUE FALSE Brief therapy provides more benefit to people with problems in one area than to people with multiple problems. (p. 651)

3. TRUE FALSE Protocol therapies are useful for people suffering from more than one disorder at a time. (p. 650)

4. TRUE FALSE Most managed care companies will approve up to 20 sessions of psychotherapy at a time. (p. 651)

5. TRUE FALSE Paradoxical intention involves encouraging behaviors that seem contradictory to the end goal of therapy. (p. 650)

Fill-in-the-Blank Questions
Complete the following paragraph by filling in the blanks with the following words:

WORD BANK	
Alcoholics Anonymous	Internet
Bibliotherapy	Support
Higher Power	Twelve
	Weekly

Self-help groups are sometimes called _____ groups and do not usually

have a clinically-trained leader. _____ was the first self-help

program and is based on _____ steps of recovery. Most such programs view a

belief in a(n) _____ as crucial to recovery, and it appears

that individuals who attend at least _____ gain the most benefit.

Support groups can also be found on the _____, although information here may not be

accurate and people may not be who they claim to be. The use of books and tapes for therapeutic

purposes is called _____. (pp. 648-651)

Multiple-Choice Questions

For each question, circle the best answer from the choices given.

1. Therapy groups typically have a _____ theoretical orientation. (p. 647)
    a. Psychodynamic
    b. Cognitive-behavioral
    c. Client-centered
    d. Any of the above

2. The most common theoretical orientation among family therapists is: (p. 647)
    a. Behavioral.
    b. Psychodynamic.
    c. Communication.
    d. Systems.

3. Research has found that it is important for clients to _____ to obtain benefits from 12-step groups such as Alcoholics Anonymous. (p. 649)
    a. Attend sessions on a regular weekly basis
    b. Do not believe in a Higher Power, such as God
    c. Own up to their responsibilities
    d. Bond with the other individuals in the group

4. When a therapist integrates specific techniques without regard for an overarching theory, the therapist is said to be using: (p. 650)
    a. Integrative modality therapy.
    b. Practical eclecticism.
    c. Psychotherapy integration.
    d. Technical eclecticism.

5. Therapy protocols are: (p. 650)
    a. Ethical guidelines for therapists.
    b. Guidelines for setting up one's office and establishing fees.
    c. Detailed session-by-session manuals of how therapy should proceed.
    d. Descriptions of particular types of clients and the types of therapy they should receive.

PRACTICE TEST #5:
WHICH THERAPY WORKS BEST?

True/False Questions

Circle TRUE or FALSE for each of the following statements about the *Consumer Reports* survey of mental health.

1.   TRUE   FALSE   Over half of respondents reported that they sought professional help for some problem. (p. 659)

2.   TRUE   FALSE   The overall finding from the survey was that treatment is effective. (p. 660)

3.   TRUE   FALSE   Treatment by a mental health professional was superior to treatment by a family doctor. (p. 660)

4.   TRUE   FALSE   Short-term therapy was as effective as long-term therapy. (p. 660)

5.   TRUE   FALSE   Patients who were active in their treatment fared better than those who were passive. (p. 660)

Multiple-Choice Questions

For each question, circle the best answer from the choices given.

1.   The *dodo bird verdict* of psychotherapy seemed to suggest that: (p. 600)
     a.   No psychotherapy is effective.
     b.   The forms of psychotherapy studied were not effective.
     c.   The forms of psychotherapy studied were equally effective.
     d.   Medication is not effective.

2.   What type of therapy would be recommended for someone with OCD? (p. 658)
     a.   Psychodynamic
     b.   Cognitive
     c.   Behavioral
     d.   Client-centered

3.   Medication can directly assist people with schizophrenia by: (p. 658)
     a.   Decreasing psychotic symptoms.
     b.   Providing the opportunity to learn new relationship skills.
     c.   Making the person more socially outgoing.
     d.   All of the above.

4. Among the curative factors of therapy are: (p. 641)
   a. Gaining a sense of hope.
   b. Uncovering unconscious motivations.
   c. Making a new friend.
   d. All of the above.

5. The TDCRP study, which investigated the relative effectiveness of four different approaches to treating depression, revealed that: (p. 656-657)
   a. Different outcome measures yielded different results.
   b. For those completing the study, cognitive behavioral therapy and interpersonal therapy were as effective as antidepressant medication.
   c. People were less willing to complete the study if they were in the non-medication groups.
   d. The bond between client and therapist is unimportant to the outcome.

6. It is especially difficult to evaluate the effectiveness of _____ therapy. (p. 662)
   a. Behavioral
   b. Psychodynamic
   c. Cognitive-behavioral
   d. Cognitive

7. Earlier studies comparing different types of therapies revealed that, in general: (p. 654)
   a. Therapy was better than no therapy.
   b. Behavior therapy was better than psychodyanamic therapy.
   c. Psychodynamic therapy was better than behavior therapy.
   d. Group therapies were superior to individual psychotherapy.

8. A drawback of using medication instead of therapy in treating depression and anxiety is that: (p. 656)
   a. Medication is simply less effective, both in the short- and long-term.
   b. When medication is discontinued, the relapse rate is high.
   c. Clients become addicted to the medications used to treat anxiety and depression.
   d. Irreversible side effects such as tardive dyskinesia can cause life-long distress.

9. Which type of treatment is most effective for panic disorder? (p. 658)
   a. CBT
   b. Interpersonal therapy
   c. Systematic desensitization
   d. Response prevention

10. Which of the following is NOT a piece of advice to use when picking a psychotherapist? (pp. 664-665)
    a. Pick someone who makes you uncomfortable, as this means that he or she is probing deeply for information.
    b. Contact several psychotherapists.
    c. Ask your insurance company for providers who they cover.
    d. Ask for referrals from friends and family.

COMPREHENSIVE PRACTICE TEST

True/False Questions

Circle TRUE or FALSE for each of the following statements.

1.   TRUE   FALSE   Dream analysis is a crucial technique for cognitive therapists. (p. 629 & 636)

2.   TRUE   FALSE   A client-centered therapist points out client's faults during therapy. (p. 639)

3.   TRUE   FALSE   For most anxiety disorders, MAOIs are the medication prescribed. (p. 642)

4.   TRUE   FALSE   ECT is effective for the majority of people who undergo it. (p. 644)

5.   TRUE   FALSE   Many insurance companies will pay for only a certain number of sessions. (p. 636)

Multiple-Choice Questions

For each question, circle the best answer from the choices given.

1.   Freud believed that psychoanalysis: (p. 636)
    a.   Was a cure for psychosis.
    b.   Could modify cognitions.
    c.   Could lead to self-actualization.
    d.   Could transform misery into unhappiness.

2.   During psychoanalysis, Susan said, "I think I hate—I mean ate—something bad." The analyst pointed out to Susan that her slip of the tongue (saying "hate" instead of "ate") was significant and suggests some underlying unconscious conflict. The analyst was using the technique of: (p. 637)
    a.   Interpretation.
    b.   Transference.
    c.   Blocking.
    d.   Incongruence.

3.   Research comparing how effective different forms of treatment are for symptoms of a particular disorder is called _____ research. (p. 654)
    a.   Systems
    b.   Outcome
    c.   Efficacy
    d.   Psychotherapeutic

4. Sometimes, when they study the effectiveness of certain therapies, researchers exclude _____ from their studies in order to _____. (p. 655-656)
   a. women; make results more clear-cut
   b. men; limit generalizability
   c. people with multiple diagnoses; make results more clear-cut
   d. people over age 40; increase validity of the study

5. The "C" of behavior therapy stands for: (p. 631)
   a. Control.
   b. Consequences.
   c. Caring.
   d. Cognition.

6. Systematic desensitization is based on principles of: (p. 625)
   a. Social learning.
   b. Psychoanalysis.
   c. Operant conditioning.
   d. Classical conditioning.

7. Julie has an overwhelming compulsion to clap her hands every time she walks through a door. Her therapist treats her by having her walk back and forth through the doorway while keeping her hands out to the side, thus preventing her from clapping them. Most likely, Julie's therapist is a(n) _____ therapist and is using the technique of _____. (p. 628)
   a. Behavior; exposure with response prevention
   b. Behavior; systematic desensitization
   c. Cognitive; behavioral restructuring
   d. Insight-oriented; interpretation

8. Which of the following is NOT a process that interferes with healthy functioning, according to Albert Ellis? (p. 630)
   a. Incongruence
   b. Hostility and rage
   c. Self-downing
   d. Low frustration tolerance

9. Which of the following therapists would be most likely to say, "Tell me about your dreams." (p. 635)
   a. Client-centered
   b. Cognitive
   c. Psychodynamic
   d. Behavioral

10. Cognitive therapists make use of psychoeducation, which is: (p. 633)
    a. Having clients try to psychoanalyze themselves.
    b. Attending continuing education conferences.
    c. Educating clients about therapy and research pertaining to their disorders.
    d. Providing education opportunities to clients who are in psychiatric hospitals

11. The MAOIs are not widely prescribed for depression because: (p. 642)
    a. They are generally effective only with atypical depression involving increased appetite and hypersomnia.
    b. They interact with certain foods to cause fatally high blood pressure.
    c. They can cause tardive dyskinesia and take several months to start working.
    d. Both A and B

12. Since the 1980s, the use of ECT has been: (p. 644)
    a. More frequent.
    b. Banned in the United States.
    c. Less frequent.
    d. Banned in Europe.

13. In family therapy, Carrie—the identified patient with bulimia—is encouraged to continue binging and purging because it is bringing her parents closer together as they attempt to help her. The therapist who tells Carrie to do this is: (p. 648)
    a. Using the technique of cognitive restructuring.
    b. Using the technique of paradoxical intention.
    c. Reframing and validating Carrie's eating patterns.
    d. Clearly unethical and should lose her license.

14. Which of the following groups suffered the greatest attrition in the TDCRP? (p. 652)
    a. Interpersonal therapy group
    b. Medication group
    c. Cognitive behavioral group
    d. Placebo group

15. For which disorders has medication been shown to be clearly superior to psychotherapy? (p. 659)
    a. Depression and anxiety
    b. Social and simple phobias
    c. Bulimia and anorexia
    d. Schizophrenia and bipolar disorder

Essay Questions

Answer each of the following questions in the space provided.

1. How is psychodynamic therapy different from psychoanalysis? _____
_____
_____
_____
_____
_____
_____

2. How does the humanistic approach to therapy differ from the psychodynamic approach?
_____
_____
_____
_____
_____
_____

3. How are Beck's and Ellis' versions of cognitive therapy similar and different? _____
_____
_____
_____
_____
_____
_____

4. Why might a systems therapist refuse to see an individual in a family? _____
_____
_____
_____
_____
_____
_____

5. Do you think that dreams are a path to the unconscious? Why or why not? Go back and read the chapter on the unconscious (Chapter 5). What are the alternative explanations for dreams? _____
_____
_____
_____
_____
_____
_____

6. Do parents put conditions of worth on their children? In what ways? Do you think that such conditions are potentially damaging and may lead the child to need therapy when older? Is unconditional positive regard appropriate for all types of clients? How about clients with antisocial personality disorder?_____

_____

_____

_____

_____

_____

_____

7. Why does electroconvulsive therapy continue to offend some people, despite its relative effectiveness? How would you feel if a friend or family member were to have ECT?

_____

_____

_____

_____

_____

_____

8. Your text mentions that there is currently no objective measure of insight. Why do you think it is difficult to measure insight? If you were to develop such a measure, what types of questions would you include?_____

_____

_____

_____

_____

_____

_____

9. If you want to know whether therapy works, why not just ask the client or therapist? What types of biases might each have? _____

_____

_____

_____

_____

_____

10. In general, which is more effective in treating psychological disorders—medication or therapy?_____

_____

_____

_____

_____

_____

When You Are Finished . . . Puzzle It Out

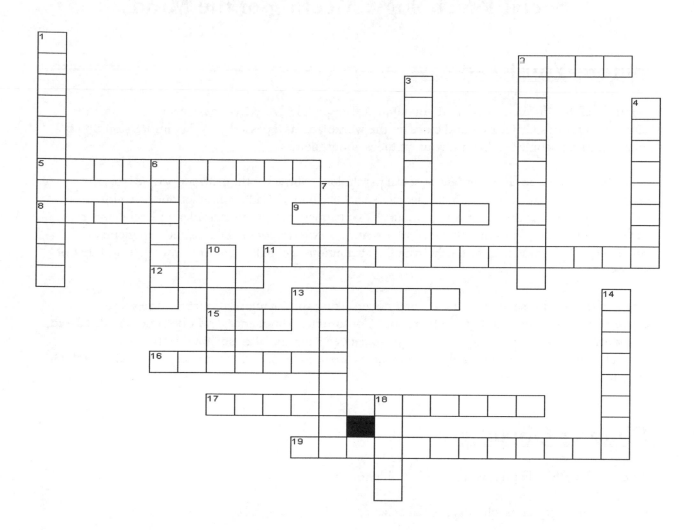

Across

2. Examples: Prozac, Zoloft, and Paxil
5. Refusal to comply with therapist
8. Developed rational-emotive therapy
9. Mood stabilizer used for schizophrenia
11. AKA support groups
12. First antidepressant medication
13. Proposed client-centered therapy
15. Controlled brain seizure as treatment
16. D in the RET therapist's ABCDEF
17. Magnifying the negative
19. Therapy over the internet

Down

1. Mismatch of ideal and real self
2. Herbal therapy for depression
3. Good therapy for panic disorder
4. Focus of cognitive therapy
6. Therapy saying no person is an island
7. Use of self-help books
10. Secondary reinforcers
14. A form of therapy
18. Developed psychoanalysis

Puzzle created with Puzzlemaker at DiscoverySchool.com.

Chapter 16
Social Psychology: Meeting of the Minds

Before You Read . . .

Think of all the different ways that you interact with people everyday—perhaps with a romantic partner, in groups like classes and clubs, in the workplace, as a passerby. What impression do you leave on these people? What are your attitudes about them?

This chapter presents an overview of social psychology—how we think about people (social cognition) and how we interact with people (social behavior). Can we predict our behaviors from our attitudes, or is it the other way around? What happens when our attitudes and behaviors are inconsistent? Sometimes our attitudes are negative, as we stereotype people and experience prejudice. Our attitudes arise partly from the attributions we make about our own fate and that of others.

The social behavior section of the chapter covers liking and loving relationships, the social organization of groups, and group behavior. Conformity, compliance, and obedience are discussed, as is decision-making in groups. Lastly, prosocial behavior and altruism are covered—the characteristics of people who help, the people we *choose* to help, and the circumstances under which we engage in helping behavior.

Chapter Objectives

After reading this chapter, you should be able to:

♦ Define social psychology, social behavior, and social cognition and explain why they are important.

♦ Describe attitudes and how they are formed.

♦ Define persuasion and why persuasion attempts work or don't work.

♦ Define stereotypes, explain how they are formed, and how they can lead to prejudice.

♦ Discuss the reasons for prejudice and how prejudice can be reduced.

♦ Define attributions and identify the various types of attributions and attributional biases.

♦ Identify and briefly describe the factors that affect interpersonal attractions.

♦ Describe the different kinds of love and explain Sternberg's triangular model of love.

- Define the following: norms, roles, and status. Also explain the effects of being in a group on the individual's behavior.

- Explain and differentiate between conformity and compliance, identify factors that affect them, and describe techniques that influence compliance.

- Describe Milgram's studies on obedience.

- Describe the factors involved in group decision-making, including social loafing and social facilitation.

- Describe the factors that affect prosocial behavior and bystander intervention.

As You Read. . . Term Identification

Make flashcards using the following terms as you go. Use the definitions in the margins of this chapter for help. If you write the definitions in your own words, though, you will remember them better!

Altruism
Attitude
Attribution
Attributional bias
Belief in a just world
Bystander effect
Cognitive dissonance
Compassionate love
Compliance
Conformity
Deindividuation
Diffusion of responsibility
Door-in-the-face technique
External attribution
Foot-in-the-door technique
Fundamental attribution error
Group
Group polarization
Groupthink
Halo effect
Impression formation
Impression management
Ingroup
Internal attribution

Lowball technique
Mere exposure effect
Norm
Obedience
Outgroup
Passionate love
Persuasion
Prejudice
Prosocial behavior
Recategorization
Role
Self-perception theory
Self-serving bias
Social cognition
Social cognitive neuroscience
Social exchange theory
Social facilitation
Social loafing
Social psychology
Status hierarchy
Stereotypes
Theory of causal attribution
Triangular theory of love

As You Read . . . Questions and Exercises

Social Cognition: Thinking About People

Making an Impression

Do you remember your first **impressions** of your psychology professor? What was it? _____
_____
_____
_____

Was your first **impression** accurate? Why or why not?_____
_____
_____
_____

Think of an example of the **halo effect** in your life and describe here. (For example, perhaps you have met someone on line, thought that this person was were very interesting, and then met him or her in the flesh and thought that person to be very attractive.) _____
_____
_____
_____

Think of an example of the **self-fulfilling prophecy** in your life and describe here._____
_____
_____
_____

GO SURFING...

...at the following site:
♦   http://p034.psch.uic.edu/marks2.htm and participate in the online study of **person perception** there.

What is the purpose of this study?_____
_____
_____
_____

What are the independent variables in this study?_____

Based on the results shown after you completed of the study, do the independent variables appear to impact participants' **impressions**?_____
_____
_____
_____

Did those variables impact *your* **impressions**? In what way?_____
_____
_____
_____

Attitudes and Behavior: Feeling and Doing

What are the three components of **attitudes**? Name and describe.

- ♦ _____
  _____
- ♦ _____
  _____
- ♦ _____
  _____

Attitudes and Cognitions

Can you think of a time when **attitudes** affected what information you processed about a specific event? (For example, this may be a time for which you and someone else have very different memories.) Describe this situation._____
_____
_____
_____

Name a time when each of the following has affected your **attitudes**.

- ♦ **Your family:**_____
  _____
- ♦ **Your personality:** _____
  _____
- ♦ **Observational learning:** _____
  _____
- ♦ **Classical conditioning:** _____
  _____

Attitudes are more likely to affect behavior when the **attitudes** are...

♦ _____
♦ _____
♦ _____
♦ _____
♦ _____

Think of an example from your life when your behavior affected your **attitude** about something. Why might this have occurred? _____
_____
_____
_____
_____
_____
_____

GO SURFING...

...at www.yale.edu/implicit. Read more about the **Implicit Association Test (IAT)** and take one of the online attitude surveys.

Describe how the IAT measures **attitudes**._____
_____
_____
_____
_____
_____

What did the online survey you took say about your **attitudes**?_____
_____
_____
_____

What is **cognitive dissonance**?_____
_____
_____
_____

Explain the two theories of **cognitive dissonance**.

♦ _____
  _____
  _____
  _____

♦ _____
  _____
  _____
  _____
  _____
  _____

What are four different ways by which we may try to decrease **cognitive dissonance**?

♦ _____
  _____
  _____

♦ _____
  _____
  _____

♦ _____
  _____
  _____

♦ _____
  _____
  _____

Attitude Change: Persuasion

What factors will increase the likelihood of **persuading** someone?

♦ _____
♦ _____
♦ _____
♦ _____
♦ _____
♦ _____

What are the four common obstacles to **persuasion**?

♦ _____
  _____

♦ _____
  _____

♦ _____
  _____

♦ _____
  _____

Stereotypes: Seen One, Seen 'Em All

Why do we **stereotype** people? _____
_____
_____

What errors do we make when **stereotyping** people?_____
_____
_____
_____
_____
_____

What is the relationship between **stereotyping** and **prejudice**?_____
_____
_____
_____
_____
_____

GO SURFING...

...at http://www.understandingprejudice.org/demos/ and do the following tests:
- The Baseline Survey.
- The Slide Tour of Prejudice (alternatively, this can be done as a group if there is Internet access in the classroom).
- Ambivalent Sexism Questionnaire.
- Slavery and the U.S. Presidents.
- What's Your Native IQ?
- Test Yourself for Hidden Biases.
- The Baseline Survey, to see if students' thinking has changed.

Describe the results of the tests here._____
_____
_____
_____
_____
_____
_____

Prejudice can stem from emotions in two ways:

♦ _____
_____

♦ _____
_____

Provide the terms for the following definitions:

Definition	Term
The tendency for people to divide the world into "us" and "them"	
The group that includes "us"	
The group that includes "them"	
The tendency to overestimate the strength of a relationship between two things	
The tendency to view "them" as all alike	
The tendency to view "us" as all different	

Explain how each of the following processes may contribute to the development and maintenance of **prejudice**:

Process	Explanation
Scarce resources	
Competition	
Social categorization and ingroup bias	
Social learning theory	

Briefly explain the two methods of **decreasing prejudice**:

♦ _____
_____
_____

♦ _____
_____
_____
_____

What conditions are necessary for intergroup contact to decrease prejudice?

- ♦ _____
  _____
- ♦ _____
  _____
- ♦ _____
  _____

Is it possible that prejudice falls along a continuum, and that most people fall somewhere in the middle? If you don't think you're prejudiced, consider how you feel when you see a couple in which the partners are of a different race, or of the same sex. How does it make you feel? What if the couple is being physically intimate? _____
_____
_____
_____
_____
_____
_____

Attributions: Making Sense of Events

In the table below, indicate the types of statements you might make about something good or bad that happened to you, assuming you make internal or external attributions.

Situation	Type of Attribution	
	Internal	External
You ace a test.		
You fail a test.		

590

GO SURFING…

…at http://discoveryhealth.queendom.com/access_lc.html and take the Locus of Control and **Attributional Style** Test.

What kind of **attributional style** do you have? Explain._____

_____

_____

_____

_____

_____

_____

What comment might a person make, if using the **fundamental attribution bias**, about the following situations?

Situation	Comment
A woman is raped.	
A waitress forgets an order.	
A homeless person asks for money.	
A man confesses to a crime.	

According to the **self-serving bias**, what types of attributions (internal/external) do you make in the following situations?

Situation	Type of Attribution
You get a good grade on an exam, despite the fact that you didn't study very hard.	
Your roommate gets a good grade on an exam, despite the fact that he didn't study very hard.	
You get a bad grade on an exam, despite the fact that you studied very hard.	
Your roommate gets a bad grade on an exam, despite the fact that he studied very hard.	

GO SURFING...

...at http://www.erzwiss.uni-halle.de/gliederung/paed/ppsych/segbjw.pdf and take the Belief in a Just World Scale. What was your score? _____ The higher your score, the more you believe in a just world.

How does **belief in a just world** lead to blaming the victim?_____
_____
_____
_____

Is there anyone for whom you have a **hostile attribution bias**? If so, who? How has this affected your relationship with that person?_____
_____
_____
_____

Looking at Levels

How do the levels of the brain, person, and group interact to explain how you feel about people who are **victims of acquaintance rape** following a long night of drinking? Draw arrows to indicate how the events at the different levels might interact.

The Brain	The Person	The Group

TRY PRACTICE TEST #1 NOW!
GOOD LUCK!

Relationships: Having a Date, Having a Partner

In light of the **repeated contact hypothesis**, what is likely to happen among men and women who live in the same dormitory?_____

_____

_____

_____

_____

What are the three factors that influence us to **like** someone else?

- ♦ _____
- ♦ _____
- ♦ _____

What features are considered **attractive** for men, world-wide?

- ♦ _____
- ♦ _____
- ♦ _____
- ♦ _____

What features are considered **attractive** for women, world-wide?

- ♦ _____
- ♦ _____
- ♦ _____

What are the three components of **consummate love**? Briefly explain each.

- ♦ _____

  _____
- ♦ _____

  _____
- ♦ _____

  _____

Think of the last romantic relationship you were in. Were you high or low on each of the three **components**, do you think?

◆ _____
◆ _____
◆ _____

Briefly describe the three major **attachment styles**:

◆ _____
_____

◆ _____
_____

◆ _____
_____

If "opposites attract" but **similarity** lasts, will that affect how you might choose a mate in the future? Consider your parents – are they more alike or more different from one another? People appear to become more similar to one another the longer they are together – do you think this is true? _____
_____
_____
_____
_____
_____
_____

GO SURFING…

…at http://p034.psch.uic.edu/cgi-bin/crq.pl and take the **Attachment Style Questionnaire**.

According to this questionnaire, what type of **attachment** do you have now? _____
_____
_____

Do you agree or disagree with these results? Why?_____
_____
_____

Fill in the table to show the interaction between **attachment** and **love relationships**. Also, indicate the percentage of Americans that fall into each category.

Attachment Type	Relationship Type	Percentage of Americans
Secure		
Avoidant		
Anxious-Ambivalent		

What are the three factors that influence the feeling of **intimacy** in a relationship?

- ◆ _____
- ◆ _____
- ◆ _____

Think of the last romantic **relationship** in which you were involved. Which of these three factors were strengths in that relationship? Which were weaknesses? _____

What four factors does Myers say will determine whether **love** will be sustained?

- ◆ _____
- ◆ _____
- ◆ _____
- ◆ _____

What role does **reciprocity** have in close relationships? _____

Can you think of a relationship in which you were involved and in which there was *not* **reciprocity**? What was the outcome of that relationship? Describe._____

Describe one study that supports the **evolutionary theory** of mate selection and one study that fails to support it.

Supports Evolutionary Theory	Refutes Evolutionary Theory

Social Organization: Group Rules, Group Roles

What four characteristics define a "**group**"?

♦ _____
♦ _____
♦ _____
♦ _____

What is **deindividuation**? Does it explain violence in anonymous crowds? Why or why not?
_____
_____
_____
_____
_____
_____
_____
_____

What are some of the **norms** at your school?_____
_____
_____
_____

What are the hidden dangers in telling children *how* to avoid drug use instead of just *why* to avoid drug use?_____
_____
_____
_____

Think of a group (either formal or informal) in which you are involved. Who are the different people in that group? What **role** (again, either formal or informal) does each person play?

Person	Role

Who are some of the **high status** members of your group? What identifies them as being high status? _____

_____
_____
_____
_____
_____

Yielding to Others: Going Along With the Group

Under what circumstances would someone be more or less likely to **conform** to a group standard or opinion?

Factors That Increase Conformity	Factors That Decrease Conformity

Conformity is a change in behavior brought about by _____, whereas **compliance** is a change in behavior brought about by _____.

What are the six principles underlying effective **compliance**?

♦ _____
♦ _____
♦ _____
♦ _____
♦ _____
♦ _____

Which of the above principles underlies the following **compliance** techniques?

♦ Foot-in-the-door: _____

♦ Lowball technique: _____

♦ Door-in-the-face: _____

Identify which of the above techniques is described below:

Compliance Scenario	Technique
Your roommate asks you to drive her home – 3 states away! You say "no," but then agree to drive her to the airport – it's only one hour away.	
Your roommate asks you if she can borrow your notes from last week when she was sick. You agree and then find yourself giving her your notes every week!	
You agree to buy a car for $15,000 (telling yourself you'll spend no more than that), but then end up driving away with a $20,000 car because you want the "extras" that didn't come with the $15,000 price tag.	

In **Milgram's study**, what percentage of people obeyed instructions to give the highest level of shock under the following conditions?

Condition	Percentage
Milgram's original study	
"Teacher" sets the voltage level.	
College student gives the order.	
Two authority figures disagree with one another.	
"Teacher" holds electrode to "learner's" skin.	
Commands are given over the phone.	

Performance in Groups: Working Together

How does the **heterogeneity** of the group affect group communication? _____

_____

_____

_____

How can the negative effects of **heterogeneity** be reduced?

♦ _____
♦ _____
♦ _____
♦ _____

What is **group polarization**? _____
_____
_____
_____

What are two reasons for **group polarization** and when does each occur?

♦ _____
    _____
    _____

♦ _____
    _____
    _____
    _____

Describe a situation in which you or someone else engaged in **social loafing**._____
_____
_____
_____

When is **groupthink** more likely to occur?

♦ _____
♦ _____
♦ _____
♦ _____

Have you worked on a group project yet? Which of the **group processes** in the chapter have you observed? Was social loafing or social facilitation present? Was there a leader and a status hierarchy? Social loafing or social compensation? Did your group have to come to some decision about something? How did the decision come about?_____
_____
_____
_____
_____
_____
_____

Helping Behavior: Helping Others

What are the characteristics of a person likely to offer **help**? Of a person likely to receive help?

Characteristics of a "Helper"	Characteristics of a "Helpee"

According to Darley and Latane, what factors are likely to increase **bystander intervention**? What factors are likely to decrease bystander intervention?

Factors Increasing Bystander Intervention	Factors Decreasing Bystander Intervention

What do you think motivates others to be helpful? If an **altruistic** act is defined as one for which you don't expect anything in return—not even a sense of feeling good—is there really any such thing as an altruistic act? _____
_____
_____
_____
_____
_____
_____

Looking at Levels

Are the factors that influence cult behavior similar to the factors that influence the behavior of students who rush a fraternity? Explain how a fraternity can exert so much power over inductees, at the **levels of the brain, person, and group**. Draw arrows to indicate how events at the different levels may interact.

The Brain	The Person	The Group

TRY PRACTICE TEST #2 NOW!
GOOD LUCK!

After You Read . . . Thinking Back

1. In Chapter 1, you learned about the ethics of psychological research. Would Milgram's study be allowed today? Why or why not? _____
    _____
    _____
    _____
    _____
    _____
    _____
    _____
    _____

2. In Chapter 10, you learned that cognition can affect emotion. In Chapter 7, you learned that emotion can affect cognition (e.g., memory). How are both of those themes reflected in this chapter? _____
    _____
    _____
    _____
    _____
    _____
    _____
    _____
    _____
    _____

3. In Chapter 12, you learned about the tasks of adulthood. Which tasks would be met by having a partner? _____
    _____
    _____
    _____
    _____

4. Why are these tasks important? _____
    _____
    _____
    _____

5. How are stereotypes similar to and different from prototypes, which you learned about in Chapter 8? _____
    _____
    _____
    _____
    _____
    _____
    _____
    _____

After You Read . . . Practice Tests

PRACTICE TEST #1:
SOCIAL COGNITION

True/False Questions
Circle TRUE or FALSE for each statement.

1. TRUE   FALSE   An attractive persuader is more effective than an unattractive one. (p. 680)

2. TRUE   FALSE   If attempting to persuade someone, you should speak slowly. (p. 680)

3. TRUE   FALSE   Persuasion is more effective when strong emotions are aroused. (p. 680)

4. TRUE   FALSE   A person who is perceived as honest is more persuasive. (p. 680)

5. TRUE   FALSE   A person will be more persuasive if he or she does not appear to be trying to persuade someone. (p. 681)

Multiple-Choice Questions
For each question, circle the best answer from the choices given.

1. An attitude is often considered a(n): (p. 674)
    a. Feeling.
    b. Thought.
    c. Behavior.
    d. Impulse.

2. Attitudes are more likely to affect behavior when the attitudes are: (p. 675)
    a. Strong.
    b. Directly relevant to the behavior.
    c. Relatively stable.
    d. All of the above.

3. When an attitude and behavior, or two attitudes, are inconsistent with one another, the resulting feeling is called: (p. 677)
    a. Intrapsychic conflict.
    b. Attitudinal conflict.
    c. Cognitive dissonance.
    d. Persuasive dissonance.

4. Persuasion would be most likely to occur when: (p. 680)
    a.   The person being persuaded has high self-esteem.
    b.   The person being persuaded feels fearful because of the message.
    c.   The person being persuaded is paying full attention to the message.
    d.   The message is a clear attempt to persuade the person.

5. When there is a conflict between a stereotype and actual behavior that is too significant to simply ignore, we tend to: (p. 683)
    a.   Change the stereotype.
    b.   Ignore the person.
    c.   Create a new subtype within the stereotype.
    d.   Switch the person to another stereotyped group.

6. Unconscious prejudice arises from: (p. 684)
    a.   The presence of negative feelings.
    b.   The absence of positive feelings.
    c.   Ambivalent feelings.
    d.   Both A and B.

7. Which of the following would NOT decrease prejudice? (p. 687)
    a.   A competition for resources
    b.   Increased contact between the different groups
    c.   Recategorization
    d.   Working toward a shared goal

8. When your friend is late meeting you for the movies, you say to yourself, "Joel is just a chronically late person – I should have known," thus making a(n) _____ attribution. (p. 691)
    a.   Internal
    b.   Situational
    c.   External
    d.   Ingroup

9. The strong inclination to attribute someone's behavior to internal causes is called the: (p. 693)
    a.   Fundamental attribution error.
    b.   In-group bias.
    c.   Self-serving bias.
    d.   Actor-observer effect.

10. After finding out that his wife was raped, Ryan blames her, saying that she shouldn't have been out at a bar that late anyway. Ryan is probably: (p. 694)
    a.   Using the self-serving bias.
    b.   Trying to maintain his belief in a just world.
    c.   Using the fundamental attribution error.
    d.   Using a theory of causal attribution.

PRACTICE TEST #2:
SOCIAL BEHAVIOR

Multiple-Choice Questions
For each question, circle the best answer from the choices given.

1. Repeated contact with a person typically leads to: (p. 696)
   a. Decreased liking for that person.
   b. No change in feelings for that person.
   c. Increased liking for that person.
   d. Feelings of love for that person.

2. People tend to rate as "attractive" those facial features that are: (p. 696)
   a. Masculine.
   b. Average.
   c. Unusual.
   d. Asymmetrical.

3. According to Sternberg, only _____ love has passion, intimacy, and commitment. (p. 697)
   a. Compassionate
   b. Agape
   c. Consummate
   d. Reciprocal

4. People who are uncomfortable with intimacy and closeness are said to have a(n) _____ attachment style. (p. 697)
   a. Secure
   b. Anxious
   c. Avoidant
   d. Ambivalent

5. A growing feeling of intimacy comes from each of the following factors, EXCEPT: (p. 697)
   a. Feeling understood by your partner.
   b. Feeling that your emotions and opinions are respected by your partner.
   c. Feeling that your partner cares for you.
   d. Feeling that you and your partner share the same interests.

6. David Buss has argued that women prefer men who: (p. 699)
   a. Are attractive.
   b. Are faithful.
   c. Have good earning potential.
   d. Have a good "pedigree."

7. Which of the following is NOT a characteristic that defines the term "group"? (p. 700)
    a. Regular interaction among members
    b. Emotional connection
    c. Physical proximity
    d. Interdependence

8. After a particularly difficult lecture, the professor asks if anyone has any questions. All students shake their head "no"; however, after class, the professor is approached by numerous students asking for clarification on specific points. The reason that students didn't raise these questions during class was probably because: (pp. 700-701)
    a. They were comparing themselves with other students, who appeared to understand the lesson.
    b. The professor didn't create an open environment where students could feel free to ask any questions.
    c. Students were obeying the professors' implicit demands for understanding students.
    d. Students were fulfilling their group roles.

9. People with a "high status" role: (p. 703)
    a. Tend to maintain eye contact.
    b. Criticize or interrupt others.
    c. Tend to be physically intrusive.
    d. All of the above.

10. In Asch's original conformity experiment, overall _____ of the participants conformed with the obviously wrong majority. (p. 704)
    a. One-fifth
    b. One-third
    c. One-fourth
    d. One-half

11. Which of the following statements about conformity is FALSE? (pp. 705-706)
    a. Rates of conformity have remained constant over the past several decades.
    b. Rates of conformity are higher in collectivist cultures.
    c. Men and women conform at the same rates.
    d. Conformity is higher for more difficult tasks.

12. A change in behavior brought about through a direct request is called: (p. 706)
    a. Conformity.
    b. Compliance.
    c. Norm readjustment.
    d. Agreement.

13. Making a ridiculously large request, followed up by a more reasonable smaller request, is called the _____ technique. (p. 706)
   a. Foot-in-the-door
   b. Door-in-the-face
   c. Lowball
   d. Big-and-then-little

14. Milgram's experiment used the _____ technique to get people to obey. (p. 708)
   a. Foot-in-the-door
   b. Forced compliance
   c. Door-in-the-face
   d. Reciprocity

15. Groups reach a better decision when: (pp. 710-711)
   a. There is a correct solution.
   b. There is a leader.
   c. The members of the group like each other.
   d. the members of the group complement each other's skills.

16. In group polarization, the attitudes of the group members: (p. 710)
   a. Become more moderate.
   b. Move in the opposite of the original direction.
   c. Become more heterogeneous.
   d. Become more extreme, in the same direction as their initial opinions.

17. Later studies using Milgram's obedience technique indicated that: (p. 708)
   a. Women were equally as likely to shock someone as men.
   b. People from other countries, such as Jordan and Germany, were equally as likely to shock someone as men.
   c. Women were less likely to shock someone as men.
   d. A & B

18. When consensus becomes more important than the critical analysis of different individual opinions, _____ has occurred. (p. 710)
   a. Group polarization
   b. Groupthink
   c. Social loafing
   d. Social compensation

19. Social facilitation is more likely to occur: (p. 711)
   a. Among homogeneous group members.
   b. Among heterogeneous group members.
   c. For difficult tasks.
   d. For well-learned tasks.

20.   Which of the following would <u>increase</u> the likelihood that a person would help someone in need? (p. 713)
a.   If the person helping were alone
b.   If the person helping were in a group
c.   If the person needing help were dissimilar to the helper
d.   If the person helping expects to experience negative consequences for helping

COMPREHENSIVE PRACTICE TEST

True/False Questions
Circle TRUE or FALSE for each of the following statements.

1. TRUE   FALSE   People are often unaware of their attitudes. (p. 677)

2. TRUE   FALSE   A good way to decrease prejudice is to engage in competitive games with the stereotyped group. (p. 687)

3. TRUE   FALSE   The old adage "opposites attract" has been supported by empirical research. (p. 696)

4. TRUE   FALSE   The majority of Americans seek closeness and interdependence in relationships and are not worried about the loss of the relationship. (p. 697)

5. TRUE   FALSE   "Just say no to drugs" is an effective way of deterring youths from using them. (p. 702)

6. TRUE   FALSE   Men and women are equally likely to conform. (p. 705)

7. TRUE   FALSE   Heterogeneity in groups can have both positive and negative effects. (p. 710-711)

8. TRUE   FALSE   As the number of bystanders increases, the likelihood of helping decreases. (p. 713)

9. TRUE   FALSE   People may be more likely to blame a rape victim if they have a strong belief in a just world. (p. 694)

10. TRUE   FALSE   People who are uncomfortable with intimacy and closeness are said to have an anxious-ambivalent attachment style. (p. 697)

Multiple-Choice Questions
For each question, circle the best answer from the choices given.

1. Repeatedly asserting an attitude—even one you did not hold previously—will have what influence on behavior? (p. 676)
    a. It will have no influence on behavior—attitudes and behavior are disconnected.
    b. It *might* have an influence on behavior, but it's unlikely.
    c. It is likely to change your behavior to conform to the stated attitude.
    d. Any of the above are equally likely.

2. Which of the following happens to minimize cognitive dissonance? (pp. 678-679)
   a. We change our attitudes.
   b. We change our behaviors.
   c. We trivialize the inconsistency between the two attitudes (or attitude and behavior).
   d. Any of the above.

3. Persuasion is *least* likely to occur when: (p. 680)
   a. The person doing the persuading is an expert.
   b. The person doing the persuading is attractive.
   c. The person doing the persuading talks slowly.
   d. Strong emotions are aroused in the attempt at persuasion.

4. Social exchange theory says that: (p. 700)
   a. People try to maximize gains and minimize losses in their relationships.
   b. People will try to seek the partners who are most similar to their opposite-sex parent as possible.
   c. People are looking for partners who maximize their chances for perpetuating their DNA.
   d. Love is based on the immediate feelings of "chemistry" that people have for each other.

5. We tend to attribute our successes to _____ causes and our failures to _____ causes. (pp. 691-692)
   a. Internal; internal
   b. External; external
   c. Internal; external
   d. External; internal

6. According to our belief in a just world: (p. 694)
   a. Chance plays a major role in what happens to people.
   b. A divine being intercedes on the behalf of all people.
   c. People deserve what they get, and get what they deserve.
   d. Our own successes are due to good fortune.

7. According to evolutionary theory, men look for women who: (pp. 698-699)
   a. Are independent and self-supporting.
   b. Are dependent upon them for support.
   c. Are older than they are.
   d. Appear "fertile" by having a well-proportioned body and symmetrical features.

8. Social status differences tend to be minimized when: (p. 703)
   a. Groups communicate via e-mail.
   b. The individuals are encouraged to interact cooperatively.
   c. A mediator is introduced to the group.
   d. The individuals in the group are of similar attitudes.

9. In which of the following situations would someone be *less* likely to conform? (p. 704)
    a. In a situation in which the task is difficult or ambiguous
    b. In a situation in which a group member openly disagrees with the consensus
    c. In a group in which the members are cohesive
    d. In a group in which the members are both male and female

10. Car salespeople are notorious for using the _____ technique to get people to buy more car than they had bargained for. (p. 707)
    a. Foot-in-the-door
    b. Door-in-the-face
    c. Lowball
    d. Kick-from-behind

11. In Milgram's original experiment, _____ percent of the participants shocked the confederate with the highest voltage. (p. 708)
    a. 15
    b. 45
    c. 65
    d. 95

12. In general, the more heterogenous a group is: (p. 710-711)
    a. The less effectively it communicates.
    b. The more likely there is to be group conflict.
    c. The more innovative and flexible the group may be.
    d. All of the above.

13. Social compensation occurs when: (p. 711)
    a. Some members of the group see the task as important, but worry that others will not work. —
    b. People accept one another's information and ideas uncritically. +
    c. Individuals work harder in a group than they do when alone. ∿
    d. Group members' opinions become more radical or extreme after discussion. ∼

14. According to Darley and Latane, bystander intervention occurs when: (p. 715)
    a. An emergency is noticed by the bystander.
    b. The bystander assumes some responsibility to intervene.
    c. The bystander is motivated to help.
    d. All of the above must occur.

15. The jigsaw technique is sometimes used to: (p. 690)
    a. Reduce conformity.
    b. Train children about the dangers of obedience.
    c. Decrease prejudice.
    d. Persuade individuals.

Essay Questions

Answer each question in the space provided.

1.   If you knew that a woman was opposed to abortion, could you predict that she would never have one?_____
_____
_____
_____
_____
_____
_____
_____
_____
_____

2.   If you wanted to persuade someone that your point of view is correct, what should you do?
_____
_____
_____
_____
_____
_____
_____
_____
_____
_____
_____

3.   If you had to design a program to combat homophobia (a negative attitude toward homosexual individuals—a type of prejudice), what elements would you include?
_____
_____
_____
_____
_____
_____
_____
_____

4.   How can the various attributional biases affect how a jury views a woman who has been raped? _____
_____
_____
_____
_____
_____
_____
_____
_____

5.   Using some social psychology principles of group behavior, explain how a fraternity can convince pledges to do things they would probably not do on their own (e.g., drink too much, or eat a live goldfish). _____

_____

_____

_____

_____

_____

_____

After You Are Done . . . Puzzle It Out

Across

4. Belief about people in category
5. Conducted famous obedience studies
9. Most common attachment style
10. Rules that govern group members
12. Difference between two conflicting attitudes
13. One's own group
14. Behavior change due to request
17. Attribution that cause is self
19. Intimacy, passion & _____
20. Attempts to change attitudes

Down

1. Loss of sense of self
2. Kitty _____
3. Behavior that benefits others
6. Liking something familiar
7. Compliance with an order
8. Behavior change to group norms
11. Triangular theory of love author
15. Negative attitude toward out-group members
16. Motivation to help another person
18. Explanation for cause of event

Puzzle created with Puzzlemaker at DiscoverySchool.com.

Answer Keys

Chapter 1: What Kind of Psychologist Are You?

A = psychodynamic   D = humanism

B = behaviorism   E = evolutionary psychology

C = cognitive psychology

Chapter 1: Practice Test #1

True/False Questions

1. T
2. F
3. F
4. F
5. T

Multiple-Choice Questions

1. A
2. D
3. D
4. B
5. C
6. A
7. B
8. D
9. A
10. B

Chapter 1: Practice Test #2

Fill-In-The-Blank Questions

Psychology

Philosophy

Science

Physiology

Structuralism

Introspection

Gestalt

Psychodynamic

Unconscious drives

Functionalism

Evolutionary

Behaviorism

Behavior

Mental processes

Cognitive

Computer

Information processing

Brain scans

Cognitive neuroscience

Brain

Matching Questions

1. E
2. C
3. G
4. A
5. D
6. H
7. B
8. F

Multiple-Choice Questions

1. B
2. D
3. A
4. B
5. B
6. A
7. D
8. B
9. D
10. B

Chapter 1: Practice Test #3

Matching Questions

1.	G
2.	D
3.	K
4.	A
5.	O
6.	M
7.	F
8.	N
9.	C
10.	I
11.	B
12.	E
13.	L
14.	H
15.	J

Multiple-Choice Questions

1. A
2. C
3. C
4. D
5. A
6. B
7. D
8. D
9. B
10. C

Chapter 1: Practice Test #4

Matching Questions

1. C
2. D
3. A
4. E
5. B

Multiple-Choice Questions

1. B
2. D
3. A
4. C
5. C
6. C
7. D
8. B
9. B
10. D

Chapter 1: Comprehensive Test

True/False Questions

1. F
2. F
3. T
4. F
5. T
6. T
7. T
8. T
9. F
10. F

Multiple-Choice Questions

1. C
2. D
3. B
4. A
5. B
6. B
7. A
8. B
9. B
10. D
11. D
12. B
13. D
14. A
15. D
16. A
17. B
18. C
19. A
20. A

Matching Questions

1. J
2. I
3. A
4. C
5. E
6. G
7. D
8. B
9. F

Puzzle It Out

Across

3. Academic
7. Three
9. Wundt
10. Gestalt
12. Social
13. Skinner
15. MD
16. Freud
18. IRB
19. Darwin
20. Debriefing

Down

1. Brain scans
2. James
4. Evolutionary
5. Computers
6. Good
8. Applied
11. Cognitive
14. Introspection
17. Deception

Chapter 2: Practice Test #1

Matching Questions

1.   B
2.   D
3.   A
4.   F
5.   E
6.   C

Multiple-Choice Questions

1.   C
2.   B
3.   D
4.   D
5.   C
6.   A
7.   B
8.   B
9.   B
10.   A

Chapter 2: Practice Test #2

True/False Questions

1.   F
2.   T
3.   T
4.   T
5.   F
6.   F
7.   T
8.   F
9.   F
10.   T

Multiple-Choice Questions

1.   A
2.   B
3.   A
4.   A
5.   B
6.   D
7.   D
8.   A
9.   D
10.   B

Chapter 2: Practice Test #3

Fill-In-The-Blank Questions

Frequency distribution
Normal distribution
Central tendency
Mean
Skewed
Median
Mode
Variability
Range
Standard deviation

Multiple-Choice Questions

1.   C
2.   D
3.   D
4.   C
5.   B
6.   C
7.   D
8.   B
9.   B
10.   B

Chapter 2: Practice Test #4

True/False Questions

1. F
2. F
3. T
4. F
5. T
6. T
7. T
8. T
9. F
10. T

Multiple-Choice Questions

1. B
2. D
3. B
4. C
5. C
6. D
7. C
8. B
9. A
10. A

Chapter 2: Comprehensive Test

Identification Questions

1. Negative
2. Negative
3. Positive
4. Positive
5. Negative

Matching Questions

1. C
2. E
3. F
4. G
5. A
6. D
7. B

Identification Questions

1. DV = occurrence of kidney stones, IV = amount of water
2. DV = size, IV = species (rats or mice)
3. DV = likelihood of anorexia, IV = whether or not girls are gymnasts
4. DV = grades, IV = completion of study guides
5. DV = children like to read, IV = presence of books

Multiple-Choice Questions

1. C
2. B
3. A
4. C
5. D
6. B
7. A
8. C
9. B
10. D
11. D
12. A
13. C
14. C
15. C

Puzzle It Out

Across

5.   Range
7.   Dependent
11. Data
12. Sample
13. Reliability
15. Survey
16. Hypothesis
18. Variability
19. Normal
20. Population

Down

1.   Mean
2.   Mode
3.   Correlation
4.   Meta-analysis
6.   Sampling bias
8.   Statistics
9.   Replication
10. Case study
14. Operational
17. Six

Chapter 3: Practice Test #1

Fill-in-the-Blank Questions

Synapse
Neurotransmitters
Neuromodulators
Glial
Excitatory
Inhibitory
Reuptake

Matching Questions

1.   C
2.   E
3.   F
4.   A
5.   D
6.   B

Multiple-Choice Questions

1.   D
2.   A
3.   A
4.   B
5.   A
6.   B
7.   C
8.   C
9.   A
10. C

Chapter 3: Practice Test #2

Matching Questions

1. F
2. A
3. I
4. J
5. B
6. H
7. C
8. E
9. D
10. K
11. G

Matching Questions

1. E
2. A
3. H
4. G
5. C
6. B
7. I
8. F
9. D

Matching Questions

1. C
2. A
3. D
4. B

Multiple-Choice Questions

1. C
2. A
3. B
4. A
5. C
6. A
7. B
8. A
9. D
10. D

Chapter 3: Practice Test #3

Fill-in-the-Blank Questions

Neuroimaging techniques
CT
MRI
PET
fMRI

Multiple-Choice Questions

1. B
2. A
3. A
4. A
5. D
6. B
7. D
8. A
9. C
10. D

Chapter 3: Practice Test #4

True/False Questions

1. T
2. T
3. F
4. F
5. T
6. T

Multiple-Choice Questions

1. C
2. B
3. C
4. A
5. C
6. C
7. B
8. C
9. A
10. B

Chapter 3: Comprehensive Practice Test

True/False Questions

1. F
2. F
3. T
4. F
5. F
6. T
7. F
8. F

Multiple-Choice Questions

1. D
2. A
3. A
4. B
5. A
6. C
7. D
8. B
9. A
10. B
11. B
12. C
13. C
14. D
15. C

Puzzle It Out

Across

5. Genotype
10. Dendrite
11. SSRI
12. Gyri
13. Lesion
14. CNS
15. Hippocampus
17. Thalamus
20. Glial cells

Down

1. Reflex
2. Lobes
3. Synapse
4. Negative
6. Heritability
7. Myelin
8. Neuron
9. Pruning
16. Plasticity
18. Amygdala
19. Mutation

Chapter 4: Practice Test #1

Matching Questions
1.   A
2.   C
3.   D
4.   B

Multiple-Choice Questions
1.   C
2.   D
3.   D
4.   B
5.   D
6.   D
7.   C
8.   C
9.   D
10.   A

Chapter 4: Practice Test #2

Multiple-Choice Questions
1.   B
2.   C
3.   B
4.   D
5.   B
6.   A
7.   C
8.   C
9.   D
10.   D

11.   B
12.   A
13.   A
14.   A
15.   B
16.   D
17.   D
18.   D
19.   A
20.   C

Chapter 4: Practice Test #3

True/False Questions
1.   F
2.   T
3.   T
4.   F
5.   F
6.   F
7.   T
8.   T
9.   T
10.   T

Matching Questions
1.   C
2.   D
3.   B
4.   A

Multiple-Choice Questions

1.	B		6.	B
2.	A		7.	A
3.	A		8.	B
4.	C		9.	B
5.	C		10.	D

Chapter 4: Comprehensive Practice Test

True/False Questions

			Identification
1.	T		Bottom-up
2.	T		Top-down
3.	F		Bottom-up
4.	T		Top-down
5.	T		
6.	T		
7.	T		
8.	F		
9.	F		
10.	F		

Multiple-Choice Questions

1.	A		9.	A
2.	B		10.	C
3.	A		11.	B
4.	D		12.	A
5.	B		13.	C
6.	C		14.	A
7.	A		15.	A
8.	D			

Puzzle It Out

Across

3.	Bias			
9.	Pupil			
10.	Afterimage			
12.	Topdown			
15.	Pheromones			
16.	Pop-out			
17.	Green			
18.	Loudness			
19.	Astigmatism			
20.	Rods			

Down

1.	Figure
2.	Kinesthetic
4.	Attention
5.	Blindspot
6.	Ganglion cells
7.	Tinnitus
8.	Pitch
11.	Taste buds
13.	Fovea
14.	Endorphins

Chapter 5: Practice Test #1

Matching Questions
1. D
2. A
3. B
4. E
5. C

True/False Questions
1. F
2. T
3. F
4. T
5. F
6. F
7. T
8. T
9. F
10. T

Multiple-Choice Questions
1. C
2. C
3. D
4. D
5. C
6. A
7. B
8. C
9. B
10. D
11. A
12. C
13. D
14. C
15. A

Chapter 5: Practice Test #2

Matching Questions
1. C
2. D
3. B
4. A

Multiple-Choice Questions
1. A
2. A
3. C
4. A
5. C
6. D
7. C
8. B
9. B
10. D
11. C
12. D
13. B
14. C
15. B

Chapter 5: Practice Test #3

Matching Questions

1. D
2. H
3. J
4. A
5. F
6. B
7. E
8. K
9. G
10. C
11. I

True/False Questions

1. T
2. T
3. T
4. F
5. T
6. T
7. T
8. F
9. F
10. F

Multiple-Choice Questions

1. A
2. D
3. D
4. A
5. C
6. C
7. A
8. A
9. A
10. B

Chapter 5: Comprehensive Test

True/False Questions

1. T
2. F
3. F
4. F
5. F
6. F
7. F
8. F
9. F
10. T
11. F
12. F
13. T
14. T
15. T

Multiple-Choice Questions

1. B
2. C
3. D
4. D
5. B
6. C
7. A
8. B
9. B
10. A
11. C
12. A
13. D
14. A
15. A
16. D
17. B
18. A
19. D
20. A

Puzzle It Out

Across

2. Rebound
4. Meditation
8. Opiate
12. Freud
13. Marijuana
14. Alcohol
16. REM
17. Hypnosis
20. Melatonin

Down

1. Hypnogogic
3. Blackout
5. Sleep apnea
6. Tolerance
7. Hallucinations
9. Trance
10. Narcolepsy
11. Crack
15. Insomnia
18. SCN
19. Latent

Chapter 6: Practice Test #1

Matching Questions

1. B
2. E
3. G
4. H
5. J
6. A
7. F
8. C
9. I
10. D

Multiple-Choice Questions

1. C
2. D
3. B
4. D
5. A
6. D
7. D
8. C
9. C
10. B
11. B
12. B
13. B
14. A
15. A

Chapter 6: Practice Test #2

Fill-In-The-Blank Questions

Discrimination
Hippocampus
Acetylcholine
Nucleus accumbens
Dopamine

Multiple-Choice Questions

1. B
2. D
3. C
4. A
5. C
6. C
7. A
8. A
9. B
10. B

Chapter 6: Practice Test #3

True/False Questions

1. F
2. T
3. F
4. T
5. T

Multiple-Choice Questions

1. A
2. B
3. D
4. B
5. B
6. B
7. A
8. B
9. A
10. D

Chapter 6: Comprehensive Test

True/False Questions

1. T
2. F
3. T
4. T
5. F
6. T
7. F
8. T
9. F
10. T

Multiple-Choice Questions

1. A
2. B
3. D
4. B
5. B
6. B
7. C
8. B

9. A
10. A
11. B
12. D
13. B
14. A
15. C
16. B
17. A
18. B
19. C
20. D

Puzzle It Out

Across

5. Primary
8. Albert
11. Shaping
12. Interval
14. Partial
16. Token
18. Positive
19. Backward
20. Thorndike

Down

1. Phobia
2. Placebo
3. Puzzle
4. Pavlov
6. Insight
7. Latent
9. Reinforcer
10. Sultan
13. Maps
15. Skinner
17. UR

Chapter 7: Practice Test #1

True/False Questions

1. F
2. T
3. T
4. T
5. T
6. F
7. T
8. T
9. F
10. T

Multiple-Choice Questions

1. B
2. C
3. A
4. D
5. C
6. A
7. B
8. D
9. B
10. C

Chapter 7: Practice Test #2

Multiple-Choice Questions

1.	C		11.	A
2.	A		12.	D
3.	D		13.	C
4.	C		14.	D
5.	C		15.	D
6.	B		16.	C
7.	C		17.	B
8.	B		18.	B
9.	A		19.	B
10.	A		20.	C

Chapter 7: Practice Test #3

True/False Questions

			## Multiple-Choice Questions	
1.	T		1.	B
2.	F		2.	D
3.	T		3.	A
4.	F		4.	D
5.	T		5.	C
6.	T		6.	C
7.	T		7.	A
8.	T		8.	C
9.	F		9.	B
10.	T		10.	B

Chapter 7: Practice Test #4

Multiple-Choice Questions

1. B
2. B
3. D
4. B
5. C
6. B
7. D
8. A
9. C
10. D

Chapter 7: Comprehensive Practice Test

True/False Questions

1. T
2. F
3. T
4. F
5. T
6. F
7. T
8. T

Multiple-Choice Questions

1. B
2. A
3. C
4. D
5. A
6. C
7. A
8. B
9. D
10. C
11. A
12. B
13. C
14. C
15. D
16. A
17. B
18. A
19. C
20. B

Puzzle It Out

Across

2. Mnemonics
4. Flashbulb
6. Ebbinghaus
7. Iconic
10. Retrograde
12. Habits
13. Decay
14. Rehearsal
15. Explicit
17. Chunk
18. Elaborative

Down

1. Semantic
2. Method of loci
3. Incidental
5. Infantile
8. Icons
9. Recognition
11. Dynamic
16. Cues

Chapter 8: Practice Test #1

True/False Questions

1.   F
2.   T
3.   T
4.   F
5.   T
6.   T
7.   F
8.   F
9.   T
10.   T

Multiple-Choice Questions

1.   B
2.   D
3.   C
4.   B
5.   C
6.   A
7.   D
8.   C
9.   D
10.   A

Chapter 8: Practice Test #2

True/False Questions

1.   F
2.   F
3.   T
4.   F
5.   T

Multiple-Choice Questions

1.   C
2.   B
3.   C
4.   C
5.   C
6.   B
7.   D
8.   B
9.   C
10.   C

Chapter 8: Practice Test #3

Fill-in-the-Blank Questions

Representation
Strategies
Algorithm
Heuristic
Insight
Incubation
Analogy

Multiple-Choice Questions

1.   A
2.   C
3.   B
4.   B
5.   B
6.   C
7.   D
8.   A
9.   C
10.   D

Chapter 8: Practice Test #4

Multiple-Choice Questions

1. D
2. A
3. B
4. B
5. C
6. C
7. D
8. A
9. B
10. D

Chapter 8: Comprehensive Practice Test

True/False Questions

1. F
2. F
3. F
4. F
5. F
6. T
7. F
8. F
9. T
10. T

Multiple-Choice Questions

1. B
2. B
3. C
4. D
5. A
6. C
7. C
8. D
9. B
10. B
11. C
12. D
13. B
14. D
15. B
16. A
17. D
18. A
19. B
20. D

Puzzle It Out

Across

2. Ten
7. Deep Fritz
8. Logic
9. Two
10. Insight
12. Chomsky
13. Problem
14. Empricism
18. Algorithm
19. Telegraphic speech
20. Semantics

Down

1. Heuristic
3. Critical period
4. Broca's
5. Nativists
6. Prototype
11. Phoneme
15. Incubation
16. CDS
17. Semantics

Chapter 9: Practice Test #1

Matching Questions
1.   C
2.   D
3.   E
4.   F
5.   B
6.   A

Multiple-Choice Questions
1.   C
2.   C
3.   D
4.   A
5.   D
6.   A
7.   D
8.   B
9.   A
10.   D
11.   D
12.   B
13.   D
14.   C
15.   D

Chapter 9: Practice Test #2

True/False Questions
1.   F
2.   T
3.   F
4.   T
5.   T
6.   F

Multiple-Choice Questions
1.   B
2.   D
3.   A
4.   C
5.   B
6.   C
7.   B
8.   A
9.   B
10.   B

Chapter 9: Practice Test #3

Matching Questions
1.   D
2.   C
3.   A
4.   E
5.   B

True/False Questions
1.   F
2.   F
3.   T
4.   F
5.   F

Multiple-Choice Questions

1.	C		9.	B
2.	A		10.	B
3.	B		11.	C
4.	D		12.	B
5.	D		13.	A
6.	C		14.	B
7.	C		15.	B
8.	B			

Chapter 9: Comprehensive Practice Test

True/False Questions

1.	T
2.	F
3.	F
4.	F
5.	T
6.	T
7.	F
8.	F
9.	F
10.	T

Multiple-Choice Questions

1.	A
2.	B
3.	B
4.	C
5.	A
6.	D
7.	C
8.	A
9.	D
10.	A
11.	B
12.	C
13.	A
14.	D
15.	A

Puzzle It Out

Across

2.	Spatial
4.	Spearman
11.	Testosterone
12.	Gifted
15.	Adoption
17.	Creativity
19.	IQ
20.	Fluid

Down

1.	Flynn effect
3.	Gardner
5.	Micro
6.	Factor analysis
7.	WAIS
8.	Test bias
9.	Prodigy
10.	Sternberg
13.	Thurstone
14.	Down syndrome
16.	Binet
18.	Termites

Chapter 10: Practice Test #1

True/False Questions

1. T
2. F
3. F
4. T
5. T
6. T
7. F
8. T
9. F
10. F

Multiple-Choice Questions

1. A
2. D
3. A
4. C
5. D
6. C
7. B
8. B
9. A
10. D

Chapter 10: Practice Test #2

Multiple-Choice Questions

1. D
2. A
3. C
4. A
5. C
6. C
7. B
8. A
9. D
10. B
11. B
12. D
13. B
14. A
15. A

Chapter 10: Practice Test #3

True/False Questions

1. F
2. F
3. F
4. T
5. F
6. T
7. F
8. F

Multiple-Choice Questions

1. A
2. A
3. C
4. C
5. B
6. C
7. C
8. C
9. A
10. A

Chapter 10: Practice Test #4

True/False Questions

1. F
2. F
3. F
4. T
5. F
6. T
7. T
8. T
9. T
10. F

Multiple-Choice Questions

1. A
2. D
3. C
4. D
5. D
6. B
7. B
8. A
9. A
10. C

Chapter 10: Comprehensive Practice Test

True/False Questions

1. T
2. T
3. T
4. F
5. F
6. T
7. F
8. F
9. F
10. F

Multiple-Choice Questions

1. A
2. C
3. D
4. B
5. A
6. B
7. D
8. A
9. C
10. B
11. A
12. A
13. D
14. D
15. C
16. A
17. D
18. B
19. A
20. D

Puzzle It Out

Across

1. Homeostasis
7. Incentive
9. Drive
12. Maslow
17. Estrogens
18. Approach
20. Implicit

Down

2. Obesity
3. Self-actualization
4. Display rules
5. Androgens
6. Need
8. LeDoux
10. Ekman
11. Insulin
13. Bisexual
14. Want
15. Polygraph
16. Set point
19. Six

Chapter 11: Practice Test #1

Multiple-Choice Questions

1.	B	11.	A
2.	C	12.	D
3.	C	13.	B
4.	A	14.	C
5.	B	15.	D
6.	C	16.	B
7.	B	17.	D
8.	A	18.	A
9.	A	19.	C
10.	A	20.	C

Chapter 11: Practice Test #2

Multiple-Choice Questions

1.	D	11.	B
2.	D	12.	A
3.	A	13.	C
4.	D	14.	A
5.	A	15.	D
6.	C	16.	C
7.	C	17.	A
8.	D	18.	D
9.	D	19.	A
10.	C	20.	D

Chapter 11: Practice Test #3

Multiple-Choice Questions

1.	A		9.	D
2.	D		10.	B
3.	B		11.	D
4.	A		12.	D
5.	A		13.	A
6.	B		14.	B
7.	C		15.	B
8.	C			

Chapter 11: Practice Test #4

True/False Questions | ## Multiple-Choice Questions

True/False #	T/F	MC #	MC
1.	T	1.	B
2.	F	2.	A
3.	T	3.	C
4.	F	4.	D
5.	F	5.	A
6.	F	6.	C
7.	T	7.	D
8.	F	8.	A
9.	F	9.	A
10.	T	10.	C

Chapter 11: Comprehensive Practice Test

True/False Questions

1.	T		6.	F
2.	F		7.	F
3.	F		8.	F
4.	T		9.	T
5.	T		10.	T

Multiple-Choice Questions

1. B
2. D
3. B
4. C
5. A
6. D
7. C
8. A
9. B

10.	C
11.	C
12.	A
13.	B
14.	C
15.	A
16.	D
17.	B
18.	A
19.	A
20.	A

Puzzle It Out

Across

1.	Neuroticism
6.	Cattell
11.	Adler
13.	Traits
14.	Heritability
15.	Id
16.	Phallic
17.	Sensation-seeking
18.	Eysenck

Down

1.	Five
2.	Harris
3.	Locus of control
5.	Maslow
6.	Collectivist
7.	Superfactors
8.	NEO-PI
9.	Rorschach
10.	Firstborns
11.	Acquiescence
12.	Rogers

Chapter 12: Practice Test #1

Fill-in-the-Blank Questions

Egg
Sperm
Gametes
Female
Male
Trimesters
Zygote
Embryo
Fetus

True/False Questions

1.	T
2.	T
3.	F
4.	T
5.	F

Multiple-Choice Questions

1.	A
2.	C
3.	A
4.	A
5.	C

6.	A
7.	C
8.	D
9.	C
10.	D

Chapter 12: Practice Test #2

True/False Questions

1. F
2. T
3. F
4. T
5. T
6. F

Fill-in-the-Blank Questions

Self-concept
Cognitive
Two
Three
Social relations
Formal operational period
Culture
Collectivist
Individualistic

Fill-in-the-Blank Questions

Schemas
Assimilation
Accommodation
Articulated
Differentiated

Multiple-Choice Questions

1. B
2. A
3. A
4. A
5. B
6. A
7. B
8. D
9. A
10. B

Chapter 12: Practice Test #3

True/False Questions

1. F
2. T
3. T
4. F
5. F

Multiple-Choice Questions

1. A
2. C
3. C
4. A
5. B
6. D
7. C
8. D
9. A
10. A

Chapter 12: Practice Test #4

True/False Questions
1. F
2. T
3. F

Multiple-Choice Questions

1. D
2. B
3. A
4. D
5. C
6. B
7. A
8. D
9. B
10. C

Chapter 12: Comprehensive Practice Test

True/False Questions
1. T
2. T
3. T
4. T
5. F
6. T
7. F
8. F
9. F
10. T

Multiple-Choice Questions
1. C
2. B
3. A
4. C
5. D
6. B
7. B
8. B
9. D
10. C
11. A
12. D
13. C
14. C
15. C

Puzzle It Out

Across
4. Kohlberg
8. Zygote
10. SIDS
13. Cohort
14. Teratogen
15. Bowlby
16. Schema
18. Habituation
19. Attachment
20. Visual cliff

Down
1. Reflex
2. Grief
3. Moro reflex
5. Girls
6. Vygotsky
7. Four
9. Preoperational
11. Adolescence
12. Genes
17. Fetus

Chapter 13: Practice Test #1

Multiple-Choice Questions

1. C
2. C
3. D
4. D
5. B

6. B
7. A
8. A
9. D
10. A

Chapter 13: Practice Test #2

Fill-in-the-Blank Questions

Immune
B cells
T cells
NK cells
Glucocorticoids
Sympathetic nervous system

Multiple-Choice Questions

1. D
2. B
3. A
4. D
5. B
6. C
7. C
8. A
9. A
10. C

Chapter 13: Practice Test #3

True/False Questions

1. F
2. F
3. T
4. T
5. F
6. T
7. T
8. F
9. T
10. T

Multiple-Choice Questions

1. C
2. A
3. C
4. A
5. D
6. C
7. B
8. D
9. B
10. D

Chapter 13: Comprehensive Practice Test

True/False Questions

1. F
2. T
3. T
4. T
5. T

Multiple-Choice Questions

1.   A
2.   B
3.   B
4.   D
5.   C
6.   D
7.   B
8.   D
9.   D
10. A
11. B
12. A
13. D
14. B
15. B

Puzzle It Out

Across

1.   B Cells
3.   Avoiders
7.   Alarm
10. Hostility
12. Stressor
13. Aggression
15. Coping
16. Selye
17. Burnout
18. Prochaska
19. Privacy

Down

2.   Cortisol
4.   Optimism
5.   Exhaustion
6.   Venting
7.   Acute
8.   Atherosclerosis
9.   Hardy
11. Primary
14. NK cells

Chapter 14: Practice Test #1

True/False Questions

1. T
2. F
3. T
4. T
5. F
6. F
7. T
8. T
9. T
10. F

Multiple-Choice Questions

1. D
2. A
3. C
4. B
5. A
6. A
7. B
8. A
9. D
10. C

Chapter 14: Practice Test #2

True/False Questions

1. F
2. F
3. F
4. F
5. T

Multiple-Choice Questions

1. A
2. A
3. A
4. B
5. D
6. C
7. B
8. A
9. B
10. B

Chapter 14: Practice Test #3

Fill-in-the-Blank Questions

Type of trauma
Crimes
Natural disasters
Locus coerulus
Limbic system
Negative reinforcement
Social support

Multiple-Choice Questions

1. C
2. D
3. C
4. A
5. D
6. D
7. B
8. A
9. C
10. D

Chapter 14: Practice Test #4

True/False Questions

1. T
2. T
3. T
4. T
5. F

Multiple-Choice Questions

1. D
2. C
3. A
4. B
5. D
6. A
7. A
8. C
9. B
10. D

Chapter 14: Practice Test #5

True/False Questions

1. T
2. F
3. T
4. T
5. T

Multiple-Choice Questions

1. C
2. B
3. A
4. C
5. B
6. D
7. D
8. B
9. B
10. A

Chapter 14: Practice Test #6

True/False Questions

1. F
2. T
3. F
4. F
5. F

Multiple-Choice Questions

1. D
2. C
3. D
4. D
5. C

6. B
7. B
8. A
9. D
10. B

Chapter 14: Comprehensive Practice Test

True/False Questions

1. F
2. T
3. T
4. F
5. F
6. T
7. F
8. T

Multiple-Choice Questions

1. C
2. D
3. A
4. C
5. C
6. B
7. A
8. D
9. B
10. C
11. A
12. A
13. D
14. C
15. C

Puzzle It Out

Across

1. Hypomania
3. PTSD
4. Delusions
7. Phobia
8. DSM
9. Negative
10. Two
12. Five
14. Dysthymia
15. Suicide
17. Bipolar

Down

1. Obsession
5. Hallucination
5. Agoraphobia
7. Panic attack
8. Diathesis
11. OCD
13. Amnesia
16. Abuse
18. Axes

Chapter 15: Practice Test #1

True/False Questions

1. F
2. T
3. F
4. T
5. F
6. T
7. T
8. F
9. F
10. T

Multiple-Choice Questions

1. C
2. D
3. C
4. D
5. C
6. D
7. A
8. A
9. B
10. D

Chapter 15: Practice Test #2

True/False Questions

1. T
2. F
3. F
4. F
5. F

Fill-in-the-Blank Questions

Hypnosis
Free association
Dreams
Interpretation
Defense mechanisms
Resistance
Transference

Multiple-Choice Questions

1. B
2. B
3. D
4. D
5. A

6. D
7. C
8. C
9. B
10. D

Chapter 15: Practice Test #3

True/False Questions

1. F
2. F
3. T
4. T
5. F
6. F
7. F
8. F

Multiple-Choice Questions

1. D
2. C
3. C
4. B
5. D
6. B
7. A
8. C
9. D
10. A

Chapter 15: Practice Test #4

True/False Questions

1.   T
2.   T
3.   F
4.   F
5.   T

Fill-in-the-Blank Questions

Support
Alcoholics Anonymous
Twelve
Higher power
Weekly
Internet
Bibliotherapy

Multiple-Choice Questions

1.   D
2.   D
3.   A
4.   D
5.   C

Chapter 15: Practice Test #5

True/False Questions

1.   T
2.   T
3.   T
4.   F
5.   T

Multiple-Choice Questions

1.   C
2.   C
3.   A
4.   A
5.   B
6.   B
7.   A
8.   B
9.   A
10.   A

Chapter 15: Comprehensive Practice Test

True/False Questions

1.   F
2.   F
3.   F
4.   F
5.   T

Multiple-Choice Questions

1.	D	9.	C
2.	A	10.	C
3.	B	11.	D
4.	C	12.	A
5.	B	13.	B
6.	D	14.	B
7.	A	15.	D
8.	A		

Puzzle It Out

Across

2.   SSRI
5.   Resistance
8.   Ellis
9.   Lithium
11.   Self-help groups
12.   MAOI
15.   ECT
16.   Dispute
17.   Mental filter
19.   Cybertherapy

Down

1.   Incongruence
2.   St. John's Wort
3.   Cognitive
4.   Thoughts
6.   Systems
7.   Bibliotherapy
10.   Tokens
14.   Modality
18.   Freud

Chapter 16: Practice Test #1

True/False Questions

1.   T
2.   F
3.   T
4.   T
5.   T

Multiple-Choice Questions

1.	A	6.	D
2.	D	7.	A
3.	C	8.	A
4.	B	9.	A
5.	C	10.	B

Chapter 16: Practice Test #2

Multiple-Choice Questions

1.	C		11.	B
2.	B		12.	B
3.	C		13.	B
4.	C		14.	A
5.	D		15.	A
6.	C		16.	D
7.	C		17.	D
8.	A		18.	B
9.	D		19.	D
10.	B		20.	A

Chapter 16: Comprehensive Practice Test

True/False Questions

1.	T
2.	F
3.	F
4.	T
5.	F
6.	T
7.	T
8.	T
9.	T
10.	F

Multiple-Choice Questions

1.	C
2.	D
3.	C
4.	A
5.	C
6.	C
7.	D
8.	A
9.	B
10.	C
11.	C
12.	D
13.	C
14.	D
15.	C

Puzzle It Out

Across

4.   Stereotype
5.   Milgram
9.   Secure
10.   Norms
12.   Dissonance
13.   In-group
14.   Compliance
17.   Internal
19.   Commitment
20.   Persuasion

Down

1.   Deindividuation
2.   Genovese
3.   Prosocial
6.   Mere exposure effect
7.   Obedience
8.   Conformity
11.   Sternberg
15.   Prejudice
16.   Altruism
18.   Attribution

NOTES

NOTES